International Operations Flight Manual

James Albright

Acknowledgments

Thanks to Debbie Stackow for her help editing this manual and for her invaluable skills as an aircraft dispatcher. She has kept my airplanes out of harms way for many years and through this manual she will help many others. Thanks also to Steven Foltz who proved invaluable with fact checking.

James' Lawyer Advises:

Always remember that James, when you get right down to it, is just a pilot. He tries to give you the facts from the source materials but maybe he got it wrong, maybe he is out of date. Sure, he warns you when he is giving you his personal techniques, but you should always follow your primary guidance (Aircraft manuals, government regulations, etc.) before listening to James.

Contents

Introduction

International flight operations can be a daunting challenge for any pilot, even more so for the very first few trips away from one's home country. Most operators require their pilots complete a recognized course and then simply turn them loose. This is a recipe for trouble.

Having a good source of written material to act at first as a tutorial and later as reference material would seem a necessity for any international pilot's bag of tricks. Sadly, most international flight operations textbooks are poorly written, based on unreferenced folklore, poorly organized as reference material, and unsuitable as introductory tutorials. I've written several international flight operations manuals over the years for various business aviation management companies. Each one was better than the one before, and I think I finally have the previously mentioned complaints solved.

Organization

This manual is organized into sections to making finding topics more logical:

I - Negotiate	-	the regulatory material and where to find them.
II - Aviate	-	the nuts and bolts of defining our location, airspace, how to plot, Reduced Vertical Separation Minima, and Global Navigation Satellite Systems.
III - Navigate	-	airspace rules throughout the world.
IV - Communicate	-	radio and datalink systems.
V - Surveillance	-	automatic dependent surveillance and transponder systems.
VI - Abnormals	-	lost communications, loss of navigation capability, loss of altitude keeping accuracy, volcanic ash, and weather deviation.
VII - Tutorial	-	a sample trip, from preparation, departure, en route, to arrival.
VIII Appendices	-	Everything else.

Tutorial

Section VII presents a tutorial on how to prepare, plan, and execute a multiple leg journey, with exact details about the many steps involved. It would be a good place to start for those who have not done this before, or for those who haven't done so in a while.

A Word About Typography

Just about everything in this manual comes from primary source material that is indicated in [brackets] where the source material can be found in the last section of the manual, the chapter called "References."

I use italics in every section except the tutorial to indicate personal techniques and opinion, those items that can't be found in the references. The tutorial is pretty much all technique and in that section italics are used when referring to the example trip.

A Few Words About Currency.

One of the challenges for every pilot is keeping abreast of the many national an international rules and regulations. Even the most basic procedures can be modified, replaced, or rendered completely useless by advances in technology and technique. Nothing remains the same, it would seem.

Even with all the reference materials cited, there is a danger that the material has become outdated. As soon as it is published, it is out of date. Some of the reference material, it would seem, is never current. Try finding CPDLC rules for continental Europe, for example.

So this is just a best effort as of January, 2016. It will get you started and give you hints about where to look for updates.

As pilots we are responsible for an unmanageable amount of information and we are left to rely on those that have gone before us. Keep up with the news, look for reliable pilot message boards and blogs, and keep "plugged in." So please be careful out there. I hope I have given you a good head start on the most challenging aspect of aviation.

— James Albright

Chapter 1

Aircraft Regulatory Compliance

*A*s strange as it may sound, many pilots who started their aviation careers in the United States do not understand that most of the world flies by a different set of rules. Stranger still, there are pilots who venture beyond their borders without a clue about the International Civil Aviation Organization (ICAO) and continue to get away with ignorance of the law. These pilots are endangering their lives and the lives of all around them. So we must begin with the legal framework that binds the U.S. pilot to the rules of the ICAO and the countries they visit.

It is often said that the sheer volume of U.S. aviation regulations is more than any one pilot can really comprehend. The number of ICAO rules is even more daunting. So step two is to learn which regulations are most important, to learn how to best access the rules that matter, and to know where to find the primary source documents when needed.

Finally, just because you know the rules as they apply to a U.S. aircraft and those that are dictated by international standards, you still have to understand what the country you are visiting (or even simply overflying) expects. These rules are sometimes posted on the Internet and in English, making life much easier. But more often than not, a copy of the rules is only available in the host country's language and often only available at great cost. You should have a method of ensuring you will be in compliance with host nation rules before you venture forward.

Why do we have an international system in the first place?

World War II highlighted the need for some standardization in the way nations operate in the airspace of other nations and in the airspace over the high seas. In 1944, 52 nations met in Chicago to agree on a set of rules that have become known as the "Chicago Convention" and on the establishment of the International Civil Aviation Organization (ICAO). The document was signed on December 7, 1944 and ratified in 1947. As of 2015 there are 191 nations who have signed on. The convention itself has 96 articles and has later become supported by 19 Annexes. Every signatory, including the United States, have agreed to comply with the convention and the annexes; but every signatory can deviate so long as they publish where the rules in their state differ.

How do I get a copy of this? The updated version is known as "ICAO Doc 7300/9" and you can type that into your Internet search engine. As of 2015 the ICAO publishes this at: http://www.icao.int/publications/Documents/7300_cons.pdf. The original version, as it was signed in 1944, is also available here: http://www.icao.int/publications/Documents/7300_orig.pdf.

1944 Chicago Convention on Civil Aviation

Where does it say I have to do any of this?

Title 14 of the United States Code of Federal Regulations, Part 91, §91.703 removes all doubt in the matter.

[14 CFR 91] §91.703 Operations of civil aircraft of U.S. registry outside of the United States.

(a) Each person operating a civil aircraft of U.S. registry outside of the United States shall—

(1) When over the high seas, comply with annex 2 (Rules of the Air) to the Convention on International Civil Aviation and with §§91.117(c), 91.127, 91.129, and 91.131;

(2) When within a foreign country, comply with the regulations relating to the flight and maneuver of aircraft there in force;

(3) Except for §§91.117(a), 91.307(b), 91.309, 91.323, and 91.711, comply with this part so far as it is not inconsistent with applicable regulations of the foreign country where the aircraft is operated or annex 2 of the Convention on International Civil Aviation; and

(4) When operating within airspace designated as Minimum Navigation Performance Specifications (MNPS) airspace, comply with §91.705. When operating within airspace designated as Reduced Vertical Separation Minimum (RVSM) airspace, comply with §91.706.

(5) For aircraft subject to ICAO Annex 16, carry on board the aircraft documents that summarize the noise operating characteristics and certifications of the aircraft that demonstrate compliance with this part and part 36 of this chapter.

(b) Annex 2 to the Convention on International Civil Aviation, Ninth Edition—July 1990, with Amendments through Amendment 32 effective February 19, 1996, to which reference is made in this part, is incorporated into this part and made a part hereof as provided in 5 U.S.C. §552 and pursuant to 1 CFR part 51.

Keep in mind this regulation was written by a bureaucrat and there are sections that don't make a lot of sense. §§91.117(c), for example, deals with speed restrictions in airspace underlying Class B airspace, hardly the thing you would worry about when operating over the high seas.

Section I - Negotiate

*H*ow do I get a copy of this? *As of 2015, all "Federal Aviation Regulations, which are more properly known as Title 14 to the U.S. Code of Federal Regulations (14 CFR), are available at: http://www.faa.gov/regulations_policies/.*

Chapter 2

Primary Source Materials (ICAO)

*A*s a pilot licensed by a country that is a signatory to the ICAO, basically *every pilot, you are constrained to operate under the rules of the ICAO except as noted by the country you happen to be flying in.*

In other words, you should know the ICAO rules if you ever plan on venturing outside your own borders. Using a secondary source, such as the Jeppesen Airways Manuals, is perfectly acceptable for routine operations. When things are not routine, however, it helps to know where to look in the primary source materials.

ICAO Annexes

ICAO Annex 1 – Personnel Licensing

Standards and Recommended Practices for Personnel Licensing were first adopted by the Council on 14 April 1948 pursuant to the provisions of Article 37 of the Convention on International Civil Aviation (Chicago 1944) and designated as Annex 1 to the Convention.

This annex includes things like licenses and ratings for pilots (Chapter 2), other crew members (Chapter 3), non-crewmembers (Chapter 4), and the medical requirements for each category (Chapter 6).

ICAO Annex 2 – Rules of the Air

In October 1945, Standards, Practices and Procedures (SARPS) for the rules of the air were published as Recommendations for Standards, Practices and Procedures — Rules of the Air in the first part of Doc 2010 and later adopted as Annex 2 on 1 September 1952.

Article 38 of the Convention requires states to notify the Organization of any differences between their national regulations and practices and the International Standards contained in this Annex and any amendments.

This annex includes things like general rules (Chapter 3), visual flight rules

(Chapter 4), instrument flight rules (Chapter 5), signals (Appendix 1), aircraft intercept rules (Appendix 2), and unlawful interference (Attachment B).

ICAO Annex 3 – Meteorological Service for International Air Navigation

Standards and Recommended Practices relating to meteorology were first adopted by the Council on 16 April 1948, pursuant to the provisions of Article 37 of the Convention on International Civil Aviation (Chicago, 1944), and designated as Annex 3 to the Convention with the title Standards and Recommended Practices — Meteorological Codes.

This annex outlines a world area forecast system and standards when it comes to things like meteorological observations and reports (Chapter 4), aircraft observations and reports (Chapter 5), forecasts (Chapter 6), and other ways weather reports are made. If you've ever wondered why your weather charts are formatted the way they are, see Appendix 1. All those codes, like DZ for drizzle and GR for hail? See Appendix 3. TAF formats are in Appendix 5.

ICAO Annex 4 – Aeronautical Charts

Standards and Recommended Practices for Aeronautical Charts were first adopted by the Council on 16 April 1948, pursuant to the provisions of Article 37 of the Convention on International Civil Aviation (Chicago, 1944), and were designated as Annex 4 to the Convention.

This annex gives the specifications to be used for aerodrome, en route, area, approach, and even plotting charts. Symbols, notes, and even the colors to be used are specified.

ICAO Annex 5 – Units of Measurement to be used in Air and Ground Operations

International Standards and Recommended Practices for Dimensional Units to be used in Air-Ground Communications were first adopted by the Council on 16 April 1948 pursuant to Article 37 of the Convention on International Civil Aviation (Chicago, 1944) and were designated as Annex 5 to the Convention.

This annex outlines the International System of Units (SI), gives conversion factors (Attachment C), and defines Coordinated Universal Time (Attachment D).

ICAO Annex 6 – Operation of Aircraft

Part I – International Commercial Air Transport Aeroplanes

Part II – International General Aviation Aeroplanes

Standards and Recommended Practices for the Operation of Aircraft — International Commercial Air Transport were first adopted by the Council on 10 December 1948 pursuant to the provisions of Article 37 of the Convention on International Civil Aviation (Chicago, 1944) and designated as Annex 6 to the Convention.

This annex includes things like flight operations, airplane performance limitations, equipment, maintenance, crew, manuals, logs, and records. You will also find the requirement for a journey log, an air operator certificate, and even the framework for a safety management system here. Part I applies to commercial aircraft and Part II to general aviation.

ICAO Annex 7 – Aircraft Nationality and Registration Marks

Annex 7 contains Standards adopted by the International Civil Aviation Organization on 8 February 1949 as the minimum Standards for the display of marks to indicate appropriate nationality and registration which have been determined to comply with Article 20 of the Convention.

This annex specifies how aircraft are marked to designate registry, what the certificate of registration should look like, and the requirement for an identification plate.

ICAO Annex 8 – Airworthiness of Aircraft

Standards and Recommended Practices for the Airworthiness of Aircraft were adopted by the Council on 1 March 1949 pursuant to the provisions of Article 37 of the Convention on International Civil Aviation (Chicago 1944) and designated as Annex 8 to the Convention.

This annex includes things like type certification, production approval, the certificate of airworthiness, and the continuing airworthiness of aircraft.

ICAO Annex 9 - Facilitation

Standards and Recommended Practices on Facilitation were first adopted by the Council on 25 March 1949, pursuant to the provisions of Article 37 of the Convention on International Civil Aviation (Chicago 1944) and designated as Annex 9 to the Convention.

This annex includes things like the documentation needed for entry and departure of aircraft, disinfection, inspection, and other passenger and cargo concerns. It also includes the need to land at an airport designated as an

15

international airport, as well as the measures when landing someplace not so designated.

ICAO Annex 10 – Aeronautical Telecommunications

Volume I – Radio Navigtion Aids

Standards and Recommended Practices for Aeronautical Telecommunications were first adopted by the Council on 30 May 1949 pursuant to the provisions of Article 37 of the Convention on International Civil Aviation (Chicago 1944) and designated as Annex 10 to the Convention.

This annex includes specifications for ILS, VOR, NDB, marker beacons, GNSS, and MLS.

Volume II – Communication Procedures including those with PANS status

Standards and Recommended Practices for Aeronautical Telecommunications were first adopted by the Council on 30 May 1949 pursuant to the provisions of Article 37 of the Convention on International Civil Aviation (Chicago 1944) and designated as Annex 10 to the Convention. Volume II contains material that has the status of Procedures for Air Navigation Services (PANS).

This annex includes procedures for voice, Aeronautical Fixed Telecommunications Network (AFTN), distress, and data link.

Volume III – Communication Systems (Digital Data and Voice Communications)

Standards and Recommended Practices for Aeronautical Telecommunications were first adopted by the Council on 30 May 1949 pursuant to the provisions of Article 37 of the Convention on International Civil Aviation (Chicago 1944) and designated as Annex 10 to the Convention.

This annex includes things like Mode S, VHF air-ground digital link (VDL), HF data link, SELCAL, and Emergency Locator Transmitter (ELT).

Volume IV – Surveillance and Collision Avoidance Systems

Standards and Recommended Practices for Aeronautical Telecommunications were first adopted by the Council on 30 May 1949 pursuant to the provisions of Article 37 of the Convention on International Civil Aviation (Chicago 1944) and designated as Annex 10 to the Convention.

This annex includes things like Secondary Surveillance Radar (SSR), Airborne Collision Avoidance System (ACAS), and Mode S.

Volume V – Aeronautical Radio Frequency Spectrum Utilization

Standards and Recommended Practices for Aeronautical Telecommunications were first adopted by the Council on 30 May 1949 pursuant to the provisions of Article 37 of the Convention on International Civil Aviation (Chicago 1944) and designated as Annex 10 to the Convention.

This annex maps out the acceptable use of various frequencies, including those used for distress.

ICAO Annex 11 – Air Traffic Services

Air Traffic Control procedures were first adopted by the Council on 18 May 1950, pursuant to Article 37 of the Convention on International Civil Aviation (Chicago, 1944), and designated as Annex 11 to the Convention.

This annex includes things like the designation of air traffic control services, flight information services, contingencies, and Traffic Information Broadcasts by Aircraft (TIBA).

ICAO Annex 12 – Search and Rescue

Standards and Recommended Practices for Search and Rescue were adopted by the Council on 25 May 1950 and designated as Annex 12 to the Convention on International Civil Aviation.

This annex includes things like the organization of search and rescue services, cooperation between the states, operating procedures, and standardized signals.

ICAO Annex 13 – Aircraft Accident and Incident Investigation

Standards and Recommended Practices for Aircraft Accident Inquiries were first adopted by the Council on 11 April 1951 pursuant to Article 37 of the Convention on International Civil Aviation (Chicago, 1944) and were designated as Annex 13 to the Convention.

This annex includes things like notification, investigation, and reporting aircraft mishaps.

ICAO Annex 14 – Aerodromes

Volume I – Aerodrome Design and Operations

Volume II - Heliports

Standards and Recommended Practices for Aerodromes were first adopted by the Council on 29 May 1951 pursuant to the provisions of Article 37 of the Convention on International Civil Aviation (Chicago 1944) and designated as Annex 14 to the Convention.

This annex includes things like pavement strength, declared distances, rescue and fire fighting, obstacle restrictions, visual markings, lights, electrical systems, and aerodrome maintenance. It also includes an attachment covering obstacle limitation surfaces.

ICAO Annex 15 – Aeronautical Information Services

Standards and Recommended Practices for Aeronautical Information Services were first adopted by the Council on 15 May 1953, pursuant to the provisions of Article 37 of the Convention on International Civil Aviation (Chicago 1944), and were designated as Annex 15 to the Convention.

This annex includes things like Aeronautical Information Publications (AIPs), Notices to Airmen (NOTAMs), Aeronautical Information Circulars (AICs), and electronic terrain and obstacle data.

ICAO Annex 16 – Environmental Protection

Volume I – Aircraft Noise

Standards and Recommended Practices for Aeronautical Information Services were first adopted by the Council on 15 May 1953, pursuant to the provisions of Article 37 of the Convention on International Civil Aviation (Chicago 1944), and were designated as Annex 15 to the Convention.

This annex is where we get our noise level standards, Chapters 2, 3, and 4 have become known as the criteria for what is called Stage 2, 3, and 4 in the United States. The higher chapters are given to propeller-driven aircraft, helicopters, and for supersonic airplanes.

Volume II – Aircraft Engine Emissions

The Council agreed in 1980 to add environmental aspects into Volume II — Aircraft Engine Emissions.

This annex includes the criteria for vented fuel and engine emissions.

ICAO Annex 17 - Security

Standards and Recommended Practices for Aeronautical Information Services were first adopted by the Council on 15 May 1953, pursuant to the provisions of Article 37 of the Convention on International Civil Aviation (Chicago 1944), and were designated as Annex 15 to the Convention.

This annex includes things like the prevention and management of acts of unlawful interference. You will also find the special SSR codes here.

ICAO Annex 18 – The Safe Transport of Dangerous Goods by Air

The provisions of Annex 18 govern the international transport of dangerous goods by air. The broad provisions of this Annex are amplified by the detailed specifications of the Technical Instructions for the Safe Transport of Dangerous Goods by Air (Doc 9284).

This annex includes things like packing, labeling, training programs, and limitations of transporting dangerous goods by air.

ICAO Documents

There are many ICAO documents that may or may not apply to what you are doing. The following are the documents that are probably the most applicable.

ICAO Doc 4444 ATM/501 – Procedures for Air Navigation Services – Air Traffic Management

The Procedures for Air Navigation Services — Air Traffic Management (PANS-ATM) are the result of the progressive evolution of the Procedures for Air Navigation Services — Air Traffic Control (PANS-ATC).

This document outlines air traffic services, including speed control, wake turbulence, position reporting, separation methods and minima, radar services, phraseologies, Automatic Dependent Surveillance (ADS), Controller Pilot Data Link Communications (CPDLC), emergency procedures and contingencies, flight plans, and incident reports.

ICAO Doc 7030 – Regional Supplementary Procedures

The ICAO Regional Supplementary Procedures (SUPPS) form the procedural part of the Air Navigation Plans to meet those needs of specific areas that are not covered in the worldwide provisions. They complement the statement of requirements for facilities and services contained in the Air

Navigation Plan publications.

This document outlines the major differences found in regions of the world with the ICAO standard. Regions are defined as Africa-Indian Ocean (AFI), Caribbean (CAR), European (EUR), Middle East/Asia (MID/ASIA), North America (NAM), North Atlantic (NAT), Pacific (PAC), and South America (SAM).

ICAO Doc 7300 – The Convention on International Civil Aviation signed at Chicago on 7 December 1944

This document contains the text of the Convention on International Civil Aviation, signed at Chicago on 7 December 1944 (hereinafter referred to as the "Convention"), in the English, French, Russian and Spanish languages as amended.

This document is simply the Chicago Convention in a format more easily read and searched than the original, which is available only as a Photostat copy and has not been updated.

ICAO Doc 7910/133 – Location Indicators

This document is the official source of ICAO location identifiers.

ICAO Doc 8168 OPS/611 – Procedures for Air Navigation Services – Aircraft Operations

The division of the PANS-OPS into the two volumes was accomplished in 1979 as a result of an extensive amendment to the obstacle clearance criteria and the construction of approach-to-land procedures.

Volume I – Flight Procedures

Flight Procedures describes operational procedures recommended for the guidance of flight operations personnel and flight crew. It also outlines the various parameters on which the criteria in Volume II are based so as to illustrate the need to adhere strictly to the published procedures in order to achieve and maintain an acceptable level of safety in operations.

Volume II – Construction of Visual and Instrument Flight Procedures

Construction of Visual and Instrument Flight Procedures is intended for the guidance of procedures specialists and describes the essential areas and obstacle clearance requirements for the achievement of safe, regular instrument flight operations. It provides the basic guidelines to States, and those operators and organizations producing instrument flight charts that will re-

sult in uniform practices at all aerodromes where instrument flight procedures are carried out.

*This document contains what in the United States is known as the U.S. Stan-
dard for Terminal Instrument Procedures (TERPS), that is, airspace construction for departure, en route, and arrival.*

ICAO Doc 8400 – ICAO Abbreviations and Codes

This document is the official source of ICAO abbreviations.

ICAO Doc 9613 AN/937 – Performance-Based Navigation (PBN) Manual

Volume I – Concept and Implementation Guidance

Volume II – Implementing RNAV and RNP

This manual identifies the relationship between RNAV and RNP applications and the advantages and limitations of choosing one or the other as the
navigation requirement for an airspace concept. It also aims at providing
practical guidance to States, air navigation service providers and airspace
users on how to implement RNAV and RNP applications, and how to ensure
that the performance requirements are appropriate for the planned application.

*This document is a primer on the concepts, which continue to be in a state of
change. The second edition was called "Manual on Required Navigation Performance" but has since become the PBN Manual. The last update came after
nearly 10 years so it can hardly be considered a timely resource, but it does get
you up to speed. (At least up to 2008, the date of the last edition.)*

ICAO Doc 9859 AN/460 – Safety Management Manual

ICAO's Standards and Recommended Practices (SARPs) require that States
establish a safety programme to achieve an acceptable level of safety in aviation operations. The acceptable level of safety shall be established by the
State(s) concerned. While the concept of safety programmes and SMS is restricted to Annexes 6, 11 and 14 at present, it is possible that the concept will
be expanded to include additional operational Annexes in the future.

*You need a safety management system to fly in some parts of the world and
you need to consider this manual to do that correctly.*

ICAO Global Operational Data Link Document (GOLD)

The GOLD provides guidance and information concerning data link operations and is intended to facilitate the uniform application of Standards and Recommended Practices contained in Annex 2 — Rules of the Air, Annex 10 — Aeronautical Telecommunications and Annex 11 — Air Traffic Services, the provisions in the Procedures for Air Navigation Services — Air Traffic Management (PANS-ATM, Doc 4444) and, when necessary, the Regional Supplementary Procedures (Doc 7030).

This manual gives you an excellent overview of data link operations. You should particularly pay attention to Chapter 5, Flight Crew Procedures and Appendix E, Regional/State-specific procedures. The manual is not updated as often as it should be and you may find regional en route charts to be a better source of datalink addresses.

Satellite Voice Guidance Material (SVGM)

The SVGM provides a comprehensive update of various regional and State guidance material for Air Navigation Service Providers (ANSPs) and aircraft operators to use SATVOICE for ATS communications. This includes the incorporation of performance-based specifications to be applied, where appropriate (i.e. RCP for controller intervention and RSP for position reporting), as well as associated guidance on data collection, monitoring, and analysis.

This manual covers SATVOICE and SATCOM, which are not the same. It also covers Required Communications Performance (RCP) and Required Surveillance Performance (RSP).

How do I get a copy of these? As of 2015, you can get the annexes at: http://www.bazl.admin.ch/dokumentation/grundlagen/02643/index.html and the documents at http://dcaa.trafikstyrelsen.dk:8000/icaodocs/ but these links tend to change and are not always up to date. The best source is obviously http://www.icao.int but they provide documents for a fee and are very expensive. You can also try creative variations of the document numbers, titles, or descriptions in your Internet search engine.

Chapter 3

Primary Source Materials (U.S.)

U.S. pilots can access various advisory circulars, the U.S. Aeronautical Information Publication (AIP) which is about the same as the Aeronautical Information Manual (AIM), various Federal Aviation Administration (FAA) orders, and Federal Aviation Regulations which are more properly known as Title 14 to the U.S. Code of Federal Regulations (14 CFR). Non-U.S. pilots can best learn the differences between ICAO and U.S. rules by looking at the U.S. AIP.

Advisory Circulars

There is a debate among some U.S. pilots about the enforceability of anything written in an advisory circular because of the word "advisory" and a statement in most of these that says "This AC is not mandatory and is not a regulation. This AC describes an acceptable means, but not the only means, to comply with applicable regulations." What these pilots are missing is the fact that any other means they choose to comply needs to be at least as well thought out as what appears in the advisory circular. No matter which means you choose, you need to be familiar with the AC.

AC 20-138D, Airworthiness Approval of Positioning and Navigation Systems

This advisory circular provides guidance material for the airworthiness approval of installed positioning and navigation equipment. Positioning and navigation equipment may be used for a variety of functions such as navigation, automatic dependent surveillance, and/or terrain awareness and warning systems.

While this AC is targeted toward manufacturers it provides background information about GNSS, GPS, SBAS, RNAV, DME/DME, RNP, Baro-VNAV, and other topics of interest to the international pilot.

AC 90-96A, Approval of U.S. Operators and Aircraft to Operate Under Instrument Flight Rules (IFR) in European Airspace Designated for Basic Area Navigation (B-RNAV) and Precision Area Navigation (P-RNAV)

This advisory circular provides operational approval and airworthiness guidance material regarding RNAV requirements for operators of U.S.-registered civil aircraft, operating in a B-RNAV or P-RNAV environment in European RNAV airspace.

European navigation requirements are changing and B-RNAV and P-RNAV are giving way to RNAV 1 and, to a lesser extent, RNAV 2. Many of the procedures will specifically state "P-RNAV OR RNAV 1 REQUIRED" in recognition that some operators have the older P-RNAV authorization. ICAO Doc 9613 says this is good enough and this AC outlines how you prove you are B-RNAV and P-RNAV qualified.

AC 91-70A, Oceanic and International Operations

This advisory circular contains general information and guidance for operators planning oceanic flights, including authorizations needed for operations outside the continental United States. This includes Special Areas of Operation (SAO) such as North Atlantic Minimum Navigation Performance Specifications (NAT/MNPS), Reduced Vertical Separation Minimum (RVSM), Area Navigation (RNAV), and Required Navigation Performance (RNP) airspace.

This is your best source of how to conduct remote and oceanic airspace operations from the perspective of a U.S. operator. It tells you how to prepare, how to plot, when you need to worry about Extended Operations (ETOPS), all about the Strategic Lateral Offset Procedure (SLOP), communications procedures, polar route procedures, and much, much more.

AC 91-85, Authorization of Aircraft and Operators for Flight in Reduced Vertical Separation Minimum Airspace

This advisory circular AC contains information on airworthiness, continuing airworthiness, and operations programs for Reduced Vertical Separation Minimum (RVSM) operations.

This AC gives you an excellent primer on what it takes to get an aircraft RVSM certified, how maintenance affects that, the monitoring requirements, and in Appendix 4 it gives you operating practices and procedures. Appendix 5 is written specifically for oceanic airspace and includes contingency examples.

AC 120-42B, Extended Operations (ETOPS and Polar Operations)

This advisory circular (AC) provides certificate holders with guidance for obtaining operational approval to conduct Extended Operations (ETOPS) under 14 CFR part 121, § 121.161.

Despite that description, ETOPS concerns more than just pilots operating under 14 CFR 121. If you are operating under 14 CFR 135 you are bound by ETOPS too, see 14 CFR 135.364. Even if you are not flying under commercial rules, this AC gives you lots to think about if you are flying outside of 180 minutes from a suitable airport or near the poles.

AC 120-47, Survival Equipment for use in Overwater Operations

The purpose of this AC is to provide information regarding the survival items that should be carried during aircraft extended overwater operations.

The scope of the AC is directed to 14 CFR 121 and 135 but provides best practices for other operators too.

How do I get a copy of these? As of 2015, you can get these advisory circulars at http://www.faa.gov/regulations_policies/advisory_circulars/, which has turned out to be one of the best parts of the www.faa.gov website. If you search for an AC that has been superseded or has expired, it will tell you.

Aeronautical Information Publications

United States Aeronautical Information Publication (AIP)

The AIP is prepared in accordance with the Standards and Recommended Practices (SARP) of Annex 15 to the Convention on International Civil Aviation and the Aeronautical Information Services Manual (ICAO Doc 8126). Charts contained in the AIP are produced in accordance with Annex 4 to the Convention on International Civil Aviation and the Aeronautical Chart Manual (ICAO Doc 8697). Differences from ICAO Standards, Recommended Practices and Procedures are given in subsection GEN 1.7.

The AIP is updated by NOTAM, which is to say the AIP you download is usually out of date. (As of July 2015 the latest AIP is over two years old.) You can certainly use it and check the NOTAMs. The Aeronautical Information Manual (AIM), however, contains about the same information and is updated more often.

Aeronautical Information Manual (AIM)

The AIM is designed to provide the aviation community with basic flight information and ATC procedures for use in the National Airspace System (NAS) of the United States. This manual contains the fundamentals required in order to fly in the United States NAS. It also contains items of interest to pilots concerning health and medical facts, factors affecting flight safety, a pilot/controller glossary of terms used in the ATC System, and information on safety, accident, and hazard reporting.

The AIM is well written and often updated. U.S. pilots should be cautioned, however, to note that the procedures given in the AIM are not always applicable when flying outside the U.S.

How do I get a copy of these? As of 2015, you can get the U.S. AIP at http://www.faa.gov/air_traffic/publications/atpubs/AIP/aip.pdf and the AIM at http://www.faa.gov/air_traffic/publications/.

FAA Orders

The Flight Standards Information Management System (FSIMS) in established by FAA Order 8900.1 and contains a lot of what determines what we can and cannot do as international pilots. There are quite a few that are worth reading.

Order 8900.1 Volume 4, Aircraft Equipment, Communications and Surveillance

Don't be fooled by the title, this volume contains a lot of information on international operations but it appears to be directed to the process of getting operations specification approval. These approval processes also pertain to getting letters of authorization and along the way reveal a lot of regulatory information.

How do I get a copy of these? As of 2015, you can find most of these at http://fsims.faa.gov but navigation is fairly difficult. The best method seems to be clicking on "8900.1 Contents" and then exploring the volumes. There is a wealth of information under Volume 4.

Federal Aviation Regulations

You could argue that all federal aviation regulations apply to a U.S. interna-

tional pilot, but here are a few to consider specifically:

§ 1.1	Definitions
§ 45.21	Nationality and Registration Marks
§ 45.31	Marking of Export Aircraft
§ 47.3	Registration Required
§ 47.5	Applicants for Aircraft Registration
§ 47.7	Certificate of US Citizenship
§ 47.11	Evidence of Ownership
§ 47.39	Effective Date of Aircraft Registration
§ 47.43	Invalid Registration
§ 91.207	Emergency Locator Transmitters
§ 91.509	Survival Equipment for Over water Operations
§ 91.511	Radio Equipment for Over water Operations
§ 91.703	Operation of Civil Aircraft of U.S. Registry Outside of the United States
§ 91.705	Operations Within the MNPS Airspace
§ 91.707	Flights Between Mexico or Canada and the United States
§ 91.709	Operations to Cuba
§ 135.43	Crewmember Certificate, International Operations: Application and Issue
§ 135.98	Operations in the North Polar Area
§ 135.145	Aircraft Proving Tests
§ 135.165	Radio and Navigation Equipment: Extended Overwater or IFR Operations
§ 135.167	Emergency Equipment: Extended Overwater Operations
§ 135.183	Performance Requirements: Land Aircraft Operated Overwater
§ 135.381	En route limitations: one engine inoperative

How do I get a copy of these? As of 2015, you can find most of these at http://www.faa.gov/regulations_policies/faa_regulations/.

Primary Source Materials (Other countries, organizations)

Before venturing to another country you should, the theory goes, consult each Aeronautical Information Publication for every country you visit and whose airspace you frequent. There are more than a few problems with this, chief among which is language. (Most are not written in English.) Another issue is you just can't find a lot of them easily. A few examples follow. If you subscribe to an international airway manual service, you have a distinct advantage.

Canada

The AIP Canada (ICAO) contains Part 1- General (GEN), Part 2 - Enroute (ENR), Part 3 - Aerodromes (AD) as well as AIP Supplements (AIP SUP) and Aeronautical Information Circulars (AIC).

How do I get a copy? As of 2015, you can find EASA regulations at: http://www.navcanada.ca/EN/products-and-services/Pages/AIP.aspx

European Aviation Safety Agency

The European Aviation Safety Agency (EASA) is the European Union authority in aviation safety. Most countries in Europe are member states and many other organizations use EASA rules and regulations.

How do I get a copy of these? As of 2015, you can find EASA regulations at: http://easa.europa.eu/document-library/regulations#basic-regulation

Jeppesen Airway Manuals

Jeppesen offers a variety of manual options, some of which include international rules and regulations translated and outlined by region. In the absence of a particular country's AIP, the Jeppesen Airway Manual text pages should suffice under most circumstances.

United Kingdom

The UK integrated AIP is available online in two files.

How do I get a copy? As of 2015, you can find this regulation at: http://www.nats-uk.ead-it.com/public/index.php.html.

Chapter 1

Coordinates

*A*s a brand new Air Force pilot in 1979, the height of my navigation skills involved holding a terrain chart in one hand while cradling the stick of a T-38 flying at "the speed of heat" 500 feet off the deck trying not to get lost. Coordinates were not important in my day-to-day flying. Years later, flying in flight levels and not feet, navigating between continents and not mountains, the coordinates that pinpoint positions on the globe are important again.

The History of Lines of Latitude and Longitude

[Sobel, page 2]

Lines of latitude and longitude began crisscrossing our world view in ancient times, at least three centuries before the birth of Christ. By A.D. 150, the cartographer and astronomer Ptolemy had plotted them on the twenty-seven maps of his first world atlas.

The Equator marked the zero-degree parallel of latitude for Ptolemy. He did not choose it arbitrarily but took it on higher authority from his predecessors, who had derived it from nature while observing the motions of the heavenly bodies. The sun, moon, and planets pass almost directly overhead at the Equator. Likewise, the Tropic of Cancer and the Tropic of Capricorn, two other famous parallels, assume their positions at the sun's command. They mark the northern and southern boundaries of the sun's apparent motion over the course of the year.

Ptolemy was free, however, to lay his prime meridian, the zero-degree longitude line, wherever he liked. He chose to run it through the Fortunate Islands (now called the Canary & Madeira Islands) off the northwest coast of Africa. As the world turns, any line drawn from pole to pole may serve as well as any other for a starting line of reference. The placement of the prime meridian is a purely political decision.

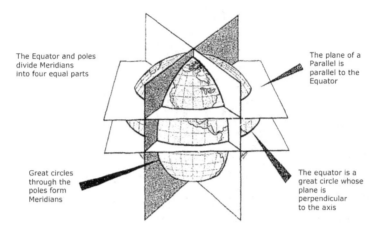

The Equator and poles divide Meridians into four equal parts

The plane of a Parallel is parallel to the Equator

Great circles through the poles form Meridians

The equator is a great circle whose plane is perpendicular to the axis

Figure: Planes of the Earth, from AFM 51-40, figure 2-3.

Great Circles

[AFM 51-40, pages 2-1 to 2-2.]

For most navigational purposes, the earth is assumed to be a perfect sphere, although in reality it is not. Inspection of the earth's crust reveals that there is a height variation of approximately 12 miles from the top of the tallest mountain to the bottom of the deepest point in the ocean.

Measured at the equator, the earth is approximately 6,887.91 nautical miles in diameter, while the polar diameter is approximately 6,864.57 nautical miles, and this difference may be used to express the ellipticity of the earth.

A great circle is defined as a circle on the surface of a sphere whose center and radius are those of the sphere itself. The arc of a great circle is the shortest distance between two points on a sphere, just as a straight line is the shortest distance between two points on a plane.

Circles on the surface of the sphere other than great circles may be defined as small circles. A small circle is a circle on the surface of the earth whose center and/or radius are not that of the sphere. A special set of small circles, called latitude, is discussed later.

From a pilot's perspective, a great circle is simply the shortest route between two points on the globe.

Latitude

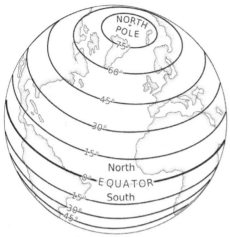

Figure: Latitude lines, from Wikimedia Commons, Pearson Scott Foresman.

[Sobel, page 2]

The zero degree parallel of latitude is fixed by the laws of nature.

Any sailor worth his salt can gauge his latitude well enough by the length of the day, or by the height of the sun or known guide stars above the horizon. Christopher Columbus followed a straight path across the Atlantic when he "sailed the parallel" on his 1492 journey, and the technique would doubtless have carried him to the Indies had not the Americas intervened.

[AFM 51-40, page 2-3.]

Once a day, the earth rotates on its north-south axis which is terminated by the two poles. The equator is constructed at the midpoint of this axis at right angles to it. A great circle drawn through the poles is called a meridian, and an infinite number of great circles may be constructed in this manner. Each meridian is divided into four quadrants by the equator and the poles. Since a circle is arbitrarily divided into 360 degrees, each of those quadrants therefore contains 90 degrees.

Take a point on one of these meridians 30 degrees north of the equator. Through this point pass a plane perpendicular to the north-south axis of rotation. This plane will be parallel to the plane of the equator as shown [in the figure] and will intersect the earth in a small circle called a parallel or parallel of latitude. The particular parallel of latitude chosen is 30° N, and every point on this parallel will be at 30° N. In the same way, other parallels can be constructed at any desired latitude, such as 10 degrees, 40 degrees, etc.

Longitude

[Sobel, page 2]

To learn one's longitude at sea, one needs to know what time it is aboard ship and also the time at the home port or another place of known longitude. Since the earth takes 24 hours to complete one full revolution of three hundred sixty degrees, one hour marks one twenty-fourth of a spin, or fifteen degrees. And so each hour's time difference between the ship and the starting point marks a progress of fifteen degrees of longitude to the east or west. Every day at sea, when the navigator resets his ship's clock to local noon when the sun reaches its highest point in the sky, and then consults the home-port clock, every hour's discrepancy between them translates into another fifteen degrees of longitude.

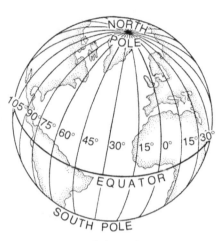

Figure: Longitude lines, from Wikimedia Commons, Pearson Scott Foresman.

Those same fifteen degrees of longitude also correspond to a distance traveled. At the Equator, where the girth of the Earth is greatest, fifteen degrees stretch fully one thousand miles. North or south of that line, however, the mileage value of each degree decreases.

[AFM 51-40, page 2-4.]

The latitude of a point can be shown as 20° N or 20° S of the equator, but there is no way of knowing whether one point is east or west or another. This difficulty is resolved by the use of the other component of the coordinate system, longitude, which is the measurement of this east-west distance.

There is not, as with latitude, a natural starting point for numbering, such as the equator. The solution has been to select an arbitrary starting point. A great many places have been used, but when the English speaking people began to make charts, they chose the meridian through their principal observatory in Greenwich, England, as the origin for counting longitude, and this point has now been accepted by most other countries of the world. This Greenwich meridian is sometimes called the prime or first meridian, though actually it is the zero meridian. Longitude is counted east and west from this meridian, through 180 degrees.

Chapter 2

Direction

*W*hile *"direction" seems to be the most basic fundamental of getting from Point A to Point B, there are quite a few pitfalls in terminology. It is quite easy to get by for years and not really understand why some directions are true and others aren't. Well let's put an end to that right now.*

The Numerical System for Determining Direction

[AFM 51-40, pages 2-5 to 2-6.]

- The numerical system, divides the horizon into 360 degrees starting with north 000 degrees, east 090 degrees, south 180 degrees, west 270 degrees, and back to north.

- The circle, called a compass rose, represents the horizon divided into 360 degrees.

True Course

[AFM 51-40, pages 2-5 to 2-6.]

- Course is the intended horizontal direction of travel.

- Heading is the horizontal direction in which an aircraft is pointed. Heading is the actual orientation of the longitudinal axis of the aircraft at any instant, while course is the direction intended to be made good.

- Track is the actual horizontal direction made by the aircraft over the earth.

- Bearing is the horizontal direction of one terrestrial point from another.

A "True Course" is the relative bearing between your course and true north. It is usually found by placing a plotter over a chart and reading the angular difference to any meridian.

Variation

[AFM 51-37, page 1-12.] The magnetic compass points to magnetic north. The angular difference between true and magnetic north is known as variation and it changes for different locations on the earth. Variation must be considered when converting true course, true headings, or true winds to magnetic direction.

This can be considered an academic exercise in understanding the difference between TRUE and MAGNETIC, except for anyone who flies at high latitudes where magnetic navigation is unreliable, or anyone who flies in Class II or oceanic airspace where plotting procedures are required. If you ever need to plot a position, variation is critical.

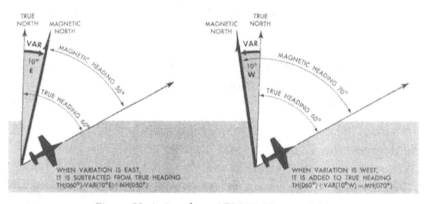

Figure: Variation, from AFM 51-37, page 1-13.

Deviation

[AFM 51-37, page 1-12.] Deviation [is] an error in compass indications caused by magnetic disturbances originating within the aircraft. The magnitude of deviation varies with operation of different electrical equipment. Periodically, the compass is checked and compensations are made to reduce the amount of deviation. Deviation errors remaining after the compass has been checked are recorded on a compass correction card in the cockpit. The STEER column on the compass correction card is the compass heading you should indicate to maintain the TO FLY magnetic heading.

At Air Force Instrument Instructor's school we were taught to fly IFR off nothing more than an attitude indicator and a magnetic compass. I came to the conclusion it would be safer to declare an emergency and get no gyro vectors. These days the chances of needing to fly off one of these cards are remote, but you should know how.

Deviation is given as degrees to steer to accomplish a desired heading, but can be thought of as positive and negative numbers to apply a magnetic heading.

True / Magnetic / Course

The navigator's text above hints at complications we pilots didn't want, so they gave us an old sailor's mnemonic: "True virgins make dull company" to which others added "Add Whiskey." Crude or not, the idea was to remember the order in which things are added to a true course to end up with what the sailor (and pilot) wanted, which was a course to sail (and fly):

B-16		COMPASS	
SWUNG 12 APR 76 BY M J R			
TO FLY	STEER	TO FLY	STEER
N	001	180	179
15	016	195	194
30	031	210	209
45	046	225	224
60	062	240	238
75	077	255	253
90	092	270	268
105	107	285	283
120	122	300	298
135	135	315	314
150	149	330	330
165	164	345	346

Figure: Compass correction card, from AFM 51-37, figure 1-15.

- *Start with a TRUE course using your handy plotter, to that you add*
- *magnetic VARIATION (explained: above) to get a*
- *MAGNETIC course; to that add*
- *DEVIATION (explained: above) to get a*
- *COMPASS heading to steer.*

The "Add Whiskey" part was to help us remember we add west variation and deviation while subtracting east variation and deviation. Another technique is to remember "East is least, west is best."

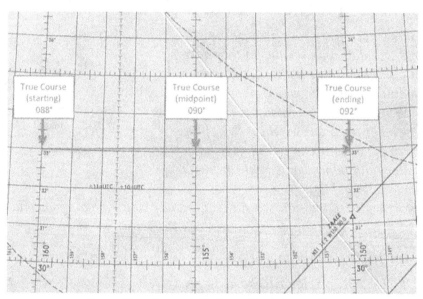

Figure: True Course initial vs. midpoint vs. ending

Chapter 3

Initial vs. Midpoint Course

Y*our plotting chart is based on a Lambert Conformal projection, the lines of longitude converge near the poles. Except for the equator, the lines of latitude are not straight, they curve toward the equator. The measurement of your true course depends on where you place the center of your plotter and it does make a difference. In the figure shown, flying from 33°N 160°W to 33°N 150°W should, intuitively, require a 090° true course. The actual course, however, depends on what you want: the starting, mid, or ending course.*

Why is this important? Most flight planning services offer either the starting or midpoint courses. Some pilots want to know what their initial course will be, others want the average course on the entire leg. It is a matter of personal preference. (I prefer using the midpoint course, since it gives you the most line for your plotter and gives you the easiest, most accurate plot. Of course I have to keep that in mind at each waypoint passage, since the FMS will be giving me the initial course.)

Course Line

In the example we draw a line from 50°N 030°W and 51°N 020°W.

Initial Course

Placing the center of the plotter compass on our initial point and the course line on top of the endpoint we see our initial true course is 077°.

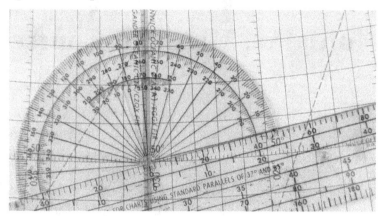

Midpoint Course

Placing the center of the plotter compass on the midpoint, 025°W in our example, we see the true course will be 081°.

We can check this mathematically using ten-degree tables at 50°N. See the Appendices, Chapter 37, True Course Ten-Degree Tables.

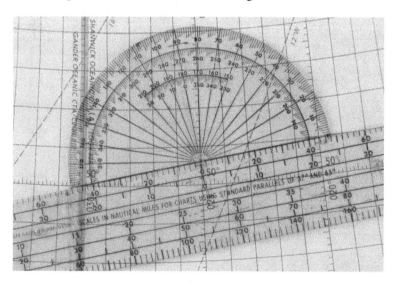

Chapter 4

Class I versus Class II

*S*o what is the difference between Class I and Class II airspace and why *should* you care? The difference boils down to your proximity to navigational aids and being in one or the other determines your ATC separation standards. While many pilots think it determines your plotting requirements that is not true.

Class I Navigation

[AC 91-70A, ¶10-1.i.] Class I navigation is any en route flight operation conducted in controlled or uncontrolled airspace that is entirely within operational service volumes of ICAO standard NAVAIDs (GNSS, VOR, VOR/DME, and NDB). The operational service volume describes a three-dimensional volume of airspace which categorizes any type of en route navigation as Class I navigation. Within this volume of airspace, IFR navigational performance must be at least as precise as IFR navigation and must use GNSS, VOR, and VOR/DME (or NDB in some countries). The definition of Class I navigation is not dependent upon the equipment installed in the aircraft. En route a VFR flight navigated by pilotage is conducting Class I navigation when operating entirely within the operational service volume. However, the VFR navigational performance in this example must be as precise as VFR pilotage operations are required to be. The operational service volumes of ICAO standard NAVAIDs solely determine the lateral and vertical extent of airspace where you conduct Class I navigation. You cannot conduct Class I navigation outside of this airspace.

(1) VFR or IFR Navigation Operations. Class I navigation also includes VFR or IFR navigation operations on the following:

- Federal airways.
- Published IFR direct routes in the United States.
- Published IFR off-airway routes in the United States.

Airways, Advisory Routes (ADR), direct routes, and off-airway routes published or approved by a foreign government provided that these routings are continuously within the operational service volume (or foreign equivalent) of ICAO standard NAVAIDs.

(2) Separation Minimums. Class I navigation requirements are directly related to separation minimums used by ATC. IFR separation minimums applied in the U.S. National Airspace System (NAS) and most other countries are based on the use of ICAO standard NAVAIDs. ATC, however, can only apply these separation minimums within areas where the NAVAIDs signal in space meets flight inspection signal strength and course quality standards. An ICAO standard NAVAID's signal in space conforms to flight inspection signal strength and course quality standards (including frequency protection) within its designated operational service volume. Therefore, you can predicate air navigation and the safe separation of aircraft within that service volume on the use of these facilities.

(3) Qualifications for Class I Navigation. Within areas where the safe separation of aircraft is based on the use of ICAO standard NAVAIDs, navigate any IFR operation with at least the same precision specified by the appropriate national separation minimums. Any operation or portion of an operation (VFR or IFR) in controlled or uncontrolled airspace with any navigation system (VOR, VOR/DME, NDB, inertial navigation system (INS) and GNSS) is Class I navigation for that portion of the route that is entirely within the operational service volume of ICAO standard en route NAVAIDs.

According to this advisory circular, if you have good GNSS / GPS reception, you are in Class I airspace. I've heard from a management pilot at a major airline that the author of this document admitted it was a mistake. Class I airspace is defined by ground navaids. But that was in 2010 and the advisory circular has not been updated.

Class II Navigation

[AC 91-70A, ¶10-1.j.] Class II navigation is any en route operation not categorized as Class I navigation and includes any operation, or portion of an operation, that takes place outside the operational service volumes of ICAO standard NAVAIDs. For example, an aircraft equipped with only VOR conducts Class II navigation when the flight operates in an area outside the operational service volumes of federal VORs/DMEs.

(2) Class II Navigation Definition. The definition of Class II navigation is not dependent upon the equipment installed in the aircraft. All airspace outside the operational service volume of ICAO standard NAVAIDs is a three-dimensional volume of airspace within which any type of en route navigation is Class II navigation. For any type of navigation within this volume of airspace, the IFR navigational performance must be as precise as the navigational performance assumed during establishment of the ATC separation minimums for that volume of airspace. The navigational performance for VFR operations in a Class II navigation volume of airspace must be only as precise as VFR navigation operations are required to be.

Standard High Altitude Service Volumes

You can have a navaid tuned and identified far outside its service volume, which means it doesn't count when making the plot / don't plot decision. Typical service volumes from [Aeronautical Information Manual, ¶1-1-8]:

- Standard High Altitude Service Volume between 18,000 and 45,000 ft: 130 nm

- Standard Low Altitude Service Volume between 1,000 and 18,000 ft: 40 nm

- Standard Terminal Service Volume between 1,000 and 12,000 ft: 25 nm

- NDB HH Service Volume: 75 nm

- NDB MH Service Volume: 25 nm

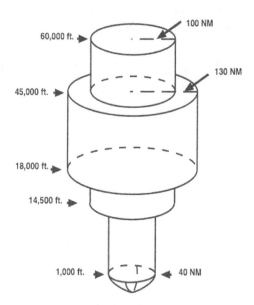

Figure: Standard High Altitude Service Volumes, from Aeronautical Information Manual, Figure 1-1-1.

Chapter 5

Plotting

W *e plot to avoid the classic one-degree error, to double-check the other pilot's FMS entries, to ensure the flight plan uplink was accurate, and to make sure the database itself is accurate.*

But wait, you say. The database itself has been QC'd, you've already checked the waypoints in the FMS, and your G450's graphical presentation makes any kind of graphical plotting completely pointless!

Well, you might have a point. You aren't going to get the standard "Ten percent of the traffic is general aviation but they are responsible for ninety percent of the gross navigational errors!" from me. That is a lie. Most of the GNEs belong to the airlines but they pay the bills and their errors are smoothed over by their companies. See, I can make a bold statement with no facts to back me up too.

But, back to the task at hand, the book says plot and maybe there is something out there lurking we don't know. Besides, lives could have been saved had plotting procedures been used. Just ask those on Korean Airlines Flight 007.

What follows comes from the references shown below. Where I think it helpful, I've added my own comments in blue.

Plotting Myths Busted

Myth: You don't need to plot over fixed track systems, like the ones between Hawaii and California

Just because the route doesn't change on a daily basis doesn't mean you or your FMS will not make mistakes. The distance between ground-based navigation aids far exceeds those required by FAA Order 8900.1, Volume 4, Chapter 1, Paragraph 4-80.A, you must plot.

A quick look at a few pilot blogs and postings confirms that few airlines require plotting over fixed track systems. Listening to the HF I've heard one or two chewed out for getting it wrong and I've heard from a POI or two that they get it wrong more often than we in the corporate world. (They get fewer violations because their companies pay most of the cost of operating the system.) But in this day and age, how are these navigation errors possible?

I think the leading cause of these navigation errors is complacency. But you could find yourself in trouble from another source. Chances are you are getting your oceanic waypoints via an uplink and those waypoints are coming from a computer. The computer got them from someone. If that someone made a mistake, chances are it will have been caught by another airplane before you. But what if you are the first after a database update? In the years since I've flown with uplinked waypoints I've caught three database errors, though none were oceanic. In my view, taking a few minutes to plot is a small price to pay to keep from hitting another airplane.

Myth: As long as you have a navaid tuned, you don't need to plot.

You can have a navaid tuned and identified far outside its service volume, which means it doesn't count when making the plot / don't plot decision. See Section II, Chapter 5.

Myth: You don't have to plot in Class I airspace.

Plotting requirements have never been tied to Class I or Class II airspace. See Section II, Chapter 5.

When is Plotting Required?

[Advisory Circular 91-70A, ¶3-6.a.]

(2) Turbojet Operations. All turbojet operations, where the route segment between the operational service volume of ICAO standard ground-based NAVAIDs exceeds 725 nm, require plotting procedures.

(3) Turboprop Operations. All turboprop operations, where the route segment between the operational service volume of ICAO standard ground-based NAVAIDs exceeds 450 nm, require plotting procedures.

(4) The Administrator requires plotting procedures for routes of shorter duration that transit airspace where special conditions exist, such as reduced lateral and vertical separation standards, high density traffic, proximity, or potentially hostile border areas.

[FAA Order 8900.1 Volume 4, Chapter 1, Paragraph 4-80.A] Plotting procedures have had a significant impact on the reduction of gross navigational errors. There is a requirement to plot the route of flight on a plotting chart and to plot the computer position, approximately 10 minutes after waypoint passage. Plotting may or may not be required, depending upon the distance between the standard ICAO ground-based NAVAIDs.

Where did these numbers come from? They appear to be arbitrary. The original version of this advisory circular came out September 6, 1994 and has the same 725 and 450 nautical mile requirements. There does not appear to be an ICAO specification. As I continue to search for the evolution of the 725 number I remind myself that I don't know everything and if the book tells me I must plot beyond 725 nautical miles from the service volume of an ICAO standard ground-based navaid, that's what I do.

Why is Plotting Required?

[Advisory Circular 91-70A, ¶3-6.a.(6)] The FAA requires crews to use a plotting chart to provide themselves with a visual presentation of the intended route. Regardless of the type of LRNS in use, operators must use plotting charts. Plotting the route will increase SA and reveal errors or discrepancies in the navigational coordinates that flight crews can correct before such errors can cause a deviation from the ATC cleared route. As the flight progresses, plotting the position approximately 10 minutes after passing each waypoint helps confirm that the flight is on course. If the plotted position indicates off track, the flight may have deviated unintentionally and the flight crew should investigate at once.

In the example chart, the crew has made a one-degree error in the FMS. After ten minutes the plotted position clearly shows something is wrong, allowing the crew to fix things before they stray too far off course.

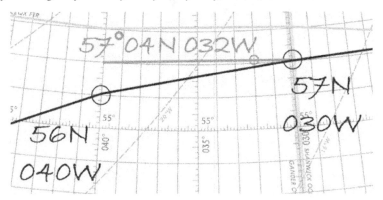

How is a common plotting chart laid out?

[ICAO Annex 4]

2.1.7 Recommendation.— The charts should be True North orientated.

2.15.1 True North and magnetic variation shall be indicated. The order of resolution of magnetic variation shall be that as specified for a particular chart.

2.15.2 Recommendation.— When magnetic variation is shown on a chart, the values shown should be those for the year nearest to the date of publication that is divisible by 5, i.e. 1980, 1985, etc.

2.18.1.1 World Geodetic System — 1984 (WGS-84) shall be used as the horizontal (geodetic) reference system. Published aeronautical geographical coordinates (indicating latitude and longitude) shall be expressed in terms of the WGS-84 geodetic reference datum.

2.18.2.1 Mean sea level (MSL) datum, which gives the relationship of gravity-related height (elevation) to a surface known as the geoid, shall be used as the vertical reference system.

Apart from saying the chart should be north up, must be based on WGS-84 and mean sea level, the chart printers are pretty much given discretion on how to print their plotting charts. There are some basic guidelines you should know for the chart you are using:

- *The horizontal lines are "parallels of latitude," usually a line for every degree with a major line every five degrees.*

- *The vertical lines are "meridians of longitude," with a line for every degree with a major line every five degrees.*

- *Longitude and latitude are subdivided into 60 parts known as minutes and labeled with a single quote mark (').*

- *Minutes are further subdivided into 60 parts known as seconds and labeled with double quote marks (").*

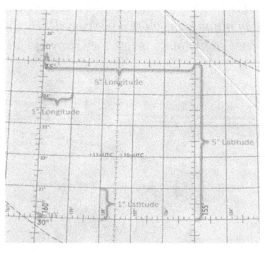

- *Bedford (KBED) airport, for example is at 42°28'11.8" N, 71°17'20.4" W; which is pronounced "forty-two degrees, twenty-eight minutes, eleven point eight seconds north, seventy-one degrees, seventeen minutes, twenty point four seconds west.*

How to Plot a Position

There are many techniques on how to do this correctly, here is mine:

- *Ensure you are in the correct quadrant: In the north the latitudes increase as you go up, in the south they increase as you go down. In the west the longitudes go up as you head west, in the east the go up as you head further east. Locate the nearest five degree line in the area of your point, in the example 30° N.*

- *Locate the five degree line just above your latitude, in our example 35° N.*

- *If your chart has one degree markings locate the nearest degree below your point, otherwise count the degree lines. In our example 33° N.*

- *Count the tick marks between degree lines on the chart you are using. In our example there are six so we conclude each tick mark represents 10 minutes of latitude. Counting up four tick marks we identify 30°40' N latitude.*

- *Notice that a line connecting 33°40' N 150° W and 33°40' N 160° W does not cross 33°40' N 155° W, it runs high. That's because the chart is a Conformal Projection which bends toward the poles. To get a more accurate position, we need to find the 33°40' point on the scale closest to our position.*

- *When dealing with longitude, we look for the nearest five degree line under our desired position, in our example 155° W.*

- *Then we look for the nearest five degree line greater than our desired position, in our example 160° W.*

- *We can now locate the nearest degree under our*

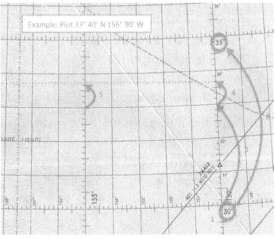

position, in our example 156° W.

- *Counting the tick marks, we see there are six so 30' of longitude will be three greater.*

- *Unlike latitude, lines of longitude appear parallel between lines of latitude, so we can draw a line at 156°30' W between tick marks and it will remain accurate.*

- *We then transpose our mark identifying 33°40' N to this line of longitude and viola, we have our position.*

How to Plot a True Course

A plotter is nothing more than a circular instrument designed to give angular differences between lines. A navigation plotter, such as the Jeppesen model shown, will typically have a hole in the center of a compass rose. To use:

- *Decide if you want the start, mid, or ending course. Most pilots will need the start course.*

- *Place the hole in the center of the compass rose over a line of longitude near the desired point, in our example we've used 40°W which is also the longitude of our start point.*

- *Align the line along the 0° mark to your desired course. You may find it helpful to insert your pencil or pen point in the hole while rotating the plotter to line up with your course.*

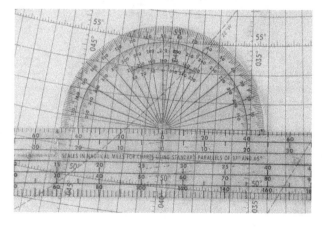

- *Read the true course along the line of selected longitude, 085° in our example.*

Note: You will have two choices aligned with the line of longitude, 085° and 275° in our example. In most cases it will be the number on top, but when dealing with courses near vertical it can be confusing. Always remember to give your answer a common sense check. In our example, we are headed to Europe and the answer should be generally easterly.

How to Measure Distance

[AFM 51-40, Page 5-8.]

- One of the disadvantages of the Lambert Conformal chart is the lack of a constant scale. If the two points between which the distance is to be measured are approximately in a north-south direction and the total distance between them can be spanned, the distance can be measured on the latitude scale opposite the midpoint. However, the total distance between any two points that do not lie approximately north or south of each other should be be spanned unless the distance is short. All distances should be measured as near the mid latitude as possible.

- In the measurement of long distances, select a mid latitude lying approximately half-way between the latitudes of the two points. By using dividers set to a convenient, reasonably short distance, such as 60 nautical miles picked off at the mid latitude scale, you may determine an approximate distance by marking off units along the line to be measures as shown [in the figure].

- The scale at mid latitude is accurate enough if the course line does not cover more than 5 degrees of latitude (somewhat less at high latitudes). If the course line exceeds this amount or if it crosses the equator, divide it into two or more legs and measure the length of each leg with the scale of its own mid latitude.

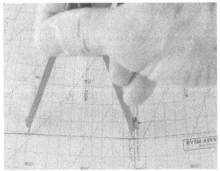

If you have a set of dividers and a flat surface you aren't afraid to scratch, finding the distance between waypoints is quite easy. First, place the points of the dividers on the start and end waypoints.

Next, find a line of longitude near the course line. It is important to use a line of longitude about the same latitude as the course, since these will change over great distances. Each degree of latitude equals 60 nautical miles.

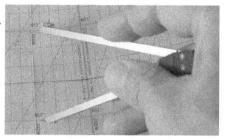

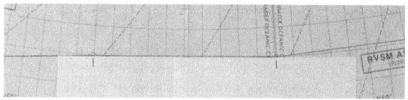

If you don't have a set of dividers — do you really want to have such a sharp instrument in the cockpit? — you can construct your own with a PostIt note or other straight-edged paper. You will be accurate within a nautical mile if you do it this way:

- Place the straight-edged paper along side the course. In our example, the PostIt note isn't long enough so we've used two, overlapping, notes.

- Place a tick mark at the starting and ending waypoints.

- Move the straight-edged paper to the nearest line of longitude at about the same latitude. Place one tick mark over a convenient line of latitude, 49°N in our example.

- Read the distance from the ending tick mark, using 60 nautical miles per degree. In our example the distance covers at least 6° of latitude, which comes to 360 nautical miles. The mark goes further by a tenth of a degree, meaning another 10 nautical miles. We conclude the distance between waypoints is therefore 370 nautical miles.

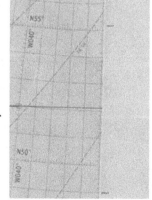

Note: You can also determine the distance using a set of "10 Degree Tables," where we would see the exact distance is actually 369 nautical miles. (Our PostIt note was off by 1 nautical mile, or had an error rate of 0.27 percent, not bad. [See the Appendices, Chapter 37, True Course Ten-Degree Tables.]

How to Determine a Magnetic Course

To determine the magnetic course, you will need to add or subtract the variation:

- *Look for the nearest lines of magnetic variation on the chart before and after the midpoint and interpolate if necessary.*

- *If the variation is West, add this value to the true course to determine magnetic course. If the variation is East, subtract this value from the true course to determine magnetic course:*

TC + West Variation = MC

TC - East Variation = MC

In our example, it appears our midpoint is very close to the "16°W" line of variation and no interpolation is necessary. Based on this we add 16 to our 270 true course and verify that our FMS and flight plan show a 286° magnetic course plus or minus a few degrees.

Note: It is not uncommon to find differences of 2 or 3 degrees in the magnetic course determined from a plotting chart and that reported in a computer flight plan. The magnetic variation changes over the years and your chart may be dated or hasn't been updated with the correct variation.

How to determine the position of a VOR radial/DME

There are many ways to turn a VOR radial/dme into a latitude and longitude, the best of these may very well be inside your FMS. If you need to do this on a plotting chart, this method works well:

- *Place the plotter hole over the VOR in question and your pencil point in the hole to hold the plotter centered over the VOR. (CON in our example.)*

- *Find the nearest line of variation. (6° West in our example.)*

- *Rotate the edge of the plotter to 360° in the northern hemisphere, 180° in the southern hemisphere, and then rotate toward the magnetic pole by the amount of the variation. (Rotate 6° to the west, in our example.)*

- *Move your pencil from the center hole to the straight line of the plotter that describes the line to the magnetic pole, move the plotter so the straight edge connects that point to the VOR. Draw a line with a flag on it from the VOR in the direction of the pole. Label this line "360° Mag" if you like. (In our example the flag points slightly left.*

- *Now return the plotter center hole to the VOR and rotate it in relation to your 360° Mag line by the number of degrees in the VOR radial. Draw a line as you did earlier by placing a tick mark, moving the plotter, and drawing the line. (In our example the line is 15° clockwise from the Magnetic north line.)*

- *Determine the distance using the Distance Measuring techniques shown above. Place a tick mark on the VOR line. (015°/85 DME in our example.)*

- *The latitude and longitude can be read directly from the chart using the Plot a Position techniques shown above. (55°15'N 8°25'W in our example.)*

If you are doing this to check the accuracy of your FMS, you might have easier tools at your disposal. [See the Appendices, Chapter 27, Navigation Accuracy Check.]

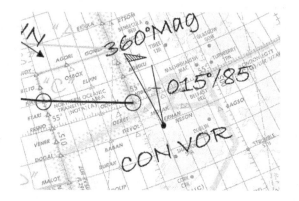

Chapter 6

Reduced Vertical Separation Minimums (RVSM)

*I*t is becoming next to impossible to fly just about anywhere in the world *without RVSM. You need to know more than just where it is in effect, the rules for getting you and your aircraft RVSM qualified, and how to keep your aircraft eligible to fly through RVSM airspace by conducting regular performance checks. You also need to know the country-specific rules that may not be what you are expecting in terms of flight level selection and contingency procedures.*

General

[AC 91-85]

- RVSM airspace is any airspace or route between FL 290 and FL 410 inclusive where aircraft are separated vertically by 1,000 ft (300 m).

- The RVSM Flight Level Orientation Scheme generally incorporates all odd flight levels from FL290 to FL410, inclusive, for aircraft on a magnetic course from 000° to 179°. The even flight levels from FL300 to FL400, inclusive, are used by aircraft of a magnetic course from 180 to 359. Regional exceptions are noted in ICAO Document 7030.

- RVSM airspace is special qualification airspace; the operator and the aircraft used by the operator must be approved by the Administrator through an FAA letter of authorization (Part 91) or operations specifications (Part 135). [14 CFR 91, Appendix G]

- RVSM has been implemented in most areas of the world above FL290. Differences in altitudes, contingency procedures, offset or other spacing procedures are covered in applicable oceanic en route charts, Jeppesen Airway Manual ATC State pages, and ICAO Document 7030.

Location

Most of the world. The exceptions are becoming rarer and you will have to check the Jeppesen State pages prior to every trip to be sure. Implementation varies by country:

- Africa / Indian Ocean. Between FL 290 and FL 410, inclusive, in selected FIRs. Consult AIPs, Jeppesen State Pages, and ICAO Document 7030, Regional Supplementary Procedures.

- Caribbean. Between FL 290 and FL 410, inclusive.

- Europe. Between FL 290 and FL 410, inclusive, except some portions of Eastern Europe. Consult AIPs, Jeppesen State Pages, and ICAO Document 7030, Regional Supplementary Procedures.

- North Atlantic. Between FL 290 and FL 410, inclusive.

- Middle East/Asia. Normally between FL 290 and FL 410, inclusive, in selected FIRs. In China, between FL 8,900m (FL 291) and FL 12,500m (FL 411), inclusive, in selected FIRs. Consult AIPs, Jeppesen State Pages, and ICAO Document 7030, Regional Supplementary Procedures.

- North America. Between FL 290 and FL 410, inclusive.

- Pacific. Between FL 290 and FL 410, inclusive, though FL 410 is available for non-RVSM approved flights. There are exceptions; consult AIPs, Jeppesen State Pages, and ICAO Document 7030, Regional Supplementary Procedures.

- South America. Between FL290 and FL410, inclusive.

Accuracy / Performance Standards

[AC 91-85 ¶6.b.] Altimetry System Error (ASE). The difference between the pressure altitude displayed to the flight crew when referenced to International System of Units (SI) standard ground pressure setting (29.92 in. Hg/1013.25 hPa) and free stream pressure altitude.

[AC 91-85 ¶8.c.(3)] The requirements in the basic RVSM envelope are as follows:

(a) At the point in the basic RVSM envelope where ASE mean reaches its largest absolute value, the absolute value should not exceed 80 ft (25 m).

(b) At the point in the basic RVSM envelope where ASE mean plus ASE3 SD reaches its largest absolute value, the absolute value should not exceed 200 ft (60 m).

[AC 91-85 ¶8.c.(4) The requirements in the full RVSM envelope are as follows:

(a) At the point in the full RVSM envelope where ASE mean reaches its largest absolute value, the absolute value should not exceed 120 ft (37 m).

(b) At the point in the full RVSM envelope where ASE mean plus of ASE3 SD reaches its largest absolute value, the absolute value should not exceed 245 ft (75 m).

The RVSM tolerance seems to be specified as tight as 80 feet but then gets confused with additives of standard deviation that bring that number as high as 245 ft.

[AC 91-85 ¶8.d.] Altitude Keeping. An automatic altitude control system should be required, and it should be capable of controlling altitude within ±65 ft (±20 m) about the acquired altitude when operated in straight and level flight under non turbulent, non gust conditions.

So how accurate does your aircraft altitude have to be? The regulations are filled with formulas based on large fleets of aircraft and do not give a cut and dried answer. For our purposes you need to keep the following two numbers in mind:

- *65 feet — Your altitude keeping device should be able to keep the airplane within 65 feet of assigned altitude.*

- *200 feet — You must notify ATC if your altimeters differ by 200 feet or more. (See Operating Practices, below.)*

Documentation / Certification

[AC 91-85 ¶12.g.]

(1) Authorization for parts 121, 125, 129, and 135 operators to operate in RVSM airspace should be granted through the issuance of an OpSpec paragraph from Part B (En Route Authorizations, Limitations, and Procedures) and Part D (Aircraft Maintenance). Each aircraft type group for which the operator is granted authority should be listed in OpSpecs. Authorization to conduct RVSM operations in an RVSM area of operations that is new to the

operator should be granted by adding the part B RVSM OpSpecs paragraph number to the appropriate area of operations in the Part B paragraph: Authorized Areas of En Route Operation Limitations and Procedures.

(2) Part 91K operators' authorization to operate in RVSM airspace should be granted through the issuance of a management specifications (MSpecs) paragraph from Part B and Part D. Each aircraft type group for which the operator is granted authority should be listed in MSpecs. Authorization to conduct RVSM operations in an RVSM area of operation that is new to the operator should be granted by adding the Part B RVSM MSpecs paragraph number to the appropriate area of operations in the Part B paragraph.

(3) Part 91 operators and part 125 operators holding a LODA should be issued an initial letter of authorization (LOA) when the initial authorization process has been completed. Part 91 operators are not required to obtain a new or amended LOA to operate in individual areas of operation where RVSM is implemented. For example, an operator that has obtained an LOA and is conducting RVSM operations in the North Atlantic is not required to obtain another LOA to conduct RVSM operations in the domestic United States.

(4) Operators issued OpSpecs are not required to also obtain an LOA for those operations when they are conducted under part 91, provided that:

(a) The aircraft is operated under the operator name listed on the OpSpecs.

(b) The flight is conducted in an area of operations listed in the OpSpecs.

(c) The aircraft is operated under the conditions under which the OpSpecs were granted (e.g., if the operator holds part 135 OpSpecs, then the pilots used for the part 91 operation must have received part 135 training. If this is not the case, then an LOA would be required).

If you want to fly just about anywhere in the world between FL290 and FL410, you are going to need an LOA or OpSpecs issued by your country of registration.

Aircraft Monitoring

[AC 91-85 ¶12.d.(8)] The operator should provide a plan for participation in the RVSM monitoring program. This program should normally entail a check of at least a portion of the operator's aircraft by an independent height-monitoring system. The FAA RVSM Documentation Web site at http://www.faa.gov/about/office_org/headquarters_offices/ato/service_units/enroute/rvsm/ contains guidance on monitoring programs for specific areas of operation.

[Reduced Vertical Separation Minimum (RVSM) Monitoring Requirements, page 1.]

- Operators, that have been issued a U.S. RVSM approval, shall ensure that a minimum of two airplanes of each [RVSM] aircraft type grouping of the operator have their height - keeping performance monitored, at least once every two years or within intervals of 1,000 flight hours per airplane, whichever period is longer. If an operator aircraft type grouping consists of a single airplane, monitoring of that airplane shall be accomplished within the specified period.

- Operators that have been issued a U.S. RVSM authorization will be required to conduct initial monitoring within six months of date of issue and must conduct monitoring every two years or within intervals of 1,000 flight hours per aircraft, whichever period is longer, in accordance with the aircraft categories as presented in the current version of the (North American) RVSM Minimum Monitoring Requirements chart.

Your aircraft needs to be monitored at least once every two years and you should carry documentation attesting to that. If you have more than two aircraft of the same type, you might not need to have every aircraft monitored. See the RVSM Minimum Monitoring Requirements chart available at http://www. faa.gov/about/office_org/headquarters_offices/ato/service_units/enroute/ rvsm/documentation/#req. Some corporate aircraft, like the G450, qualify for the two aircraft per fleet proviso. Others require at least 60% or even 100% monitoring. If you have more than two aircraft of the same type, it would be worth your trouble to investigate further.

Equipment Requirements

[AC 91-85 ¶9.a.] The minimum equipment fit should be as follows:

(1) Two Independent Altitude Measurement Systems. Each system should be composed of the following elements:

(a) Cross-coupled static source/system, provided with ice protection if located in areas subject to ice accretion;

(b) Equipment for measuring static pressure sensed by the static source, converting it to pressure altitude and displaying the pressure altitude to the flight crew;

(c) Equipment for providing a digitally coded signal corresponding to the displayed pressure altitude, for automatic altitude reporting purposes;

(d) SSEC, if needed to meet the performance requirements of paragraphs 8c(3) and 8c(4), or 8c(8), as appropriate; and

(e) The equipment fit should provide reference signals for automatic control and alerting at selected altitude. These signals should preferably be derived from an altitude measurement system meeting the full requirements of this document, but must in all cases meet the requirements of paragraphs 9b(6) and 9c. (See Appendix 7 for additional guidance for configurations found on older model "legacy" airplanes for which RVSM approval is sought.)

(2) One Secondary Surveillance Radar (SSR) Altitude Reporting Transponder. If only one is fitted, it should have the capability for switching to obtain input from either altitude measurement system.

(3) An Altitude Alert System. The altitude alert system should be capable of operation from either of the two required independent altitude measurement systems.

(4) An Automatic Altitude Control System. The automatic altitude control system should be capable of operation from either of the two required independent altitude measurement systems.

The altitude alert system is required to activate when altitude deviates more than 300' (aircraft certified before 1997) or 200' (aircraft certified after 1997).

Operating Practices

Flight Planning

[AC 91-85, Appendix 4, ¶2.]

a. Verifying that the aircraft is approved for RVSM operations.

b. Annotating the flight plan to be filed with the Air Traffic Service Provider to show that the aircraft and operator are authorized for RVSM operations.

Preflight Procedures

[AC 91-85, Appendix 4, ¶3.]

a. Review maintenance logs and forms to ascertain the condition of equipment required for flight in the RVSM airspace. Ensure that maintenance action has been taken to correct defects to required equipment.

b. During the external inspection of aircraft, pay particular attention to the condition of static sources and the condition of the fuselage skin near each static source and any other component that affects altimetry system accuracy.

c. Before takeoff, the aircraft altimeters should be set to the local altimeter atmospheric pressure at nautical height (QNH) setting and should display a known elevation (e.g., field elevation) within the limits specified in aircraft operating manuals. The difference between the known elevation and the elevation displayed on the altimeters should not exceed 75 ft. The two primary altimeters should also agree within limits specified by the aircraft operating manual. An alternative procedure using atmospheric pressure at field elevation (QFE) may also be used;

d. Before takeoff, equipment required for flight in RVSM airspace should be operational, and indications of malfunction should be resolved.

In-flight Procedures

[AC 91-85, Appendix 4, ¶5.]

a. During cleared transition between levels, the aircraft should not be allowed to overshoot or undershoot the cleared flight level by more than 150 ft (45 m);

b. NOTE: It is recommended that the level off be accomplished using the altitude capture feature of the automatic altitude-control system, if installed.

c. An automatic altitude-control system should be operative and engaged during level cruise, except when circumstances such as the need to retrim the aircraft or turbulence require disengagement. In any event, adherence to cruise altitude should be done by reference to one of the two primary altimeters;

d. The altitude-alerting system should be operational;

e. At intervals of approximately 1 hour, make crosschecks between the primary altimeters and the stand-by altimeter. A minimum of two primary altimeters should agree within 200 ft (60 m) or a lesser value if specified in the aircraft operating manual.

The section goes on to say "The normal pilot scan of cockpit instruments should suffice for altimeter crosschecking on most flights." When oceanic, however, I would recommend recording altimeter performance on the master document.

Hourly Checks

[ICAO Doc 9574, ¶5.1.1.(e)] Regular (hourly) crosschecks between the altimeters should be made, and a minimum of two RVSM MASPS-compliant systems must agree within 60 m (200 ft). Failure to meet this condition will require that the system be reported as defective and notified to ATC.

Standby Altimeter Performance

While there are no in-flight standby altimeter tolerances which would necessitate an in-flight abort, the standby altimeter should be evaluated against 14 CFR 43, Appendix E tolerances for subsequent maintenance action. The tolerances are altitude dependent.

Contingencies

[AC 91-85, ¶4.b.]

(1) Do not interpret guidance for contingency procedures in any way that prejudices the final authority and responsibility of the pilot in command (PIC) for the safe operation of the aircraft.

(2) If the pilot is unsure of the vertical or lateral position of the aircraft or the aircraft deviates from its assigned altitude or track for cause without prior ATC clearance, then the pilot must take action to mitigate the potential for collision with aircraft on adjacent routes or flight levels.

NOTE: In this situation, the pilot should alert adjacent aircraft by making

Altitude	Equivalent pressure (inches of mercury)	Tolerance ±(feet)
0	29.921	20
1,000	28.856	20
2,000	27.821	30
4,000	25.842	35
6,000	23.978	40
8,000	22.225	60
10,000	20.577	80
12,000	19,029	90
14,000	17.577	100
16,000	16.216	110
18,000	14.942	120
20,000	13.750	130
22,000	12.636	140
25,000	11.104	155
30,000	8.885	180
35,000	7.041	205
40,000	5.538	230
45,000	4.355	255

Table: Standby Altimeter Tolerance, from 14 CFR 43, Appendix E., Table 1.

maximum use of aircraft lighting and broadcasting position, flight level (FL), and intentions on 121.5 megahertz (MHz) (as a back-up, the appropriate very high frequency (VHF) inter-pilot air-to-air frequency may be used).

(3) Unless the nature of the contingency dictates otherwise, the pilot should advise ATC as soon as possible of a contingency situation and if possible, request an ATC clearance before deviating from the assigned route or FL.

(4) If a revised ATC clearance cannot be obtained in a timely manner and action is required to avoid potential conflict with other aircraft, then the aircraft should:

(a) Acquire and maintain in either direction a track laterally separated by 28 km (15 nm) from the assigned route; and

(b) Once established on the offset track, climb or descend to select a FL which differs from those normally used by 150 m (500 ft);

(c) The pilot may also consider descending below FL 285 or climbing above FL 410. (The vast majority of oceanic traffic operates between FL 290 and

410. Flight above FL 410 or below FL 285 may limit exposure to conflict with other aircraft.)

(5) When executing a contingency maneuver the pilot should:

(a) Watch for conflicting traffic both visually and by reference to Airborne Collision Avoidance System (ACAS) or Traffic Alert and Collision Avoidance System (TCAS), if equipped.

(b) Continue to alert other aircraft using 121.5 MHz (as a back-up, the VHF inter-pilot air-to-air frequency (VHF 123.45) may be used) and aircraft lights.

(c) Continue to fly offset tracks or altitudes until an ATC clearance is obtained.

(d) Obtain an ATC clearance as soon as possible.

Chapter 7

Global Navigation Satellite System (GNSS)

A lot of rules for using GPS have changed over the years and what you can and cannot do also depends on where in the world you are.

For example, can you fly the "VOR Rwy 23" to Bedford, Massachusetts using GPS? No, the U.S. overlay program that said you could a few years ago was in Advisory Circular 90-94 which was cancelled in 2009. In the U.S., the approach has to have the term "GPS" in the title. What about the "VOR DME Rwy 31" to Sibu, Malaysia? Yes, they are WGS-84 compliant and ICAO rules say you can. In the case of the U.S. approach, it would be a good idea to have the GPS up for position awareness and in Malaysia you should probably have the VOR tuned for back up.

What about an approach that references GNSS and not GPS? Well, it depends. If your airplane lists it as a viable approach, if the country is WGS-84 compliant, and if the country's rules allow you to, then probably. It is a confusing world out there.

Overview

[FAA-H-8083-15B, pg. 9-25]

- The Department of Defense (DOD) developed and deployed GPS as a space-based positioning, velocity, and time system. The DOD is responsible for the operation of the GPS satellite constellation and constantly monitors the satellites to ensure proper operation. The GPS system permits Earth-centered coordinates to be determined and provides aircraft position referenced to the DOD World Geodetic System of 1984 (WGS-84). Satellite navigation systems are unaffected by weather and provide global navigation coverage that fully meet the civil requirements for use as the primary means of navigation in oceanic airspace and certain remote areas. Properly certified GPS equipment may be used as a supplemental means of IFR navigation for domestic en route, terminal operations, and certain IAPs. Navigational values, such as distance and bearing to a waypoint and groundspeed, are computed from the aircraft's current position (latitude and longitude) and the location of the next waypoint. Course guidance is provided as a linear deviation from the desired track of a great circle route between defined waypoints.

- The space element [of GPS] consists of 24 Navstar satellites. This group of satellites is called a constellation. The satellites are in six orbital planes (with four in each plane) at about 11,000 miles above the Earth. At least five satellites are in view at all times. The GPS constellation broadcasts a pseudo-random code timing signal and data message that the aircraft equipment processes to obtain satellite position and status data. By knowing the precise location of each satellite and precisely matching timing with the atomic clocks on the satellites, the aircraft receiver/processor can accurately measure the time each signal takes to arrive at the receiver and, therefore, determine aircraft position.

How GPS Works

There is obviously much more to it than what follows, but this gives you what you need to understand how GPS has changed the way we fly airplanes. . .

The Transmitted Signal

[AFAIS Performance-Based Navigation Presentation] Each Navstar satellite transmits on two frequencies:

- L1: 1575.42 MHz — C/A and P codes
- L2: 1227.6 MHz — P code only

Coarse Acquisition (C/A) code is available to all users without limitations and includes

- Ephemeris (position, altitude, speed information from the satellite)
- Time (from the onboard atomic clock, including a time correction factor to make up for the clock's internal errors)
- Satellite health status
- GPS Almanac (predicted positions for entire GPS constellation, often

good for months). A receiver that keeps the almanac in memory can predict from a cold start where to look for satellites, speeding acquisition times.

P-Code provides navigation/targeting data for U.S. government users with an encryption key:

- Position data

- Broadcast on both frequencies, allowing qualified receivers to compare both frequencies and correct for any ionospheric delays.

- Once decrypted P-code becomes Y-code.

[FAA-H-8083-15, pg. 7-22] The aircraft GPS receiver measures distance from a satellite using the travel time of a radio signal. Each satellite transmits a specific code, called a coarse/acquisition (CA) code, which contains information on the satellite's position, the GPS system time, and the health and accuracy of the transmitted data. Knowing the speed at which the signal traveled (approximately 186,000 miles per second) and the exact broadcast time, the distance traveled by the signal can be computed from the arrival time. The distance derived from this method of computing distance is called a pseudo-range because it is not a direct measurement of distance, but a measurement based on time. In addition to knowing the distance to a satellite, a receiver needs to know the satellite's exact position in space; this is know as its ephemeris. Each satellite transmits information about its exact orbital location. The GPS receiver uses this information to precisely establish the position of the satellite.

Each GPS satellite transmits these two frequencies and chances are your receiver captures the L1. There are no limits to the number of receivers since there is no interaction from these receivers back to the satellites. You will need four satellites to determine your position . . .

One satellite

Each satellite sends out a signal that includes its own position and the time. The receiver calculates the time it took the signal to travel and multiplies that by the speed of light) to compute the distance. That distance ("r" in the figure) defines a sphere. The receiver could be at any point on that sphere; more than just the black line, it is the entire outer shell of the sphere. This is true in theory but there is an issue with the time synchronization when dealing with only one satellite. (The problem goes away with more than one satellite since they can be synchronized. But we are just illustrating a point here.)

Two satellites

With two satellites you have an intersection of two spheres and the receiver could be in any position along those intersecting spheres. It is more than just the black lines in the diagram, your position could be at any point inside the three-dimensional shape described by the black line.

Three satellites

With three satellites you narrow the possible location down to one of two points (the two black points).

Four satellites

With one more satellite, you have narrowed the universe of possible intersections to just one (the single black point). Errors, of course, are possible.

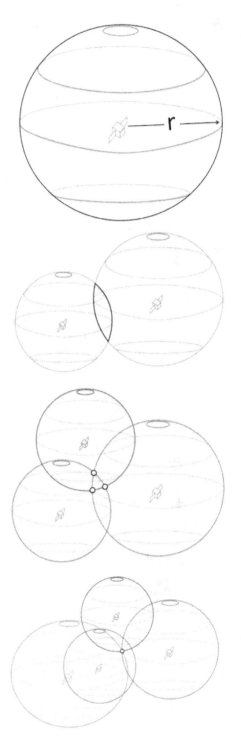

Position Errors

[AFAIS Performance-Based Navigation Presentation] Errors are possible due to:

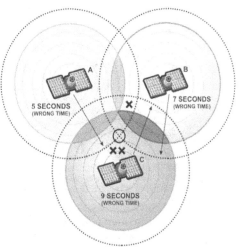

- Minor disturbances in satellite orbits from gravitational variations from the sun and the moon or solar wind.

- Ionospheric signal delays caused by water vapor in the atmosphere; this is the biggest source of signal error.

Figure: GPS Position errors, from AFAIS Performance-Based Navigation Presentation.

- Slight fluctuations in the satellite atomic clocks.

- Receiver quality (faulty clocks or internal noise).

- Multi-path signal reflections off structures.

Any errors from even a single satellite can throw off the estimated distance computations and therefore your estimated position. The drawing makes light of a 5 second error, but at the speed of light that would be 930,000 miles, exceeding the satellite's orbit. We must obviously be talking about very small time errors.

The performance of each satellite is measured and corrected to ensure accuracy . . .

GPS Ground Stations

[AFAIS Performance-Based Navigation Presentation] There are 6 monitoring stations, including the master station at Colorado Springs.

- Collect position and timing data from satellites every 12 hours.

- Send information to master control station.

- Master control station computes corrections and uploads to satellites.

Some receivers are capable of greater accuracy than others, but the issue isn't as extreme as some would have you believe . . .

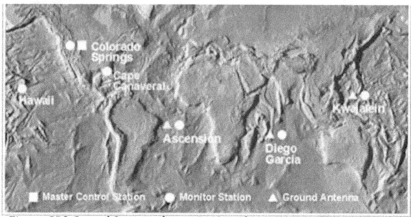

Figure: GPS Ground Stations, from AFAIS Performance-Based Navigation Presentation.

Positioning Services

[AFAIS Performance-Based Navigation Presentation]

Standard Positioning Service (SPS)

- Uses C/A code – for all users
- Single frequency (L1)

Precise Positioning Service (PPS)

- Uses P-code – for military
- Two frequencies (L1 and L2) – more accurate
- Requires Decryption Key do use it

Selective Availability

[AFAIS Performance-Based Navigation Presentation]

- Selective Availability was designed into the system to provide non-military or non-governmental users intentionally limited accuracy.
- The system was turned off in 2000 and we are told the newer satellites don't even have the capability.

As the world became more dependent on GPS they became more worried that one day the U.S. government would turn on selective availability and send airplanes into mountains. The U.S. government promises us that they've abandoned the concept entirely.

Satellite Tracks

The signal coverage is supposed to be worldwide, but the satellites do not cover the world. How can that be?

[http://www.colorado.edu/geography/gcraft/notes/gps/gps_f.html] The nominal GPS Operational Constellation consists of 24 satellites that orbit the earth in 12 hours. There are often more than 24 operational satellites as new ones are launched to replace older satellites. The satellite orbits repeat almost the same ground track (as the earth turns beneath them) once each day. The orbit altitude is such that the satellites repeat the same track and configuration over any point approximately each 24 hours (4 minutes earlier each day). There are six orbital planes (with nominally four SVs in each), equally spaced (60 degrees apart), and inclined at about fifty-five degrees with respect to the equatorial plane. This constellation provides the user with between five and eight SVs visible from any point on the earth.

There are some who say you cannot get a GPS signal at either pole because they are inclined at 55° from the equator, they even have anecdotal evidence.

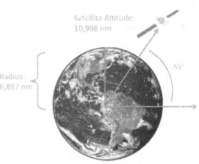

NASA offers a website to track each satellite and it is true they never get higher than 55° but there are lots of reports of excellent GPS signals at each pole. What gives?

Each GPS satellite traces a track over the earth from 55° North to 55° South every twelve hours. At their maximum latitudes they are actually "looking down" on the poles:

Height Above Pole=10998cos(55)–6887=2122

Of course you have no guarantee you will have at least one satellite that high in its orbit. In order to have line of sight on the pole, a satellite would have to be at least 39° latitude:

Minimum Latitude to See Pole=arcsin(6887/10998)=39

I've not found anything in writing that tells you there will always be at least four satellites above 39° North and 39° South, but it appears so. You should have a good GPS position at either pole.

GNSS versus GPS

[AC 20-138D, ¶1-4.e.(2)(a)] GNSS is used internationally to indicate any satellite-based positioning system or augmentation system. The acronym 'GNSS' includes satellite constellations, such as GPS, GLONASS, Galileo, or Beidou, along with augmentation systems such as 'SBAS' and 'GBAS'; all of which provide a satellite-based positioning service.

The Global Navigation Satellite System (GNSS) includes navigation satellites and ground systems that monitor satellite signals and provide corrections and integrity messages, where needed, to support specific phases of flight. Currently, there are two navigation satellite systems in orbit: the U.S. Global Positioning Satellite (GPS) System and the Russian global navigation satellite system (GLONASS). The U.S. and Russia have offered these systems as the basis for a GNSS, free of direct user charges.

So GPS is a subset of GNSS which means all GPS approaches are GNSS but not all GNSS approaches are GPS. If the approach is marked RNAV (GNSS) you might be okay, but you have some homework to do first: Is GNSS in your flight manual's list of allowed approaches? If you are a commercial operator, do you have the necessary OpSpec? Are there any host-nation prohibitions?

U.S. Requirements to Use GPS

General IFR Requirements

[Aeronautical Information Manual ¶1-1-19.d.]

1. Authorization to conduct any GPS operation under IFR requires that:

(a) GPS navigation equipment used must be approved in accordance with the requirements specified in Technical Standard Order (TSO) TSO-C129, or equivalent, and the installation must be done in accordance with Advisory Circular AC 20-138, Airworthiness Approval of Global Positioning System (GPS) Navigation Equipment for Use as a VFR and IFR Supplemental Navigation System, or Advisory Circular AC 20-130A, Airworthiness Approval of Navigation or Flight Management Systems Integrating Multiple Navigation Sensors, or equivalent. Equipment approved in accordance with TSO-C115a does not meet the requirements of TSO-C129. Visual flight rules (VFR) and hand-held GPS systems are not authorized for IFR navigation, instrument approaches, or as a principal instrument flight reference.

During IFR operations they may be considered only an aid to situational awareness.

(b) Aircraft using GPS navigation equipment under IFR must be equipped with an approved and operational alternate means of navigation appropriate to the flight. Active monitoring of alternative navigation equipment is not required if the GPS receiver uses RAIM for integrity monitoring. Active monitoring of an alternate means of navigation is required when the RAIM capability of the GPS equipment is lost.

(c) Procedures must be established for use in the event that the loss of RAIM capability is predicted to occur. In situations where this is encountered, the flight must rely on other approved equipment, delay departure, or cancel the flight.

(d) The GPS operation must be conducted in accordance with the FAA-approved aircraft flight manual (AFM) or flight manual supplement. Flight crew members must be thoroughly familiar with the particular GPS equipment installed in the aircraft, the receiver operation manual, and the AFM or flight manual supplement. Unlike ILS and VOR, the basic operation, receiver presentation to the pilot, and some capabilities of the equipment can vary greatly. Due to these differences, operation of different brands, or even models of the same brand, of GPS receiver under IFR should not be attempted without thorough study of the operation of that particular receiver and installation. Most receivers have a built-in simulator mode which will allow the pilot to become familiar with operation prior to attempting operation in the aircraft. Using the equipment in flight under VFR conditions prior to attempting IFR operation will allow further familiarization.

(e) Aircraft navigating by IFR approved GPS are considered to be area navigation (RNAV) aircraft and have special equipment suffixes. File the appropriate equipment suffix in accordance with TBL 5-1-2, on the ATC flight plan. If GPS avionics become inoperative, the pilot should advise ATC and amend the equipment suffix.

(f) Prior to any GPS IFR operation, the pilot must review appropriate NOTAMs and aeronautical information. (See GPS NOTAMs/Aeronautical Information.)

(g) Air carrier and commercial operators must meet the appropriate provisions of their approved operations specifications.

Section II - Aviate

IFR Oceanic

[Aeronautical Information Manual ¶1-1-19.e.1.] GPS IFR operations in oceanic areas can be conducted as soon as the proper avionics systems are installed, provided all general requirements are met. A GPS installation with TSO-C129 authorization in class A1, A2, B1, B2, C1, or C2 may be used to replace one of the other approved means of long-range navigation, such as dual INS. (See TBL 1-1-5 and TBL 1-1-6.) A single GPS installation with these classes of equipment which provide RAIM for integrity monitoring may also be used on short oceanic routes which have only required one means of long-range navigation.

Domestic En Route

[Aeronautical Information Manual ¶1-1-19.e.2.] GPS domestic en route and terminal IFR operations can be conducted as soon as proper avionics systems are installed, provided all general requirements are met. The avionics necessary to receive all of the ground-based facilities appropriate for the route to the destination airport and any required alternate airport must be installed and operational. Ground-based facilities necessary for these routes must also be operational.

Terminal Area Operations

[Aeronautical Information Manual ¶1-1-19.e.3.] The GPS Approach Overlay Program is an authorization for pilots to use GPS avionics under IFR for flying designated nonprecision instrument approach procedures, except LOC, LDA, and simplified directional facility (SDF) procedures. These procedures are now identified by the name of the procedure and "or GPS" (e.g., VOR/DME or GPS RWY 15). Other previous types of overlays have either been converted to this format or replaced with stand-alone procedures. Only approaches contained in the current onboard navigation database are authorized. The navigation database may contain information about non-overlay approach procedures that is intended to be used to enhance position orientation, generally by providing a map, while flying these approaches using conventional NAVAIDs. This approach information should not be confused with a GPS overlay approach (see the receiver operating manual, AFM, or AFM Supplement for details on how to identify these approaches in the navigation database).

[Aeronautical Information Manual ¶1-1-19.e.3.] Additionally:

72

- All approach procedures to be flown must be retrievable from the current airborne navigation database

- Prior to using a procedure or waypoint retrieved from the airborne navigation database, the pilot should verify the validity of the database.

- Determine that the waypoints and transition names coincide with names found on the procedure chart. Do not use waypoints, which do not exactly match the spelling shown on published procedure charts.

- Determine that the waypoints are generally logical in location, in the correct order, and that their orientation to each other is as found on the procedure chart, both laterally and vertically.

ICAO Requirements to Use GPS

[FAA-H-8083-15, pg. 7-21] GPS may not be approved for IFR use in other countries. Prior to its use, pilots should ensure that GPS is authorized by the appropriate countries.

WGS-84

[ICAO Doc 9613, Attachment 2, ¶3.4 a)] Navigation data may originate from survey observations, from equipment specifications/settings or from the airspace and procedure design process. Whatever the source, the generation and the subsequent processing of the data must take account of the following: (a) all coordinate data must be referenced to the World Geodetic System — 1984 (WGS-84).

Not every country uses the same system to map coordinates. While the differences are minor for en route navigation, they can be significant on approach. See the Appendices, Chapter 40, World Geodetic System 84 (WGS-84).

Operational Approval

[ICAO Doc 8168 Vol 1 ¶1.2.1]: Aircraft equipped with basic GNSS receivers (either as stand-alone equipment or in a multi-sensor environment) that have been approved by the State of the Operator for departure and non-precision approach operations may use these systems to carry out RNAV procedures provided that before conducting any flight, the following criteria are met: a) the GNSS equipment is serviceable; b) the pilot has a current knowledge of how to operate the equipment so as to achieve the optimum level of navigation performance; c) satellite availability is checked to support the intended operation; d) an alternate airport with conventional navaids has been selected; and e) the procedure is retrievable from an airborne navigation database.

Navigation Database

[ICAO Doc 8168 Vol 1 ¶1.2.3]: Departure and approach waypoint information is contained in a navigation database. If the navigation database does not contain the departure or approach procedure, then the basic GNSS stand-alone receiver or FMC shall not be used for these procedures.

Receiver Autonomous Integrity Monitoring (RAIM)

[AFAIS Performance-Based Navigation Presentation] For a GPS receiver to be certified for IFR navigation, it must have RAIM or an equivalent function. RAIM is simply a computer algorithm that evaluates the integrity of the GPS signal. That means it judges whether enough satellites are in view and in a good geometry to compute a sufficiently accurate position. RAIM checked now evaluates the current satellites in view. Predictive RAIM is based solely on the Almanac. In other words, RAIM uses the Almanac data to estimate where satellites are supposed to be for the future time entered. Sometimes, the number and position of satellites may result in an accuracy good enough only for certain phases of flight, ie, en route, terminal, or approach.

[Aeronautical Information Manual ¶1-1-19.a.]

3. Receiver Autonomous Integrity Monitoring (RAIM). When GNSS equipment is not using integrity information from WAAS or LAAS, the GPS navigation receiver using RAIM provides GPS signal integrity monitoring. RAIM is necessary since delays of up to two hours can occur before an erroneous satellite transmission can be detected and corrected by the satellite control segment. The RAIM function is also referred to as fault detection. Another capability, fault exclusion, refers to the ability of the receiver to exclude a failed satellite from the position solution and is provided by some GPS receivers and by WAAS receivers.

4. The GPS receiver verifies the integrity (usability) of the signals received from the GPS constellation through receiver autonomous integrity monitoring (RAIM) to determine if a satellite is providing corrupted information. At least one satellite, in addition to those required for navigation, must be in view for the receiver to perform the RAIM function; thus, RAIM needs

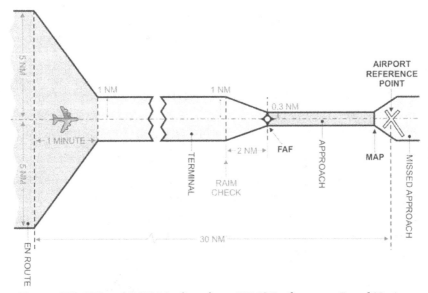

Figure: GPS CDI and RAIM Scaling, from AFAIS Performance-Based Navigation Presentation.

a minimum of 5 satellites in view, or 4 satellites and a barometric altimeter (baro-aiding) to detect an integrity anomaly. [Baro-aiding satisfies the RAIM requirement in lieu of a fifth satellite.] For receivers capable of doing so, RAIM needs 6 satellites in view (or 5 satellites with baro-aiding) to isolate the corrupt satellite signal and remove it from the navigation solution. Baro-aiding is a method of augmenting the GPS integrity solution by using a nonsatellite input source. GPS derived altitude should not be relied upon to determine aircraft altitude since the vertical error can be quite large and no integrity is provided. To ensure that baro-aiding is available, the current altimeter setting must be entered into the receiver as described in the operating manual.

5. RAIM messages vary somewhat between receivers; however, generally there are two types. One type indicates that there are not enough satellites available to provide RAIM integrity monitoring and another type indicates that the RAIM integrity monitor has detected a potential error that exceeds the limit for the current phase of flight. Without RAIM capability, the pilot has no assurance of the accuracy of the GPS position.

Fault Detection and Exclusion (FDE)

[FAA Order 8900.1, Vol. 4, Ch. 1, §4, ¶4-78.C.]

Definitions.

1.   Primary means of navigation—Navigation equipment that provides the only required means on the aircraft of satisfying the necessary levels of accuracy, integrity, and availability for a particular area, route, procedure, or operation.

2.   Class II navigation—Any en route flight operation or portion of an en route operation (irrespective of the means of navigation) which takes place outside (beyond) the designated operational service volume of ICAO standard airway navigation facilities (VOR, VOR/DME, NDB).

3.   Fault detection and exclusion (FDE)—Capability of GPS to:

a.   Detect a satellite failure which effects navigation; and

b.   Automatically exclude that satellite from the navigation solution.

4.   All operators conducting GPS primary means of Class II navigation in oceanic/remote areas under 14 CFR parts 91, 121, 125, or 135 must utilize an FAA-approved FDE prediction program for the installed GPS equipment that is capable of predicting, prior to departure, the maximum outage duration of the loss of fault exclusion, the loss of fault detection, and the loss of navigation function for flight on a specified route. The "specified route of flight" is defined by a series of waypoints (to include the route to any required alternates) with the time specified by a velocity or series of velocities. Since specific ground speeds may not be maintained, the pre-departure prediction must be performed for the range of expected ground speeds. This FDE prediction program must use the same FDE algorithm that is employed by the installed GPS equipment and must be developed using an acceptable software development methodology (e.g., RTCA/DO-178B). The FDE prediction program must provide the capability to designate manually satellites that are scheduled to be unavailable in order to perform the prediction accurately. The FDE prediction program will be evaluated as part of the navigation system's installation approval.

5.   Any predicted satellite outages that affect the capability of GPS equipment to provide the navigation function on the specified route of flight requires that the flight be canceled, delayed, or rerouted. If the fault exclu-

sion capability outage (exclusion of a malfunctioning satellite) exceeds the acceptable duration on the specific route of flight, the flight must be canceled, delayed, or rerouted.

6.   Prior to departure, the operator must use the FDE prediction program to demonstrate that there are no outages in the capability to navigate on the specified route of flight (the FDE prediction program determines whether the GPS constellation is robust enough to provide a navigation solution for the specified route of flight).

7.   Once navigation function is ensured (the equipment can navigate on the specified route of flight), the operator must use the FDE prediction program to demonstrate that the maximum outage of the capability of the equipment to provide fault exclusion for the specified route of flight does not exceed the acceptable duration (fault exclusion is the ability to exclude a failed satellite from the navigation solution). The acceptable duration (in minutes) is equal to the time it would take to exit the protected airspace (one-half the lateral separation minimum) assuming a 35-nautical mile (nm) per hour cross-track navigation system error growth rate when starting from the center of the route. For example, a 60-nm lateral separation minimum yields 51 minutes acceptable duration (30 nm divided by 35 nm per hour). If the fault exclusion outage exceeds the acceptable duration, the flight must be canceled, delayed, or rerouted.

This can be confusing so let's break it into a few pieces:

- *Class II navigation in oceanic/remote areas means anytime you are outside the service volume of authorized navigation aids. More about this: Airspace / Class I versus Class II.*

- *"GPS primary means of Class II navigation" means that the only way you have of long range navigation is GPS. If you have an IRS, you have another means.*

- *If your aircraft relies on GPS, and GPS only, for Class II navigation, your manufacturer should either provide or point you to a qualified FDE program you can load on a computer device to satisfy this requirement.*

Availability / NOTAMS

[Aeronautical Information Manual, §1-1-18, ¶a.2.(a)] The status of GPS satellites is broadcast as part of the data message transmitted by the GPS satellites. GPS status information is also available by means of the U.S. Coast Guard navigation information service: (703) 313–5907, Internet: http://www.navcen.uscg.gov/?Do=constellationStatus. Additionally, satellite status is available through the Notice to Airmen (NOTAM) system.

NOTAMS are available here: https://pilotweb.nas.faa.gov/PilotWeb/.

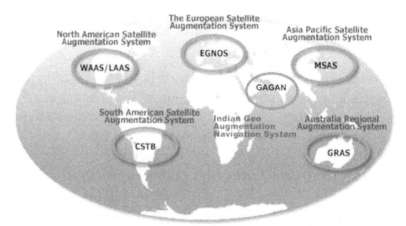

Figure: SBAS, from AFAIS PBN Presentation

Satellite-Based Augmentation System (SBAS)

[AC 20-138D, ¶1-4.e.(2)(b)] The acronyms 'SBAS' and 'GBAS' are the respective international designations for satellite-based and ground-based augmentation systems complying with the International Civil Aviation Organization (ICAO) standards and recommended practices (SARPs). Several countries have implemented their own versions of 'SBAS' and 'GBAS' that have specific names and acronyms. For example, WAAS is the U.S. implementation of an 'SBAS' while EGNOS is the European implementation.

[ICAO Doc 8168 - Aircraft Operations - Vol I, chapter 2, ¶2.1.]

- An SBAS augments core satellite constellations by providing ranging, integrity and correction information via geostationary satellites. The system comprises a network of ground reference stations that observe satellite signals, and master stations that process observed data and generate SBAS messages for uplink to the geostationary satellites, which broadcast the SBAS message to the users.

• By providing extra ranging signals via geostationary satellites and enhanced integrity information for each navigation satellite, SBAS delivers a higher availability of service than the core satellite constellations.

These geostationary satellites are above and beyond the GPS constellation. Their positions are constantly update by reference to the ground stations and provide a high degree of accuracy.

Accuracy

[AFAIS Performance-Based Navigation Presentation]

a. Lateral Accuracy - better than GPS — More like Localizer

b. Vertical Accuracy – much better than GPS — Good enough for Vertical Guidance (glideslope)

c. LPV minima — "Localizer Performance with Vertical Guidance" (GPS 95% Standard / GPS Actual Performance), (Horizontal 36m / 2.74m), (Vertical 77m / 3.89m)

	WAAS 95% Standard	WAAS Actual Performance
Horizontal	16 m	1.08 m
Vertical	4 m	1.26 m

WAAS

The U.S. implementation of SBAS is WAAS. The U.S. system is compatible with the European (EGNOS) and Asia Pacific (MSAS) systems.

[AC 90-107 ¶6.b.] WAAS improves the accuracy, integrity, availability and continuity of GPS signals. Additionally, the WAAS geostationary satellites provide ranging sources to supplement the GPS signals. If there are no airworthiness limitations on other installed navigation equipment, WAAS avionics enable aircraft navigation during all phases of flight from takeoff through vertically guided approaches and guided missed approaches. WAAS avionics with an appropriate airworthiness approval can enable aircraft to fly to the LPV, LP, LNAV/VNAV and LNAV lines of minima on RNAV (GPS) approaches. One of the major improvements WAAS provides is the ability to generate glide path guidance independent of ground equipment. Temperature and pressure extremes do not affect WAAS vertical guidance unlike when baro-VNAV is used to fly to LNAV/VNAV line of minima. However, like most other navigation services, the WAAS network has service volume limits, and some airports on the fringe of WAAS coverage may experience reduced availability of WAAS vertical guidance. When a pilot selects an approach procedure, WAAS avionics display the best level of service supported by the combination of the WAAS signal-in-space, the aircraft avionics, and the selected RNAV (GPS) instrument approach.

WAAS Channel Number/Approach ID

[AIM 5-4-5.m.7.(g)] The WAAS Channel Number is an optional equipment capability that allows the use of a 5–digit number to select a specific final approach segment without using the menu method. The Approach ID is an airport unique 4–character combination for verifying the selection and extraction of the correct final approach segment information from the aircraft database. It is similar to the ILS ident, but displayed visually rather than aurally. The Approach ID consists of the letter W for WAAS, the runway number, and a letter other than L, C or R, which could be confused with Left, Center and Right, e.g., W35A. Approach IDs are assigned in the order that WAAS approaches are built to that runway number at that airport. The WAAS Channel Number and Approach ID are displayed in the upper left corner of the approach procedure pilot briefing.

Depending on your avionics suite, approach verification may depend on the WAAS Channel Number, the Approach ID, or both. You will need to select the approach from a database and simply verify the necessary item for approach verification is present.

Chapter 1

Area Navigation (RNAV)

*S*o what is area navigation (RNAV), when you get right down to it? It started *out as pilots flying with basic compass cards and doing fix-to-fix navigation and ended with global navigation satellites making everything much easier. RNAV airspace generally mandates a certain level of equipment and assumes you have a 95% chance of keeping to a stated level of navigation accuracy. Unlike Required Navigation Performance (RNP) standards, in the next chapter, RNAV will not alert you when there is a problem.*

Examples of RNAV airspace include B-BRAV, P-RNAV, and the RNAV 1 and RNAV 2 routes found in the United States. MNPS is not exactly RNAV airspace, but is often thought of as just that. RNP-10, despite the name, is RNAV airspace. It can be confusing.

The Big Picture

[AC 90-100A, ¶4.b.] Area Navigation (RNAV). A method of navigation which permits aircraft operation on any desired flight path within the coverage of station-referenced navigation aids or within the limits of the capability of self-contained aids, or a combination of these. For the purposes of this AC, the specified RNAV accuracy must be met 95% of the flight time.

[ICAO Doc 9613, pg. I-(iii)] RNAV systems evolved in a manner similar to conventional ground-based routes and procedures. A specific RNAV system was identified and its performance was evaluated through a combination of analysis and flight testing. For domestic operations, the initial systems used very high frequency omnidirectional radio range (VOR) and distance measuring equipment (DME) for estimating their position; for oceanic operations, inertial navigation systems (INS) were employed. These "new" systems were developed, evaluated and certified. Airspace and obstacle clearance criteria were developed based on the performance of available equipment; and specifications for requirements were based on available capabilities. In some cases, it was necessary to identify the individual models of equipment that could be operated within the airspace concerned. Such prescriptive requirements resulted in delays to the introduction of new RNAV system capabilities and higher costs for maintaining appropriate certification.

In the old days we would navigate IFR from navaid to navaid and when we had to, we would fly fix-to-fix by mentally visualizing the airspace and estimating a course to fly. Then various boxes appeared that did this better than we could and "area navigation" was born. It is simply a method of navigation that allows us to fly along any desired flight path.

Equipment Requirements

RNAV routes typically specify minimum equipment levels needed to satisfy navigation accuracy. For example:

[AC 90-100A, ¶8.b.] U.S. RNAV operations are based upon the use of RNAV equipment that automatically determines aircraft position in the horizontal plane using inputs from the following types of positioning sensors (no specific priority).

(1) Global Navigation Satellite System (GNSS) in accordance with TSO-C145a, TSO- C146a, and TSO-C129/C129a. Positioning data from other types of navigation sensors may be integrated with the GNSS data provided it does not cause position errors exceeding the total system error requirements. The use of GPS equipment approved to TSO-C129() is limited to those which include the minimum system functions specified in Appendix 3. As a minimum, integrity should be provided by ABAS [Aircraft-Based Augmentation System]. In addition, GPS stand-alone equipment should include the following additional functions:

- Pseudorange step detection
- Health word checking.

For procedures requiring GPS and/or aircraft approvals requiring GPS, if the navigation system does not automatically alert the flight crew of a loss of GPS, the operator must develop procedures to verify correct GPS operation.

(2) DME/DME RNAV equipment complying with the criteria in appendix 1. Based on current DME availability evaluations, coverage is not sufficient to support DME/DME RNAV operations without additional IRU augmentation or using GPS.

(3) DME/DME/IRU RNAV equipment complying with the criteria in appendix 2.

An example of a suitable Aircraft-Based Augmentation System (ABAS) is receiver autonomous integrity monitoring (RAIM).

Total System Error

Total System Error (TSE) is simply a measure of how far off course the airplane can be. In RNP-1 or RNAV-1 airspace, for example, the TSE = 1. Is RNP more accurate than RNAV? No.

[AC 20-138D, ¶1-4.f.(2)]

RNAV systems conform to the ICAO performance-based navigation specification for total system error (TSE). RNAV total system error is the 95% probability that the navigation system accuracy remains within the limits defined for the RNAV operation. For example, during an RNAV-1 operation the TSE remains within one nautical mile of the desired path 95% of the time.

Looking at the figure, you see that RNAV-1 keeps the aircraft within 1 nautical mile of centerline 95% of the flight time.

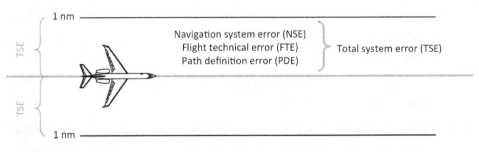

RNAV: Aircraft remains within Total System Error (ex: +/- 1 nm) for 95% of flight time

RNAV 1   *Idea is the same for RNAV 2, RNAV 5, etc.*

RNAV Airspace

Basic Area Navigation (B-RNAV) — ± 5 nm for 95% of flight time, will eventually be replaced but remains a requirement in European Civil Aviation Conference member States.

Minimum Navigation Performance Specification (MNPS) — lateral deviation standard of 6.3 nm, used in the north Atlantic and a few other regions, should eventually be replaced worldwide by RNP-4 or RNP-10. (MNPS isn't really RNAV or RNP, but it fits better into the RNAV category.)

Precision Area Navigation (P-RNAV) — +/- 1 nm for 95% of flight time, will eventually be replaced but remains a requirement in many parts of the world.

Required Navigation Performance-10 (RNP-10) — +/- 10 nm for 95% of the flight flight; despite the name, RNP-10 is an RNAV system without performance monitoring and alert capability. The ICAO elected to retain "RNP-10" when in fact it should be "RNAV-10" because many areas of the world adopted "RNP-10" before the RNP specification was made. The affected regions complained it would be too costly to change all the manuals and charts, so the ICAO made this exception.

RNAV-1 and RNAV-2

[90 AC-100A, ¶4.b.] Area Navigation (RNAV). A method of navigation which permits aircraft operation on any desired flight path within the coverage of station-referenced navigation aids or within the limits of the capability of self-contained aids, or a combination of these. For the purposes of this AC, the specified RNAV accuracy must be met 95% of the flight time.

- RNAV 1 requires a total system error of not more than 1 nm for 95% of the total flight time.

- RNAV 2 requires a total system error of not more than 2 nm for 95% of the total flight time.

The line between what is RNAV airspace and what is more properly called Required Navigation Performance (RNP) airspace gets blurred because of the naming conventions. It really isn't that difficult, as the next chapter illustrates.

Chapter 2

Required Navigation Performance (RNP)

Which is better: RNAV or RNP? Because the equipment requirements tend to be higher and the certification rules are certainly stricter, we tend to think of Required Navigation Performance (RNP) as the higher standard. But which is more accurate? Their accuracy standards are the same. Surprised? The key difference is that RNP includes the concept of containment.

The Big Picture

[ICAO Doc 9613, pg. I-(iii)]

- Performance-based navigation (PBN). The PBN concept specifies that aircraft RNAV system performance requirements be defined in terms of the accuracy, integrity, availability, continuity and functionality, which are needed for the proposed operations in the context of a particular airspace concept. The PBN concept represents a shift from sensor-based to performance-based navigation. Performance requirements are identified in navigation specifications, which also identify the choice of navigation sensors and equipment that may be used to meet the performance requirements. These navigation specifications are defined at a sufficient level of detail to facilitate global harmonization by providing specific implementation guidance for States and operators.

- Under PBN, generic navigation requirements are defined based on operational requirements. Operators then evaluate options in respect of available technology and navigation services, which could allow the requirements to be met. An operator thereby has the opportunity to select a more cost-effective option, rather than a solution being imposed as part of the operational requirements. Technology can evolve over time without requiring the operation itself to be reviewed, as long as the expected performance is provided by the RNAV system. As part of the future work of ICAO, it is anticipated that other means for meeting the requirements of the navigation specifications will be evaluated and may be included in the applicable navigation specifications, as appropriate.

Performance based navigation incorporates RNAV and adds the ability to continuously monitor the accuracy and utility of the system, alerting the pilot when the system isn't as good as it is supposed to be.

Equipment Requirements

True RNP, that using Performance Based Navigation, does not specify equipment but may require more than just navigation capability:

[ICAO Doc 9613, page I-(iii)]

PBN offers a number of advantages over the sensor-specific method of developing airspace and obstacle clearance criteria, i.e.:

- reduces the need to maintain sensor-specific routes and procedures, and their associated costs;

- avoids the need for developing sensor-specific operations with each new evolution of navigation systems, which would be cost-prohibitive;

- allows for more efficient use of airspace (route placement, fuel efficiency and noise abatement);

- clarifies how RNAV systems are used; and

- facilitates the operational approval process for operators by providing a limited set of navigation specifications intended for global use.

Within an airspace concept, PBN requirements will be affected by the communication, surveillance and ATM environments, the navaid infrastructure, and the functional and operational capabilities needed to meet the ATM application. PBN performance requirements also depend on what reversionary, non-RNAV means of navigation are available and what degree of redundancy is required to ensure adequate continuity of functions.

Total System Error

Total System Error (TSE) is simply a measure of how far off course the airplane can be. In RNP-1 or RNAV-1 airspace, for example, the TSE = 1. Is RNP more accurate than RNAV? No.

[AC 20-138D, ¶1-4.f.(2)]

- RNAV systems conform to the ICAO performance-based navigation specification for total system error (TSE). RNAV total system error is the 95% probability that the navigation system accuracy remains within the limits defined for the RNAV operation. For example, during an RNAV-1 operation the TSE remains within one nautical mile of the desired path 95% of the time.

- RNP systems conform to a performance-based navigation specification based on RNAV capability that also includes requirements for on-board performance monitoring and alerting. For example, during an RNP 1.0 operation, the TSE remains within one nautical mile of the desired path 95% of the time, and on-board performance monitoring provides the pilot with an alert when the probability that TSE exceeds 2xRNP is greater than 10^{-5}.

- RNP is an RNAV subset that also includes a requirement to provide on-board navigation system accuracy performance monitoring and alerting which means an RNP system is also an RNAV system. GNSS equipment provides accuracy performance monitoring and alerting which, by definition, makes it both an RNAV and RNP capable system.

Both RNAV-1 and RNP-1 keep the aircraft within 1 nautical mile of centerline 95% of the flight time. The difference is that under RNP-1, the pilot is notified when the system thinks there is a greater than 0.00001 probability (.001%) that the airplane could wander outside of 2 nautical miles.

- *RNAV says you should be on course,*

- *RNP says you should be on course, monitors system performance, and alerts you when it thinks there is a problem.*

Containment

So what makes RNP different than RNAV?

Let's first look at what makes them the same:

- *The system defines navigation accuracy as being able to stay within the total system error at least 95% of the total flight time. This applies to BOTH RNAV and RNP.*

- *In our example, with RNAV-1 or RNP-1, the airplane will be within 1 nautical mile 95% of the flight time.*

The following applies ONLY to RNP

- *The system considers itself adequately contained as long as the probability of the airplane being inside an area twice the total system error value at least 99.999% of the time. The regulations seem to confuse the term "containment" as either the 95% navigation accuracy limit or the 99.999% alert limit.*

- *Regardless of terminology, remember that twice the stated number is where the airplane will be 99.999% of the time before issuing an alert.*

- *In our example, with RNP-1, the airplane will alert the pilot if there is greater than a 0.001% chance the airplane could be more than 2 nautical miles off course.*

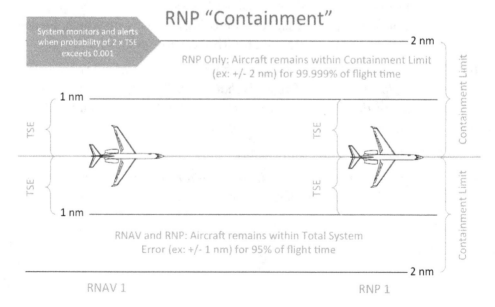

RNP "Containment"

System monitors and alerts when probability of 2 x TSE exceeds 0.001

RNP Only: Aircraft remains within Containment Limit (ex: +/- 2 nm) for 99.999% of flight time

RNAV and RNP: Aircraft remains within Total System Error (ex: +/- 1 nm) for 95% of flight time

RNAV 1   RNP 1

[ICAO Doc 9613, §II-A-2-4, ¶2.3.7] The PBN concept uses the term on-board performance monitoring and alerting instead of the term containment. This is to avoid confusion between existing uses of containment in various documents by different areas of expertise. For example:

a.   "Containment" refers to the region within which the aircraft will remain 95 percent of the time. The associated terms have been "containment value" and "containment distance" and the related airspace protection on either side of an RNAV ATS route.

b.   Within the industry standards of RTCA/DO-236 and EUROCAE/ED-75, "containment" refers to the region that the aircraft will remain when there is no alert (0.99999 probability), and defines a requirement for how often an alert occurs (0.9999). The associated terms are "containment limit", "containment integrity", "containment continuity", and "containment region".

c.   Within PANS-OPS material, "containment" has referred to the region used to define the obstacle clearance, and the aircraft is expected to remain within or above that surface (regardless of alerting) with very high probability. The associated terms have been "containment area", "airspace containment", "obstacle clearance containment" and related obstacle protection areas.

[ICAO Doc 9613, §II-A-2-4, ¶2.3.8] The previous ICAO expressions of "containment value" and "containment distance" have been replaced by the navigation accuracy of TSE.

RNP Airspace

Required Navigation Performance-4 (RNP-4) — ±4 nm for 95% of flight time plus integrity, continuity, performance and alerting requirements. Intended for oceanic and remote operations.

There is more to RNP than navigation accuracy, it may also require specific communications and surveillance capabilities such as CPDLC and ADS-C.

GNSS and RNAV (or) RNP

[AC 20-138D, ¶5-1.a.] There have been questions on whether GNSS is an RNAV or RNP system. The answer is GNSS is both an RNAV and RNP system because RNP is a subset of RNAV that also includes a requirement to provide on-board navigation system accuracy performance monitoring and alerting. Therefore, an RNP system is also capable of RNAV. GNSS equipment provides accuracy performance monitoring and alerting which, by definition, makes it an RNP capable system.

Comparisons

Criteria	B-RNAV (aka RNAV 5)	MNPS	P-RNAV (aka RNAV 1)	RNAV 1	RNAV 2	RNP-4	RNP-10
Location	Europe en route arrival	Atlantic Caribbean * Parts of Canada *	Europe * en route arrival approach departure	U.S. en route arrival approach departure	U.S. en route arrival departure	Asia * Pacific * oceanic remote	Worldwide * oceanic remote
Accuracy	+/- 5 nm 95% time	6.3 nm lateral *	+/- 1 nm 95% time	+/- 1 nm 95% time	+/- 2 nm 95% time	+/- 4 nm 95% time	+/- 10 nm 95% time
Performance	N/A	N/A	N/A	N/A	N/A	Integrity Continuity Monitoring Alert	N/A
Aircraft Apvl	AFM Statement	State Apvl *	AC 90-96A JAA TGL-10	AFM Statement	AFM Statement	AFM * STC *	AFM
Operator Apvl (91)	None Req.	LOA	LOA	None Req.	None Req.	LOA	LOA
Operator Apvl (Commercial)	B034	B039	B034	B035	B035	B036	B036
Regulatory	AC 90-96A	ICAO Doc 7030 FAA Order 8900	AC 90-96A	AC 90-100A	AC 90-100A	ICAO Doc 7030 FAA Order 8900	ICAO Doc 7030 FAA Order 8900

Chapter 3

Future Air Navigation System (FANS)

I was a staff officer at the Pentagon when I first heard about FANS and thought it was madness. It was envisioned as a system that completely revolutionized communications, navigation, and surveillance when flying anywhere in the world and, in 1992, it sounded like science fiction. Three years later the Boeing Aircraft Company came up with a way to do the communications part and that became FANS-1. A few years later Airbus did their version and that was known as FANS-A. Now we have a few variants but they are basically called FANS-1/A and you must have FANS-1/A to fly in some parts of the world. So what is FANS-1/A?

It is basically nothing more than a CPDLC system that uses the ICAO Aeronautical Telecommunications Network (ATN) over Satcom or VHF and Automatic Dependent Surveillance – Contract (ADS-C) as specified by the ICAO.

Definition

[ICAO SVGM, pg 1-14] Future air navigation system 1/A — As defined by [Radio Technical Commission for Aeronautics] RTCA DO-258A / [European Organization for Civil Aviation Equipment] EUROCAE ED-100A, or previous standards that defined the FANS 1/A capability. FANS 1/A generally means that the data link system on an aircraft, the [Air Traffic Service Unit] ATSU ground system, and communication service provision comply with the standard. In certain cases, specific reference is made to a particular type of FANS 1/A aircraft as follows:

• FANS 1/A+ means that the aircraft completely complies with Revision A of the standard, which includes message latency timer; and

• FANS 1/A ADS-C means that the aircraft complies with data link initiation capability and ADS-C applications, but does not include the CP-

DLC application.

[ICAO GOLD, table 2-1]

- FANS 1/A --- Initial future air navigation system (FANS 1/A) ATS applications, CPDLC and ADS-C, supported by FANS 1/A over ACARS. Note.— FANS 1/A typically involve communication (CPDLC), navigation (RNAV/RNP) and surveillance (ADS-C).

- FANS 1/A+ --- Same as FANS 1/A, except with additional features, such as the message latency monitor function.

- FANS 1/A ADS-C --- ATS applications, AFN and ADS-C, supported by FANS 1/A over ACARS. No CPDLC.

FANS mandates were a big deal about ten years ago, with everyone fretting on how they were going to comply. Most of the mandatory dates have come to pass and you will be denied some airspace throughout the world if you are not FANS compliant. But you hardly ever see the FANS terminology any more. The mandatory requirements are given for CPDLC and ADS-C. That is where your focus needs to be.

History

[ICAO SVGM, pg vi]

- In the early 1980s, civil aviation recognized the increasing limitations of the present communications, navigation, and surveillance (CNS) systems for air traffic management (ATM) and the need to make improvements to overcome them and meet future needs. Thus the Council of ICAO established the Special Committee on Future Air Navigation Systems (FANS) to study new concepts and new technologies and to recommend a system that would overcome the present and foreseen problems. The Committee made an extensive study of existing systems and the application of new technologies. It concluded that the limitations of the existing systems are intrinsic to the systems themselves and that problems could not be overcome on a global scale except by the exploitation of satellite technology. Thus a new concept of air navigation based on satellite technology was developed and consequently endorsed by the Tenth Air Navigation Conference in September 1991.

- The potential for improvement in efficiency resulting from the adoption of satellite technology was discussed at length during the Limited NAT Regional Air Navigation (LIM/NAT/RAN) Conference in Cascais, Portugal, in 1992. Although both data and voice communications were evaluated, it was recognised that data offered greater economic benefit and that the emphasis should be put on that form of communications. This was not seen as precluding the use of voice in abnormal circumstances but the use of SATCOM voice for routine communications was not seen as viable.

- In 1995, the initial future air navigation system (FANS 1/A) provided an integrated airborne CNS package. In addition to required navigation performance (RNP) and global navigation satellite system (GNSS) capabilities, FANS 1/A includes controller pilot data link communications (CPDLC) and automatic dependent surveillance – contract (ADS-C) capabilities using SATCOM, VHF, and HF data links. CPDLC and ADS-C were seen as the normal or preferred means of ATS communications and surveillance in procedural airspace. However, voice communications would continue to be required as an alternative means of ATS communications. At the same time, aircraft were equipped with SATVOICE capability.

[ICAO Doc 9613, pg. I-(xii)]

- The Special Committee on Future Air Navigation Systems (FANS) identified that the method most commonly used over the years to indicate required navigation capability was to prescribe mandatory carriage of certain equipment. This constrained the optimum application of modern on-board equipment. To overcome this problem, the committee developed the concept of required navigation performance capability (RNPC). FANS defined RNPC as a parameter describing lateral deviations from assigned or selected track as well as along track position fixing accuracy on the basis of an appropriate containment level.

- The RNPC concept was approved by the ICAO Council and was assigned to the Review of the General Concept of Separation Panel (RGCSP) for further elaboration. The RGCSP, in 1990, noting that capability and performance were distinctly different and that airspace planning is dependent on measured performance, rather than designed-in capability, changed RNPC to required navigation performance (RNP).

- The RGCSP then developed the concept of RNP further by expanding it to be a statement of the navigation performance necessary for operation within a defined airspace. It was proposed that a specified type of RNP should define the navigation performance of all users within the airspace to be commensurate with the navigation capability available within the airspace. RNP types were to be identified by a single accuracy value as envisaged by FANS. While this was found to be appropriate for application in remote and oceanic areas, the associated guidance for route separation was not sufficient for continental RNAV applications; this was due to a number of factors, including the setting of performance and functional standards for aircraft navigation systems, working within the constraints of available airspace, and using a more robust communication, surveillance and ATM environment. It was also due to practical considerations stemming from the gradual development of RNAV capability together with the need to derive early benefits from the installed equipment. This resulted in different specifications of navigation capability with common navigation accuracy. It was noted that such developments were unlikely to cease as vertical (3D) navigation and time (4D) navigation evolved and was subsequently applied by ATM to increase airspace capacity and efficiency.

It is true that Required Navigation Performance Capability (RNPC) was changed to Required Navigation Performance (RNP). But there is more to it that that. We also have Required Communications Performance (RCP) and Required Surveillance Performance (RSP).

Chapter 4

Performance Based Navigation

*T*he Performance-Based Navigation (PBN) system is a concept of how we ensure our aircraft are where we say they are, when we say they are. The designation is mostly consistent, but not completely. How you qualify and how you prove your qualification is pretty much up to the State. But that approval isn't listed as "PBN" but as the individual levels of compliance, i.e., RNP-4.

The Concept

[ICAO Doc 9613, ¶1.1.1]

- The performance-based navigation (PBN) concept specifies that aircraft RNAV system performance requirements be defined in terms of accuracy, integrity, availability, continuity and functionality required for the proposed operations in the context of a particular airspace concept, when supported by the appropriate navigation infrastructure. In that context, the PBN concept represents a shift from sensor-based to performance-based navigation. Performance requirements are identified in navigation specifications, which also identify the choice of navigation sensors and equipment that may be used to meet the performance requirements. These navigation specifications provide specific implementation guidance for States and operators in order to facilitate global harmonization.

- Under PBN, generic navigation requirements are first defined based on the operational requirements. Operators then evaluate options in respect of available technology and navigation services. A chosen solution would be the most cost-effective for the operator, as opposed to a solution being established as part of the operational requirements. Technology can evolve over time without requiring the operation itself to be revisited as long as the requisite performance is provided by the RNAV system.

The Navigation Specification

[ICAO Doc 9613, ¶1.2]

A navigation specification details the performance required of the RNAV system in terms of accuracy, integrity, availability and continuity; which navigation functionalities the RNAV system must have; which navigation sensors must be integrated into the RNAV system; and which requirements are placed on the flight crew.

On-board performance monitoring and alerting is the main element that determines if the navigation system complies with the necessary safety level associated to an RNP application; it relates to both lateral and longitudinal navigation performance; and it allows the aircrew to detect that the navigation system is not achieving, or cannot guarantee with 10^{-5} integrity, the navigation performance required for the operation. Both RNAV and RNP specifications include requirements for certain navigation functionalities. At the basic level, these functional requirements may include:

- continuous indication of aircraft position relative to track to be displayed to the pilot flying on a navigation display;

- display of distance and bearing to the active (To) waypoint;

- display of ground speed or time to the active (To) waypoint;

- navigation data storage function; and

- appropriate failure indication of the RNAV system, including the sensors.

The 10^{-5} integrity is the 0.9999 probability concept. The monitoring and alerting is the key component of a PBN specification.

[ICAO Doc 9613, ¶1.2.5]

- For oceanic, remote, en-route and terminal operations, an RNP specification is designated as RNP X, e.g. RNP 4. An RNAV specification is designated as RNAV X, e.g. RNAV 1. If two navigation specifications share the same value for X, they may be distinguished by use of a prefix, e.g. Advanced-RNP 1 and Basic-RNP 1.

- For both RNP and RNAV designations, the expression "X" (where stated) refers to the lateral navigation accuracy in nautical miles, which is expected to be achieved at least 95 per cent of the flight time by the population of aircraft operating within the airspace, route or procedure.

- Approach navigation specifications cover all segments of the instrument approach. RNP specifications are designated using RNP as a prefix and an abbreviated textual suffix, e.g. RNP APCH or RNP AR APCH. There are no RNAV approach specifications.

- Because specific performance requirements are defined for each navigation specification, an aircraft approved for an RNP specification is not automatically approved for all RNAV specifications. Similarly, an aircraft approved for an RNP or RNAV specification having a stringent accuracy requirement (e.g. RNP 0.3 specification) is not automatically approved for a navigation specification having a less stringent accuracy requirement (e.g. RNP 4).

- *If your airplane is approved for RNP 0.3 and RNP 10, you might think RNP 4 is automatically included. But it isn't. RNP 0.3 does not have the same communications and surveillance requirements of RNP 4, specifically CPDLC and ADS-C. RNP 10 isn't a PBN specification at all. So you cannot infer you are RNP 4 qualified.*

- *If you have an RNP 4 qualification you are good to go for RNP 10. In fact, if you had an LOA that said RNP 10 and got approval for RNP 4, the RNP 10 disappears. Be careful about RNP 4. Some U.S. FSDOs are granting RNP 4 LOAs based on the mistaken notion that aircraft with P-RNAV approval are more accurate than RNP 4. That might be true and it will work in the Caribbean. But it won't work in the rest of the world where RNP 4 also requires CPDLC and ADS-C.*

- The existing RNP 10 designation is inconsistent with PBN RNP and RNAV specifications. RNP 10 does not include requirements for onboard performance monitoring and alerting. For purposes of consistency with the PBN concept, RNP 10 is referred to as RNAV 10 in this manual. Renaming current RNP 10 routes, operational approvals, etc., to an RNAV 10 designation would be an extensive and expensive task, which is not cost-effective. Consequently, any existing or new operational approvals will continue to be designated RNP 10, and any charting annotations will be depicted as RNP 10.

- In the past, the United States and member States of the European Civil Aviation Conference (ECAC) used regional RNAV specifications with different designators. The ECAC applications (P-RNAV and B-RNAV) will continue to be used only within those States. Over time, ECAC RNAV applications will migrate towards the international navigation specifications of RNAV 1 and RNAV 5. The United States migrated from the USRNAV Types A and B to the RNAV 1 specification in March 2007.

- Aircraft operating in the North Atlantic airspace are required to meet a minimum navigation performance specification (MNPS). The MNPS specification has intentionally been excluded from the above designation scheme because of its mandatory nature and because future MNPS implementations are not envisaged.

If you want to attach some kind of accuracy standard to MNPS, it is about 6.3 nm either side of track. (It is often called a "12.6 nm standard.") The eventual plan is to move all oceanic airspace to RNP-4 and when that happens MNPS will no longer exist.

Airworthiness Approval

[ICAO Doc 9613, ¶3.4.2]

- The airworthiness approval process assures that each item of the RNAV equipment installed is of a type and design appropriate to its intended function and that the installation functions properly under foreseeable operating conditions.

- The RNAV system installed should be compliant with a set of basic performance requirements as described in the navigation specification, which defines accuracy, integrity and continuity criteria. It should also be compliant with a set of specific functional requirements, have a navigation database, and support each specific path terminator as required by the navigation specification.

- The aircraft must be equipped with an RNAV system enabling the flight crew to navigate in accordance with operational criteria as defined in the navigation specification. The State of the Operator is the authority responsible for approving flight operations. The authority must be satisfied that operational programmes are adequate. Training programmes and operations manuals should be evaluated.

You do not get approved for PBN, rather you get approved for each specification, such as for RNP-4.

Chapter 5

Class A through Class G Airspace

*T*he U.S. airspace classification method changed a few years back to more closely align with the International Civil Aviation Organization (ICAO). They are close but not exact.

[ICAO Annex 11, Air Traffic Services §2.6.1] ATS airspaces shall be classified and designated in accordance with the following:

- Class A. IFR flights only are permitted, all flights are provided with air traffic control service and are separated from each other.

- Class B. IFR and VFR flights are permitted, all flights are provided with air traffic control service and are separated from each other.

- Class C. IFR and VFR flights are permitted, all flights are provided with air traffic control service and IFR flights are separated from other IFR flights and from VFR flights. VFR flights are separated from IFR flights and receive traffic information in respect of other VFR flights.

- Class D. IFR and VFR flights are permitted and all flights are provided with air traffic control service, IFR flights are separated from other IFR flights and receive traffic information in respect of VFR flights, VFR flights receive traffic information in respect of all other flights.

- Class E. IFR and VFR flights are permitted, IFR flights are provided with air traffic control service and are separated from other IFR flights. All flights receive traffic information as far as is practical. Class E shall not be used for control zones.

- Class F. IFR and VFR flights are permitted, all participating IFR flights receive an air traffic advisory service and all flights receive flight information service if requested.

Note.— Where air traffic advisory service is implemented, this is considered normally as a temporary measure only until such time as it can be replaced by air traffic control. (See also PANS-ATM, Chapter 9.)

- Class G. IFR and VFR flights are permitted and receive flight information service if requested.

Class	Type of flight	Separation provided	Service provided	Speed limitation*	Radio communication requirement	Subject to an ATC clearance
A	IFR only	All aircraft	Air traffic control service	Not applicable	Continuous two-way	Yes
B	IFR	All aircraft	Air traffic control service	Not applicable	Continuous two-way	Yes
	VFR	All aircraft	Air traffic control service	Not applicable	Continuous two-way	Yes
C	IFR	IFR from IFR IFR from VFR	Air traffic control service	Not applicable	Continuous two-way	Yes
	VFR	VFR from IFR	1) Air traffic control service for separation from IFR; 2) VFR/VFR traffic information (and traffic avoidance advice on request)	250 kt IAS below 3 050 m (10 000 ft) AMSL	Continuous two-way	Yes
D	IFR	IFR from IFR	Air traffic control service, traffic information about VFR flights (and traffic avoidance advice on request)	250 kt IAS below 3 050 m (10 000 ft) AMSL	Continuous two-way	Yes
	VFR	Nil	IFR/VFR and VFR/VFR traffic information (and traffic avoidance advice on request)	250 kt IAS below 3 050 m (10 000 ft) AMSL	Continuous two-way	Yes
E	IFR	IFR from IFR	Air traffic control service and, as far as practical, traffic information about VFR flights	250 kt IAS below 3 050 m (10 000 ft) AMSL	Continuous two-way	Yes
	VFR	Nil	Traffic information as far as practical	250 kt IAS below 3 050 m (10 000 ft) AMSL	No	No
F	IFR	IFR from IFR as far as practical	Air traffic advisory service; flight information service	250 kt IAS below 3 050 m (10 000 ft) AMSL	Continuous two-way	No
	VFR	Nil	Flight information service	250 kt IAS below 3 050 m (10 000 ft) AMSL	No	No
G	IFR	Nil	Flight information service	250 kt IAS below 3 050 m (10 000 ft) AMSL	Continuous two-way	No
	VFR	Nil	Flight information service	250 kt IAS below 3 050 m (10 000 ft) AMSL	No	No

* When the height of the transition altitude is lower than 3 050 m (10 000 ft) AMSL, FL 100 should be used in lieu of 10 000 ft.

Figure: Airspace Classification, from ICAO Annex 11, Air Traffic Services, Appendix 4

Chapter 6

Basic Area Navigation (B-RNAV)

In the days before Performance Based Navigation (PBN), countries would specify a track keeping accuracy needed to fly a route and you would certify that you had the right equipment to do just that. The standard was "sensor based." PBN systems must be able to monitor their own performance and alert the crew when there are problems. B-RNAV comes from before PBN and is being replaced by RNAV-5. You hardly ever see it; it is just as easy to meet RNAV-1 these days. But it still exists as a standard and you will need to have it to fly in Europe. If you are from the United States your B-RNAV authorization counts for RNAV-5. Under 14 CFR 91 you will need an AFM statement, under 14 CFR 135 you will need OpSpec B034.

Location

Europe

[ICAO Doc 7030, §EUR, ¶4.1.1.5.2] Precision RNAV (P-RNAV) and basic RNAV (B-RNAV)

4.1.1.5.2.1 The provisions in respect of en-route operations, as specified in 4.1.1.5.2.6 and 4.1.1.5.2.7, shall apply to all such operations conducted under IFR on the entire ATS route network as notified by the appropriate authorities in the following flight information regions (FIRs)/upper flight information regions (UIRs):

Amsterdam, Ankara, Athinai, Barcelona, Berlin, Bodø, Bordeaux, Bratislava, Bremen, Brest, Brindisi, Bruxelles, Bucuresti, Budapest, Canarias (AFI area of applicability), Casablanca, Chisinau, Düsseldorf, France, Frankfurt, Hannover, Istanbul, Kharkiv, København, Kyiv, Lisboa, Ljubljana, London, L'viv, Madrid, Malta, Marseille, Milano, München, Nicosia, Odessa, Oslo, Paris, Praha, Reims, Rhein, Riga, Roma, Rovaniemi, Scottish, Shannon, Simferopol, Skopje, Sofia, Stavanger, Sweden, Switzerland, Tallinn, Tampere, Tbilisi, Tirana, Trondheim, Tunis (FL 245 and above), Varna, Vilnius, Warszawa,

Wien, Yerevan, Zagreb.

4.1.1.5.2.6 Only aircraft approved for B-RNAV operations may plan for operations under IFR on the ATS routes of the FIRs/UIRs identified in 4.1.1.5.2.1. Aircraft not equipped with RNAV but having a navigation accuracy meeting RNP 5 will be restricted to operations on ATS routes which States may designate within their lower airspace in accordance with 4.1.1.5.2.7.

4.1.1.5.2.7 Until such time as VOR facilities cease to be available, the carriage of a single RNAV system not meeting an average continuity of service of 99.99 percent of flight time may be approved for B-RNAV operations if the aircraft is also carrying VOR and distance-measuring equipment (DME) equipment.

There are exceptions, but for the most part, if you fly in Europe you will need B-RNAV.

Accuracy / Performance Standards

Accuracy

[AC 90-96A, ¶4.b.] Basic Area Navigation (B-RNAV). B-RNAV is defined as RNAV that meets a track keeping accuracy equal to or better than ±5 nm for 95 percent of the flight time. This value includes signal source error, airborne receiver error, display system error, and flight technical error. This navigation performance assumes the necessary coverage provided by satellite or ground-based navigation aids is available for the intended operation.

Accuracy versus Performance

[ICAO Doc 9613 ¶1.1.1.1] The performance-based navigation (PBN) concept specifies that aircraft RNAV system performance requirements be defined in terms of accuracy, integrity, availability, continuity and functionality required for the proposed operations in the context of a particular airspace concept, when supported by the appropriate navigation infrastructure. In that context, the PBN concept represents a shift from sensor-based to performance-based navigation. Performance requirements are identified in navigation specifications, which also identify the choice of navigation sensors and equipment that may be used to meet the performance requirements. These navigation specifications provide specific implementation guidance for States and operators in order to facilitate global harmonization.

[ICAO Doc 9613 ¶1.2.3.1] On-board performance monitoring and alerting is the main element that determines if the navigation system complies with the necessary safety level associated to an RNP application; it relates to both lateral and longitudinal navigation performance; and it allows the aircrew to detect that the navigation system is not achieving, or cannot guarantee with 10–5 integrity, the navigation performance required for the operation.

What we have grown up with, accuracy standards, specify what it takes to fly the airspace in question and permit properly equipped aircraft and trained crews to fly there. Performance Based Navigation, on the other hand, mandates a performance standard that includes navigation accuracy but also includes other parameters, such as the ability to self monitor and alert the crew of integrity issues.

B-RNAV is an accuracy standard that lives in a middle ground, as the PBN manual states:

[ICAO Doc 9613 ¶1.2.5.5.2] In the past, the United States and member States of the European Civil Aviation Conference (ECAC) used regional RNAV specifications with different designators. The ECAC applications (P-RNAV and B-RNAV) will continue to be used only within those States. Over time, ECAC RNAV applications will migrate towards the international navigation specifications of RNAV 1 and RNAV 5. The United States migrated from the USRNAV Types A and B to the RNAV 1 specification in March 2007.

Documentation / Certification

Aircraft System Eligibility

[AC 90-96A, Appendix 1 ¶1.b.(1)] The aircraft should be considered eligible for B-RNAV operations, if the AFM or POH shows the appropriate instrument flight rules (IFR) navigation system installation has received airworthiness approval in accordance with this advisory circular (AC) or with one of the following Federal Aviation Administration (FAA) ACs: AC 90-45A, AC 20-121A, AC 20-130, AC 20-138, or AC 25-15.

Part 91 Aircraft/Operator Approval

[AC 90-96A, Appendix 1 ¶1.b.(2)] U.S. part 91 operators should review their AFM or POH to ensure aircraft system eligibility as detailed in Appendix 1, paragraph 1b(1). Once aircraft system eligibility has been established, the operator should take steps to ensure B-RNAV operations are conducted in accordance with the guidance contained in Appendix 1, paragraph 1d, 2, 3, and 4, as well as any other established operational or airspace requirements. Operators must ensure the required functions of Appendix 1 are met. Once these actions are completed, the operator may begin to conduct B-RNAV operations. A letter of authorization (LOA) is not required when eligibility is based on the AFM or POH. See Appendix 1, paragraph 1c, for actions to take if the operator is unable to determine from the AFM or POH whether the aircraft system has been approved and installed in accordance with an appropriate FAA AC.

If your AFM or POH has the necessary statement, you have what you need to operate B-RNAV under 14 CFR 91. (An LOA is not needed.) Otherwise, there are other means listed in AC 90-96A to get approval.

U.S. Air Carrier Aircraft/Commercial Operator Approval

[AC 90-96A, Appendix 1 ¶1.b.(3)] Part 121, 125, or 135 operators should present the following documentation to their certificate-holding district office (CHDO): sections of the AFM that document airworthiness approval in accordance with an appropriate FAA AC as detailed in Appendix 1, paragraph 1b(1) and training and operations manuals that reflect the operating policies of Appendix 1, paragraph 1d, 2, 3, 4 as well as any other operational or airspace requirements established by European authorities. Operators must ensure the required functions of Appendix 1 are met.

[FAA Order 8900.1, Vol 3, Chapter 18, OPSEC B034, ¶B.] B034 also authorizes an operator to conduct IFR operations in designated European Basic RNAV (B-RNAV) and European Precision RNAV (P-RNAV) airspace.

If your AFM or POH has the necessary statement, you have what you need to apply for OpSpec B034 under 14 CFR 135. Otherwise, there are other means listed in AC 90-96A to get approval.

Minimum Navigation Performance Specification (MNPS)

*T*he *Minimum Navigation Performance Specification (MNPS) was created in the seventies as a way of setting some kind of standard for who could and could not fly the North Atlantic and was adopted by a few other regions, because it was really the only standard of its kind. Just about all of those regions have adopted RNP 4 or RNP 10 and it will eventually be eliminated in the North Atlantic too. But for now, if you fly between the United States and Europe you need to know about MNPS.*

Location

[ICAO Doc 7030, §CAR, ¶4.1.1.5.1] Caribbean — For flights in transit to or from the NAT MNPS airspace, while operating in the control area of the San Juan FIR, a lateral separation minimum of 110 km (60 nm) may be applied. . . . Aircraft must meet the NAT MNPS specifications.

[ICAO Doc 7030, §NAT, ¶4.1.1.5.1] North Atlantic — The MNPS shall be applicable in that volume of airspace between FL 285 and FL 420 within the Oceanic Control Areas of Santa Maria, Shanwick, Reykjavik, Gander Oceanic and New York Oceanic, excluding the area west of 60°W and south of 38°30'N.

[Transport Canada AIM, ¶2.6] Canada — The airspace from FL330 to FL410 within the lateral dimensions of the NCA [Northern Control Area], the ACA [Arctic Control Area] and the northern part of the SCA has been designated CMNPS airspace. More about: International Operations / High Latitude Operations.

Note: this is an ever-decreasing list. Far off places like Hong Kong once used MNPS but are gravitating toward RNP-4.

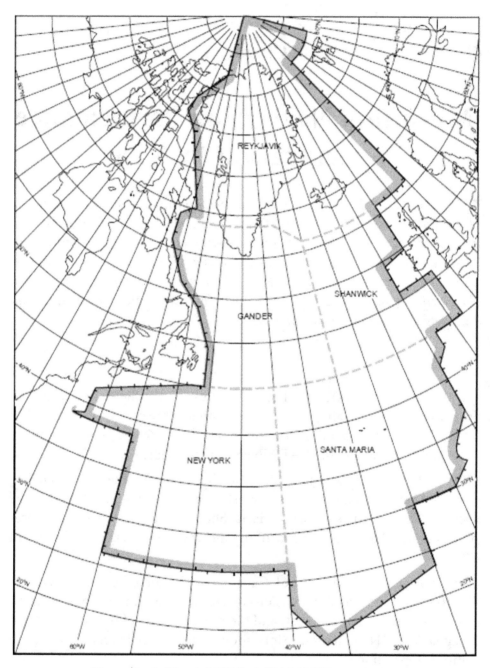

Figure: North Atlantic MNP from ICAO NAT Doc 007, cover

Accuracy / Performance Standards

[ICAO NAT Doc 007 § 1.3.3] In terms of accuracy, an aircraft which is approved for operations within NAT MNPS Airspace shall have a navigation performance capability such that:

- the standard deviation of lateral track errors shall be less than 6.3 nm (11.7 km);

- the proportion of total flight time spent by the aircraft 30 nm (56 km) or more off the cleared track shall be less than 5.3 x 10-4;

- the proportion of total flight time spent by the aircraft between 50 and 70 nm (93 and 130 km) off the cleared track shall be less than 13 x 10-5.

Documentation / Certification

[ICAO NAT Doc 007 § 1.2.1] All flights within NAT MNPS Airspace must have the approval of either the State of Registry of the aircraft, or the State of the Operator. Aircraft operating in RVSM Airspace are required to be compliant with the altimetry minimum aircraft system performance specification (MASPS) and hold an issued approval. Approval for MNPS operations will require the checking by the State of Registry or State of the Operator of various aspects affecting navigation performance. These aspects include: the navigation equipment used, together with its installation and maintenance procedures; plus the crew navigation procedures employed and the crew training requirements.

[ICAO NAT Doc 007 § 1.2.2] Since MNPS Airspace is now designated as RVSM airspace at all levels (i.e. FL290-410 inclusive) specific State RVSM Approval is also required to operate within MNPS Airspace.

14 CFR 135 Approval

[8900.1, Volume 4, Chapter 1, Paragraph 4-98.D.] All NAT/MNPS approvals are granted by issuing OpSpec paragraph B039, Operations within North Atlantic (NAT) Minimum Navigation Performance Specifications (MNPS) Airspace, and by adding that area of en route operation to paragraph B050, Authorized Areas of En Route Operation, Limitations, and Procedures, of the standard OpSpecs.

14 CFR 91 Approval

[14 CFR 91, §91.705] Operations within airspace designated as Minimum Navigation Performance Specification Airspace.

a.   Except as provided in paragraph (b) of this section, no person may operate a civil aircraft of U.S. registry in airspace designated as Minimum Navigation Performance Specifications airspace unless—

  1.   The aircraft has approved navigation performance capability that complies with the requirements of appendix C of this part; and

  2.   The operator is authorized by the Administrator to perform such operations.

b.   The Administrator may authorize a deviation from the requirements of this section in accordance with Section 3 of appendix C to this part.

[14 CFR 91, Appendix C, §3] Air traffic control (ATC) may authorize an aircraft operator to deviate from the requirements of §91.705 for a specific flight if, at the time of flight plan filing for that flight, ATC determines that the aircraft may be provided appropriate separation and that the flight will not interfere with, or impose a burden upon, the operations of other aircraft which meet the requirements of §91.705.

Under 14 CFR 91 you will need an LOA.

Chapter 8

Precision Area Navigation (P-RNAV)

P-*RNAV is giving way to RNAV-1 under Performance Based Navigation but in the United States the existing authorization process is written for P-RNAV. Some procedures allow for either, but even without that, the ICAO rules allow you to fly a RNAV-1 procedure with a P-RNAV authorization.*

Location

Europe

[ICAO Doc 7030, §EUR, ¶4.1.1.5.2] Precision RNAV (P-RNAV) and basic RNAV (B-RNAV)

4.1.1.5.2.2 The provisions in respect of precision area navigation (P-RNAV) shall be applied whenever RNAV terminal control area (TMA) procedures, excluding the final and missed approach segments, are used.

You used to see these all over Europe and other places, such as Hong Kong. As the world gravitates to RNP-1 for the terminal sector they are becoming a bit more scarce. If applicable, you should see "RNAV-1" or "P-RNAV APPROVAL REQUIRED" annotated on the arrival or departure procedure.

Accuracy / Performance Standards

[AC 90-96A, ¶4.c.] P-RNAV is defined as RNAV that meets a track keeping accuracy equal to or better than ±1 nm for 95 percent of the flight time. This value includes signal source error, airborne receiver error, display system error, and flight technical error. This navigation performance assumes the necessary coverage provided by satellite or ground-based navigation aids is available for the intended operation.

Documentation / Certification

Aircraft P-RNAV System Eligibility

[AC 90-96A, Appendix 2 ¶1.c.(1)] Consider the aircraft eligible for P-RNAV operations, if the AFM or POH shows the appropriate instrument flight rules (IFR) navigation system installation has received airworthiness approval in accordance with this AC or has a statement of compliance to the performance and functional requirements of JAA TGL-10.

Part 91 Aircraft/Operator Approval

[AC 90-96A, Appendix 2 ¶1.c.(2)] U.S. part 91 operators present the following documentation to their FSDO: sections of the AFM or POH as appropriate to establish P-RNAV system eligibility; and, evidence of meeting the requirements contained in Appendix 2, sections 3, 4 and 5. The FSDO issues LOA or similar operational approval documentation authorizing P-RNAV operations to part 91 operators. Appendix 2, paragraph 1d provides guidance for operators not able to determine from the AFM or POH that the aircraft system has been approved and installed in accordance with an appropriate FAA AC.

U.S. Air Carrier Aircraft/Commercial Operator Approval

[AC 90-96A, Appendix 2 ¶1.c.(3)] Part 121, 125, or 135 operators should present the following documentation to their CHDO: sections of the AFM or POH that establish P-RNAV eligibility. Once the operator has satisfied the requirements described in Appendix 2, sections 3, 4, and 5; the CHDO: issues OpSpecs to reflect Basic Area Navigation (B-RNAV) and P-RNAV approval; and, approves changes to the minimum equipment list (MEL) to account for B-RNAV and P-RNAV operations. Appendix 2, paragraph 1d provides guidance if the operator is unable to determine from the AFM or POH whether the aircraft system is approved in accordance with an appropriate FAA AC.

[FAA Order 8900.1, Vol 3, Chapter 18, OPSEC B034, ¶B.] B034 also authorizes an operator to conduct IFR operations in designated European Basic RNAV (B-RNAV) and European Precision RNAV (P-RNAV) airspace.

If your AFM or POH has the necessary statement, you have what you need to apply for OpSpec B034 under 14 CFR 135 or an LOA under 14 CFR 91. Otherwise, there are other means listed in AC 90-96A to get approval.

Chapter 9

Required Navigation Performance-4 (RNP-4)

*T**he Required Navigation Performance-4 (RNP-4) standard is performance based, requiring on-board performance monitoring and alerting. This is as opposed to the older RNAV systems which are an equipment-based standard that do not require on-board performance monitoring and alerting.*

Of the current RNP designations, RNP-4 is the specification used for oceanic and remote continental navigation applications. While RNP-10 is also used, it is not a true Performance Based Navigation standard.

As of 2015, only a handful of places in the world say RNP-4 is required but they all have work arounds in place if you are RNP-10 authorized. To get your RNP-4 authorization you will first need CPDLC and ADS. Then, under 14 CFR 91 you will need an LOA and under 14 CFR 135 you will need OpSpec B036.

Location

Asia

[ICAO Doc 7030, §MID/ASIA, ¶4.1.2.1.2] For flights on designated controlled oceanic routes or areas within the Auckland Oceanic, Brisbane, Fukuoka, Honiara, Melbourne, Nauru, New Zealand and Port Moresby FIRs, a longitudinal separation minimum of 55.5 km (30 nm) derived by RNAV may be applied between RNAV-equipped aircraft approved to RNP 4 or better, in accordance with the provisions of the PANS-ATM, 5.4.2.6.

Pacific

[ICAO Doc 7030, §PAC, ¶4.1.2.1.2] For flights on designated controlled oceanic routes or areas within the Anchorage Arctic, Anchorage Continental, Anchorage Oceanic, Auckland Oceanic, Nadi, Oakland Oceanic and Tahiti FIRs, a longitudinal separation minimum of 55.5 km (30 nm) derived by

RNAV may be applied between RNAV-equipped aircraft approved to RNP 4 or better, in accordance with the provisions of the PANS-ATM, 5.4.2.6.

In both the Asia and Pacific instances, the 30 nm longitudinal separation "may be applied." If you do not have RNP-4 authorization the following PANS-ATM provisions are cited:

RNAV Provisions

[ICAO Doc 4444, ¶5.4.2.6] LONGITUDINAL SEPARATION MINIMA BASED ON DISTANCE USING RNAV WHERE RNP IS SPECIFIED

5.4.2.6.2.2 Direct controller-pilot communications shall be maintained while applying a distance-based separation minima. Direct controller-pilot communications shall be voice or CPDLC. The communication criteria necessary for CPDLC to satisfy the requirement for direct controller-pilot communications shall be established by an appropriate safety assessment.

5.4.2.6.3 Longitudinal distance-based separation minima in an RNP RNAV environment not using ADS.

5.4.2.6.3.1 For aircraft cruising, climbing or descending on the same track, the following separation minimum may be used:

Separation minimum	RNP type	Communication requirement	Surveillance requirement	Distance verification requirements
93 km (50NM)	10	Direct controller-pilot communications	Procedure position reports	At least every 24 minutes

5.4.2.6.4 Longitudinal distance-based separation minima in 5.4.2.6.4 an RNP RNAV environment using ADS.

5.4.2.6.4.3 For aircraft cruising, climbing or descending on the same track, the following separation minima may be used:

Separation minimum	RNP type	Maximum ADS periodic reporting interval
93 km (50NM)	10	27 minutes
93 km (50NM)	4	32 minutes
55.5 km (30NM)	4	14 minutes

If you do not have ADS and are not RNP-4 authorized, controllers have the option of accepting you but using increased separation standards provided: you are RNP-10 qualified, you are in direct communications with the controller, and you make position reports at least every 24 minutes.

Accuracy / Performance Standards

[ICAO Doc 9613, Volume II, Part C,¶1.3.3.5]

- During operations in airspace or on routes designated as RNP 4, the lateral total system error must be within ±4 nm for at least 95% of the total flight time. The along-track error must also be within ±4 nm for at least 95% of the total flight time. An FTE of 2.0 nm (95%) may be assumed.

- Malfunction of the aircraft navigation equipment is classified as a major failure condition under airworthiness regulations (i.e. 10^{-5} per hour).

- Loss of function is classified as a major failure condition for oceanic and remote navigation. The continuity requirement is satisfied by the carriage of dual independent long-range navigation systems (excluding signal-in-space).

- The RNP system, or the RNP system and pilot in combination, shall provide an alert if the accuracy requirement is not met, or if the probability that the lateral TSE exceeds 8 nm is greater than 10^{-5}.

- If using GNSS, the aircraft navigation equipment shall provide an alert if the probability of signal-in-space errors causing a lateral position error greater than 8 nm exceeds 10^{-7} per hour (Annex 10, Volume I, Table 3.7.2.4-1).

Note.— Compliance with the performance monitoring and alerting requirement does not imply an automatic monitor of flight technical error. The on-board monitoring and alerting function should consist at least of a navigation system error (NSE) monitoring and alerting algorithm and a lateral deviation display enabling the crew to monitor the flight technical error (FTE). To the extent operational procedures are used to monitor FTE, the crew procedure, equipment characteristics, and installation are evaluated for their effectiveness and equivalence as described in the functional requirements and operating procedures. Path definition error (PDE) is considered negligible due to the quality assurance process (1.3.6) and crew procedures (1.3.4).

[ICAO Doc 9613, Volume II, Part C,¶1.3.4.1] It is important to understand that additional requirements will have to be met for operational authorization in RNP 4 airspace or on RNP 4 routes. Controller-pilot data link communications (CPDLC) and automatic dependent surveillance — contract (ADS-C) systems will also be required when the separation standard is 30 nm lateral and/or longitudinal. The on-board navigation data must be current and include appropriate procedures.

[FAA Order 8400.33, ¶9.c.] Operators should use the appropriate FAA or ICAO flight plan designation specified for the RNP route flown. The letter "R" should be placed in block 10 of the ICAO flight plan to indicate that the pilot has reviewed the planned route of flight to determine RNP requirements and the aircraft and operator have been approved by the FAA to operate in areas or on routes where RNP is a requirement for operation. Additional information needs to be displayed in the remarks section that indicates the accuracy capability such as RNP-4 versus RNP-10. It is important to understand that additional requirements will have to be met for operational authorization in RNP-4 airspace or routes. Controller-Pilot Data Link Communication (CPDLC) and Air Data System (ADS) will also be required when the separation standard is 30 nm lateral and/or longitudinal.

This is a potential "gotcha" in the works. The FAA can issue an OpSpec/MSpec/ LOA for RNP-4 authorization to aircraft without CPDLC and ADS and you could file the appropriate flight plan designation. But you could be granted access to RNP-4 airspace where air traffic control is assuming they will see your aircraft on ADS and can reach you via CPDLC. When ATC figures that out, they will fear you could cause a loss of separation with an aircraft that has all the necessary navigation and communications equipment. If that happens, guess who will be found to blame? My advice: skip the RNP-4 authorization until you meet the requirements to use it worldwide.

Documentation / Certification

Determining Eligibility of Aircraft

[FAA Order 8400.33, ¶6.b.] New systems may demonstrate compliance with RNP-4 oceanic and remote operations as part of their airworthiness approval. For existing systems, the Aircraft Manufacturer should determine compliance with RNP-4 Oceanic and Remote Operations capability as listed in the Aircraft Flight Manual (AFM) supplement, or additional airworthiness documentation, or as obtained per amended type certificate (TC) or Supplemental Type Certificate (STC). Confirmation from the manufacturer documenting that the aircraft meets RNP-4 performance requirements in this order will be required if the operator chooses to claim additional performance beyond original airworthiness approval or as stated in the AFM, amended TC, or STC. Navigation performance must consider the navigation infrastructure used in original airworthiness approval.

14 CFR 91

[FAA Order 8400.33, ¶6.a.(2)] *[These operators should]* Contact their local FSDO to start the process for RNP-4 authorization. The responsible FSDO will issue the LOA, authorizing RNP-4 oceanic or remote operations. The LOA will identify conditions or limitations (e.g., navigation systems or procedures required, routes or areas authorized).

14 CFR 135

[FAA Order 8400.33, ¶6.a.(1)] *[These operators should]* Notify the certificate management office (CMO) or CHDO which holds its operating certificate of its intent to request authorization for RNP-4 operations (OpSpecs B036). RNP-4 authorizations for air carriers will be addressed through issuance of approved OpSpecs. The OpSpecs will identify conditions or limitations (e.g., navigation systems or procedures required, routes or areas authorized (OpSpecs B050)).

[FAA Order 8900.10 Vol 3, Chapter 18, Part B, §B036, ¶k)] OpSpec/MSpec Entries.

4. For RNP 4 operations, an aircraft must meet a cross-track keeping accuracy and along-track positioning accuracy of no greater than +7.4 km (4 nm) for 95% of the flight time. Different routes that require RNP-4 may have different separation, equipment, and communications requirements. It is possible in the future that a route or airspace could be established that would require RNP-4 navigation capability with VHF communication and radar. Some examples of routes that require RNP-4 are:

- Australian Tasman Sea; detailed guidance is contained in Australian Government, Civil Aviation Authority, AC 91U-3(0), Required Navigation Performance 4 (RNP-4) Operational Certificate;

- Easter Russia, the Magadan region; requires FANS 1/A-equiped aircraft; and

"Easter Russia" is probably a typo, most likely means eastern Russia.

- Western region of China and north of the Himalayas, Route 888; because of the remoteness of the area, RNP-4 CPDLC, and ADS are required.

5. Eligibility of aircraft and certification of its navigation equipment for RNP-4 must be determined:

- For RNP-4 operations in oceanic or remote airspace, at least two fully serviceable independent LRNS, with integrity such that the navigation system does not provide misleading information, must be fitted to the aircraft. These will form part of the basis upon which RNP-4 operational approval is granted;

- For aircraft incorporating GPS, AC 20-138A or equivalent documents provide an acceptable means of complying with installation requirements for aircraft that use but do not integrate the GNSS output with that of other sensors. AC 20-130A describes an acceptable means of compliance for multi-sensor navigation systems that incorporate GPS; and

- Flightcrew training and operating procedures for the navigation systems to be used must be identified by the operator.

Example Compliance

Authorized Aircraft Operation: RNP 4

Max EPU Value: 4

Authorization Required (Part 91): Yes

Aircraft complies with RNP RNAV as defined in RTCA/DO-236B and DO-283, with the limitations and exceptions noted in the AFM Limitations Section. Operation must be authorized by civil aviation authorities via Letter of Authorization or Ops Specs.

You should have a similar statement in your AFM or POH, or other proof of eligibility.

Under 14 CFR 91 you will need an LOA.

Under 14 CFR 135 you will also need OpSpec B036:

Note that this operations specification, with at least RNP 10, is required before getting authorizations B037 (Operations in Central East Pacific airspace), B038 (North Pacific Operations), B039 (Operations within North Atlantic Minimum Navigation Performance Specifications airspace), and B040 (Operations in Areas of Magnetic Unreliability).

Chapter 10

Required Navigation Performance-10 (RNP-10)

equired Navigation Performance (RNP) standards are almost always per-formance based, requiring on-board performance monitoring and alerting. This is as opposed to the older RNAV systems which are an equipment-based standard that do not require on-board performance monitoring and alerting. We say almost always because RNP-10 is an exception . . .

Inconsistent RNP Designation

[ICAO Doc 9613, Volume I, Part A, ¶1.2.5.1] The existing RNP 10 designation is inconsistent with PBN RNP and RNAV specifications. RNP 10 does not include requirements for on-board performance monitoring and alerting. For purposes of consistency with the PBN concept, RNP 10 is referred to as RNAV 10 in this manual. Renaming current RNP 10 routes, operational approvals, etc., to an RNAV 10 designation would be an extensive and expensive task, which is not cost-effective. Consequently, any existing or new operational approvals will continue to be designated RNP 10, and any charting annotations will be depicted as RNP 10.

Location

Africa

[ICAO Doc 7030, §AFI, ¶4.1.1] For flights on designated controlled oceanic routes or areas within the Canarias FIR (southern sector), Dakar Oceanic, Recife and Sal Oceanic FIRs, and on designated routes over continental Africa, a lateral separation minimum of 93 km (50 nm) may be applied.

For flights in the EUR/SAM corridor (Canarias (southern sector), Dakar Oceanic, Recife and Sal Oceanic FIRs), a longitudinal separation minimum of 93 km (50 nm) derived by RNAV may be applied between RNAV-equipped aircraft approved to RNP 10 or better, in accordance with the provisions of the PANS-ATM, 5.4.2.6.

Longitudinal distance-based separation minima of 93 km (50 nm) between RNAV aircraft on the same track on RNP 10 routes over continental Africa shall not be used.

Asia

[ICAO Doc 7030, §MID/ASIA, ¶4.1.1] For flights on designated controlled oceanic routes or areas within the Auckland Oceanic, Brisbane, Fukuoka, Honiara, Melbourne, Nauru, New Zealand and Port Moresby FIRs, a lateral separation minimum of 93 km (50 nm) may be applied.

For flights on designated controlled oceanic routes or areas within the Auckland Oceanic, Brisbane, Fukuoka, Honiara, Melbourne, Nauru, New Zealand and Port Moresby FIRs, a longitudinal separation minimum of 93 km (50 nm) derived by RNAV may be applied between RNAV-equipped aircraft approved to RNP 10 or better, in accordance with the provisions of the PANS-ATM, 5.4.2.6.

Pacific

[ICAO Doc 7030, §PAC, ¶4.1.1]

For flights on designated controlled oceanic routes or areas within the Anchorage Arctic, Anchorage Continental, Anchorage Oceanic, Auckland Oceanic, Nadi, Oakland Oceanic and Tahiti FIRs, a lateral separation minimum of 93 km (50 nm) may be applied.

For flights on designated controlled oceanic routes or areas within the Anchorage Arctic, Anchorage Continental, Anchorage Oceanic, Auckland Oceanic, Nadi, Oakland Oceanic and Tahiti FIRs, a longitudinal separation minimum of 93 km (50 nm) derived by RNAV may be applied between RNAV-equipped aircraft approved to RNP 10 or better, in accordance with the provisions of the PANS-ATM, 5.4.2.6.

South America

[ICAO Doc 7030, §SAM, ¶4.1.1] For flights on designated controlled oceanic routes or areas within the Canarias FIR (southern sector), Dakar Oceanic, Recife and Sal Oceanic FIRs a lateral separation minimum of 93 km (50 nm) may be applied.

For flights in the EUR/SAM corridor (Canarias (southern sector), Dakar Oceanic, Recife and Sal Oceanic FIRs), a longitudinal separation minimum of 93 km (50 nm) derived by RNAV may be applied between RNAV-equipped aircraft approved to RNP 10 or better, in accordance with the provisions of the PANS-ATM, 5.4.2.6.

RNAV Provisions

[PANS-ATM ICAO Doc 4444] LONGITUDINAL SEPARATION MINIMA BASED ON DISTANCE USING RNAV WHERE RNP IS SPECIFIED

5.4.2.6.2.2 Direct controller-pilot communications shall be maintained while applying a distance-based separation minima. Direct controller-pilot communications shall be voice or CPDLC. The communication criteria necessary for CPDLC to satisfy the requirement for direct controller-pilot communications shall be established by an appropriate safety assessment.

5.4.2.6.3 Longitudinal distance-based separation minima in an RNP RNAV environment not using ADS

5.4.2.6.3.1 For aircraft cruising, climbing or descending on the same track, the following separation minimum may be used:

Separation minimum	RNP type	Communication requirement	Surveillance requirement	Distance verification requirements
93 km (50NM)	10	Direct controller-pilot communications	Procedure position reports	At least every 24 minutes

Accuracy / Performance Standards

[ICAO Doc 9613, Volume II, Part C,¶1.3.4.1]

Accuracy: During operations in airspace or on routes designated as RNP 10, the lateral total system error must be within ±10 nm for at least 95 percent of the total flight time. The along-track error must also be within ±10 nm for at least 95 percent of the total flight time.

Note 1.— For RNP 10, operational approval of aircraft capable of coupling the area navigation (RNAV) system to the flight director or autopilot, a navigational positioning error is considered to be the dominant contributor to cross-track and along-track error. Flight technical error, path definition error and display errors are considered to be insignificant for the purposes of RNP 10 approval.

Note 2.— When the data collection method described in Appendix 1 of FAA Order 8400.12A (as amended) is used as the basis for an RNP 10 operational approval, these error types are included in the analysis. However, when the data collection method described in Appendix 6 of FAA Order 8400.12A is used, these errors are not included since that method is more conservative. The Appendix 6 method uses radial error instead of cross-track and along-track error.

- Integrity: Malfunction of the aircraft navigation equipment is classified as a major failure condition under airworthiness regulations (i.e. 10^{-5} per hour).

- Continuity: Loss of function is classified as a major failure condition for oceanic and remote navigation. The continuity requirement is satisfied by the carriage of dual independent LRNSs (excluding signal-in-space).

- Signal-in-space: If using GNSS, the aircraft navigation equipment shall provide an alert if the probability of signal-in- space errors causing a lateral position error greater than 20 nm exceeds 10^{-7} per hour.

Documentation / Certification

Determining Eligibility of Aircraft

FAA Order 8400.12A was written in 1998 and details an extensive process to determine aircraft eligibility. The process has pretty much aligned itself with other RNP approvals; an AFM statement seems to suffice.

14 CFR 91

[FAA Order 8400.12A, ¶8.b.(2)] These operators should contact their local FSDO to start the process for RNP-10 authorization. Operators under part 91 will receive an LOA, which authorizes RNP-10 operations. The LOA will identify any conditions or limitations necessary (e.g., navigation systems or procedures required, time limits, routes or areas authorized).

14 CFR 135

[FAA Order 8400.12A, ¶8.b.(1)] These operators should notify the Certificate Management Office (CMO) or CHDO which holds its operating certificate of its intent to request approval for RNP-10 operations. RNP-10 authorizations for air carriers will be addressed through issuance of approved operations specifications. The operations specifications will identify any conditions or limitations necessary (e.g., navigation systems or procedures required, time limits, routes or areas authorized).*Under 14 CFR 91 you will need an LOA.*

Section IV – Communicate

Chapter 1

Required Communications Performance (RCP)

*M*ost pilots who have flown internationally in the last decade or so are well acquainted with the concept of Required Navigation Performance (RNP), the idea that where you can fly will be determined on how accurately you can fly and how well the system alerts you when things are less than promised. The same concept holds true for communications and surveillance. In the case of communications, the number attached to your Required Communications Performance (RCP) is the number of seconds it takes for an instruction to travel from the ground to you and your acknowledgement back to the ground. Does it matter? Yes, the lower the number the tighter the airspace you will be allowed to fly. Put another way: the higher the number, the more airspace around the world that will be denied you.

History

[ICAO Doc 9869, ¶1.1.4] The fourth meeting of the Aeronautical Mobile Communications Panel (AMCP/4) (Montreal, April 1996) recognized the absence of objective criteria to evaluate communication performance requirements. This objective criteria was seen as a set of values for parameters, which would be based on the operational requirements for communication systems in the various phases of flight. The meeting agreed that there was an urgent need to assess the various technical options of communication systems against such a set values for these parameters. The term RCP type is used to denote a set of values for these parameters.

This all grew out of the initial efforts to formalize the Future Air Navigation System (FANS) that led to the development of a Required Navigation Performance (RNP) standard. RCP is the underlying principle behind getting rid of HF and moving toward SATCOM. That also spawned the need to differentiate SATVOICE versus SATCOM.

121

Concept

[ICAO Doc 9869, ¶2.2]

- The RCP concept characterizes the performance required for communication capabilities that support ATM functions without reference to any specific technology and is open to new technology. This approach is essential to evolving operational concepts using emerging technologies. An ATM function is an individual operational component of air traffic services. Examples of ATM functions include the application of separation between aircraft, the re-routing of aircraft, and the provision of flight information.

- The RCP concept assesses operational communication transactions in the context of an ATM function, taking into account human interactions, procedures, and environmental characteristics.

- The contribution of the human can be significant to RCP. Communication is the accurate transfer of information between sender and receiver, the content of which can be readily understood by both.

- An operational communication transaction is the process a human uses to send an instruction, clearance, flight information, and/or request, and is completed when that human is confident that the transaction is complete.

- The RCP concept is based upon "operationally significant" benchmarks to attain confidence that the operational communications supporting the ATM functions will be conducted in an acceptably safe manner.

- The benchmark of choice is the round trip time between a controller's instruction to a pilot and the pilot's acknowledgement back to the controller.

- The basis for the development of the RCP concept was the need for objective operational criteria, in the form of an RCP type, to evaluate a variety of communication technologies. Once these criteria have been set and accepted, a specific implementation, considering system technical and human performance, may be assessed for its viability against acceptable operational criteria.

- An RCP type is a label (e.g., RCP 240) that defines a performance standard for operational communication transactions. Each RCP type denotes values for communication transaction time, continuity, availability, and integrity applicable to the most stringent operational communication transaction supporting an ATM function.

RCP Type

[ICAO Doc 9869, ¶3.2]

In order to simplify RCP type naming convention and to make the required communication transaction time readily apparent to airspace planners, aircraft manufacturers and operators, the RCP type is specified by the value for the communication transaction time associated with the ATM function.

An RCP type comprises values assigned to the parameters: communication transaction time, continuity, availability, and integrity.

RCP type parameters

• Communication transaction time - The maximum time for the completion of the operational communication transaction after which the initiator should revert to an alternative procedure.

• Continuity - The probability that an operational communication transaction can be completed within the communication transaction time.

• Availability - The probability that an operational communication transaction can be initiated when needed.

• Integrity - The probability that communication transactions are completed within the communication transaction time with undetected error.

This is good stuff for a comm geek but really not that pertinent to a pilot. But it helps to understand what is to follow:

[ICAO Doc 9869, ¶3.3]

• There may be multiple operational communication transactions that support an ATM function. These transactions are assessed to determine the most stringent. The value for the communication transaction time parameter is based on the time needed to complete the most stringent transaction.

• The assessment would take into consideration the time needed to safely execute the contingency procedure and can include simulations, demonstrations, operational trials, and analysis of empirical data applicable to the operational communication transaction times needed to support the ATM function.

- Separation assurance is an ATM function for which the operational communication transaction time can be determined by collision risk modeling. Collision risk modeling considers the operational communication transaction times in the communications and controller intervention buffer supporting separation assurance.

RCP type	Transaction time (sec)	Continuity (probability/ flight hour)	Availability (probability/ flight hour)	Integrity (acceptable rate/ flight hour)
RCP 10	10	0.995	0.99998	10^{-5}
RCP 60	60	0.99	0.9995	10^{-5}
RCP 120	120	0.99	0.9995	10^{-5}
RCP 240	240	0.99	0.9995	10^{-5}
RCP 400	400	0.99	0.999	10^{-5}

Figure: Recommended RCP Types, from ICAO Document 9869, Table 3-1.

Here you see the crux of the RCP issue for a pilot. If you are flying in an environment where you have 50 nm or more lateral spacing, you are probably flying in an RCP-400 environment. The turn around time from the controller to the radio operator to you and back is 400 seconds. An HF will suffice. But, on the other hand, if you are flying with only 30 nm of lateral spacing and reduced longitudinal separation, you are probably dealing with an RCP-240 environment. Now you need CPDLC. If you combine CPDLC with ADS, you can get even lower. See Section V, Chapter 1, Required Surveillance Performance (RSP).

RCP specification	Intended uses for which the RCP specification is applicable
RCP 240	When CPDLC is the normal means of communications supporting the application of separation minima predicated on communication performance (e.g. 30 NM lateral and 30 NM or 50 NM longitudinal).
RCP 400	When a technology other than HF voice radio is the normal means of communication and the ATS function specifies a requirement for RCP 400.
	When a technology other than HF voice radio is the alternative means of communication supporting the application of separation minima predicated on communication performance (e.g. 30 NM lateral and 30 NM or 50 NM longitudinal).

Figure: Examples of applying RCP, from ICAO GOLD, Table 2-3.

Chapter 2

High Frequency (HF) Radio

*T*here is much about HF to be confused about. It is a High Frequency (HF), for example, which turns out to be lower than most of the frequencies we deal with on a daily basis. Younger pilots often hear from the older pilots about just how difficult it was to make a position report "back in the day," but it seems rather easy these days. It is true that technology has made the radios easier to use and the transmitted signals much clearer. But there are still a few things to be gained from learning the technical stuff behind the technology.

Principles of Radio Communications

Amplitude, frequency, and wave lengths

[Radio Communications, Chapter 1]

Radio waves belong to the electromagnetic radiation family, which includes x-ray, ultraviolet, and visible light. Much like the gentle waves that form when a stone is tossed into a still lake, radio signals radiate outward, or propagate, from a transmitting antenna. However, unlike water waves, radio waves propagate at the speed of light. We characterize a radio wave in terms of its amplitude, frequency, and wavelength.

Radio wave amplitude, or strength, can be visualized as its height being the distance between its peak and its lowest point. Amplitude, which is measured in volts, is usually expressed in terms of an average value called root-mean-square, or RMS.

The frequency of a radio wave is the number of repetitions or cycles it completes in a given period of time. Frequency is measured in Hertz (Hz); one Hertz equals one cycle per second. Thousands of Hertz are expressed as kilohertz (kHz), and millions of Hertz as megahertz (MHz). You would typically see a frequency of 2,345,000 Hertz, for example, written as 2,345 kHz or 2.345 MHz.

Radio wavelength is the distance between crests of a wave. The product of wavelength and frequency is a constant that is equal to the speed of propagation. Thus, as the frequency increases, wavelength decreases, and vice versa. Radio waves propagate at the speed of light (300 million meters per second). To determine the wavelength in meters for any frequency, divide 300 by the frequency in megahertz. So, the wavelength of a 10 MHz wave is 30 meters, determined by dividing 300 by 10.

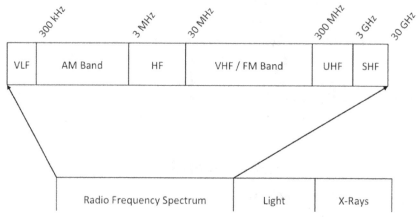

Figure: Radio Frequency Spectrum.

The HF Spectrum

[Radio Communications, Chapter 1]

The HF band is defined as the frequency range of 3 to 30 MHz. In practice, most HF radios use the spectrum from 1.6 to 30 MHz. Most long haul communications in this band take place between 4 and 18 MHz. Higher frequencies (18 to 30 MHz) may also be available from time to time, depending on ionospheric conditions and the time of day.

Sidebands

[Radio Communications, Chapter 1]

Today's common methods for radio communications include amplitude modulation (AM), which varies the strength of the carrier in direct proportion to changes in the intensity of a source such as the human voice. In other words, information is contained in amplitude variations. The AM process creates a carrier and a pair of duplicate sidebands — nearby fre-

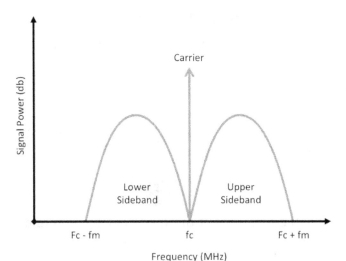

Figure: AM Signal Sidebands.

quencies above and below the carrier. AM is a relatively inefficient form of modulation, since the carrier must be continually generated. The majority of the power in an AM signal is consumed by the carrier that carries no information, with the rest going to the information-carrying sidebands.

You can think of the data as existing in the fat lobes of the signal where as the center has no space for any data at all. Shortwave radio enthusiasts can use either or both sidebands.

In a more efficient technique, single sideband (SSB), the carrier and one of the sidebands are suppressed. Only the remaining sideband — upper (USB) or lower (LSB) — is transmitted. An SSB signal needs only half the bandwidth of an AM signal and is produced only when a modulating signal is present. Thus, SSB systems are more efficient both in the use of the spectrum, which must accommodate many users, and of transmitter power. All the transmitted power goes into the information-carrying sideband.

In aviation we used to note our frequency as "Upper" or "Lower" to differentiate between the two. You would say, "transmitting 8060 upper," for example. All aircraft HF communication, outside of the military, seems to have gravitated to the upper sideband so we no longer need to say it. (It is assumed.)

Line of Sight / Minimum Altitude

So, at what point does your VHF lose its air-to-ground capability? A little geometry:

$$(r_p + h)^2 = r_p^2 + d_{los}^2$$

Where r_p is the radius of the earth (20,025,643 feet at the equator), h is the height of the aircraft, and d_{los} is the line of sight distance from the aircraft to the horizon. Solving for d_{los} we get:

$$d_{los} = \sqrt{h(2r_p + h)}$$

Which gives us the line of sight distance available at minium altitudes, as shown in the table:

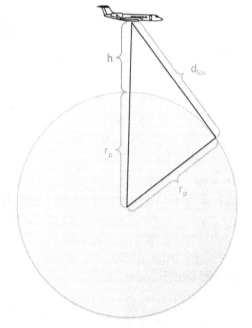

Altitude (feet)	Distance (nm)
10,000	104
20,000	147
30,000	180
40,000	208
50,000	233

Figure: Line of sight.

You can use your VHF or HF for line of sight communications, but to go beyond the horizon, you will need to bounce an HF signal off the ground, water, or the ionosphere.

Sky Wave Propagation

[Radio Communications, Chapter 2]

The ionosphere is a region of electrically charged particles or gases in the earth's atmosphere, extending from approximately 50 to 600 km above the earth's surface. Ionization, the process in which electrons are stripped from atoms and produces electrically charged particles, results from solar radiation. When the ionosphere becomes heavily ionized, the gases may even glow and be visible. This phenomenon is known as Northern and Southern Lights.

Why is the ionosphere important in HF radio? Well, this blanket of gases is like nature's satellite, making HF BLOS radio communications possible. When radio waves strike these ionized layers, depending on frequency, some are completely absorbed, others are refracted so that they return to the earth, and still others pass through the ionosphere into outer space. Absorption tends to be greater at lower frequencies, and increases as the degree of ionization increases.

The angle at which sky waves enter the ionosphere is known as the incident angle. This is determined by wavelength and the type of transmitting antenna. Like a billiard ball bouncing off a rail, a radio wave reflects from the ionosphere at the same angle it hits it. Thus, the incident angle is an important factor in determining communications range. If you need to reach a

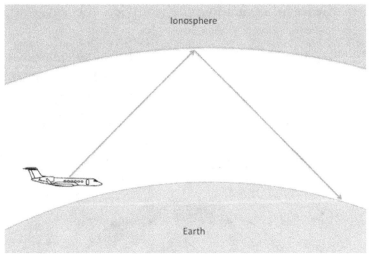

Figure: Sky wave propagation.

station that is relatively far from you, you would want the incident angle to be relatively large. To communicate with a nearby station, the incident angle should be relatively small.

Ground station HF radio operators worry about the angle of incidence as a way of aiming their signals to a desired distance. Since aircraft are closer to the ionosphere, the achievable angles are far greater as is the achievable distance. The pilot doesn't need to worry about the angle, other than to know how the angle can be affected by atmospheric conditions.

Ionosphere Layers

[Radio Communications, Chapter 2]

Within the ionosphere, there are four layers of varying ionization. Since ionization is caused by solar radiation, the higher layers of the ionosphere tend to be more highly ionized, while the lower layers, protected by the outer layers, experience less ionization. Of these layers, the first was designated E for electric waves. Later, D and F were discovered and noted by these letters. Additional ionospheric phenomena were discovered through the 1930s and 1940s, such as sporadic E and aurora.

In the ionosphere, the D layer is the lowest region affecting HF radio waves. Ionized during the day, the D layer reaches maximum ionization when the sun is at its zenith and dissipates quickly toward sunset.

The E layer reaches maximum ionization at noon. It begins dissipating to-

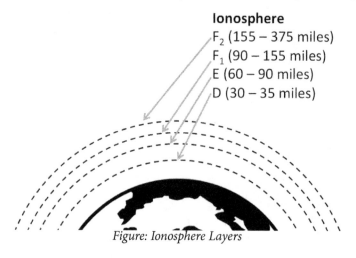

Ionosphere
F_2 (155 – 375 miles)
F_1 (90 – 155 miles)
E (60 – 90 miles)
D (30 – 35 miles)

Figure: Ionosphere Layers

ward sunset and reaches minimum activity at midnight. Irregular cloud-like formations of ionized gases occasionally occur in the E layer. These regions, known as sporadic E, can support propagation of sky waves at the upper end of the HF band and beyond.

The most heavily ionized region of the ionosphere, and therefore the most important for long-haul communications, is the F layer. At this altitude, the air is thin enough that the ions and electrons recombine very slowly, so the layer retains its ionized properties even after sunset.

In the daytime, the F layer consists of two distinct layers, F1 and F2. The F1 layer, which exists only in the daytime and is negligible in winter, is not important to HF communications. The F2 layer reaches maximum ionization at noon and remains charged at night, gradually decreasing to a minimum just before sunrise.

During the day, sky wave reflection from the F2 layer requires wavelengths short enough to penetrate the ionized D and E layers, but not so short as to pass through the F layer. Generally, frequencies from 10 to 20 MHz will accomplish this, but the same frequencies used at night would penetrate the F layer and pass into outer space. The most effective frequencies for long-haul nighttime communications are normally between 3 and 8 MHz.

There are free electrons everywhere and when these electrons attach themselves to molecules in the atmosphere these molecules are said to be ionized. An ionized molecule is good for bouncing radio waves so an ionized layer of atmosphere is good for long distance communications. Where the knowledge shown here comes in handy is when selecting a frequency. During the day the lowest ionosphere is as ionized as it gets and a higher frequency (with the longest wavelength) bounces best. During the night this layer isn't so effective so you want to pass through it. So a lower frequency (with a shorter wavelength) will pass through the D layer on its way to the F layers where a better bounce can be had. That validates the old pilot's rule of thumb: the higher the sun, the higher the frequency.

Atmospheric Ionization Factors

[Radio Communications, Chapter 2]

The intensity of solar radiation, and therefore ionization, varies periodically. Hence, we can predict solar radiation intensity based on time of day and the season, and make adjustments in equipment to limit or optimize ionization effects.

Ionization is higher during spring and summer because the hours of daylight are longer. Sky waves are absorbed or weakened as they pass through the highly charged D and E layers, reducing, in effect, the communication range of most HF bands.

Because there are fewer hours of daylight during autumn and winter, less radiation reaches the D and E layers. Lower frequencies pass easily through these weakly ionized layers. Therefore, signals arriving at the F layer are stronger and are reflected over greater distances.

Another longer term periodic variation results from the 11-year sunspot cycle. Sunspots generate bursts of radiation that cause higher levels of ionization. The more sunspots, the greater the ionization.

During periods of low sunspot activity, frequencies above 20 MHz tend to be unusable because the E and F layers are too weakly ionized to reflect signals back to earth. At the peak of the sunspot cycle, however, it is not unusual to have worldwide propagation on frequencies above 30 MHz.

In addition to these regular variations, there is a class of unpredictable phenomena known as sudden ionospheric disturbances (SID), which can affect HF communications as well. SIDs are random events due to solar flares that can disrupt sky wave communication for hours or days at a time. Solar flares produce intense ionization of the D layer, causing it to absorb most HF signals on the side of the earth facing the sun.

Magnetic storms often follow the eruption of solar flares within 20 to 40 hours. Charged particles from the storms have a scattering effect on the F layer, temporarily neutralizing its reflective properties.

Required for Oceanic?

U.S. Requirement

[AC 91-70A, ¶3-3.c.] Notwithstanding the fact that pilots must comply with all regulations applicable to their flight, all aircraft operating over the high seas must equip suitable instruments and navigation equipment appropriate to the route to be flown. The aircraft must also equip a functioning two-way radio to maintain a continuous listening watch on the appropriate radio frequency and establish two-way radio communications with the appropriate ATC unit. It is not acceptable to depend on radio relay operations to satisfy this requirement.

ICAO Requirement

[ICAO Annex 2, §3.6.5.1] An aircraft operated as a controlled flight shall maintain continuous air-ground voice communication watch on the appropriate communication channel of, and establish two-way communication as necessary with, the appropriate air traffic control unit, except as may be prescribed by the appropriate ATS authority in respect of aircraft forming part of aerodrome traffic at a controlled aerodrome.

Note 1. SELCAL or similar automatic signalling devices satisfy the requirement to maintain an air-ground voice communication watch.

Note 2. The requirement for an aircraft to maintain an air-ground voice communication watch remains in effect after CPDLC has been established.

[ICAO Annex 2, §5.1.1] Aircraft shall be equipped with suitable instruments and with navigation equipment appropriate to the route to be flown.

North Atlantic Requirement

[ICAO Doc 7030, §NAT, ¶3.4.1] Within the NAT Region, aircraft equipped for SATCOM voice shall restrict the use of such equipment to emergencies and non-routine situations. An unforeseen inability to communicate by voice radio constitutes a non-routine situation. Since oceanic traffic typically communicates through aeradio facilities, a SATCOM call due to an unforeseen inability to communicate by other means should be made to such a facility rather than the ATC centre unless the urgency of the communication dictates otherwise. Dedicated SATCOM telephone numbers (short codes) for aeradio facilities and air traffic control facilities are published in national AIPs.

Yes, you can use your SATCOM for position reporting if you really needed to, and yes, you do make position reports with CPDLC. But the requirement remains: you need the HF when beyond VHF coverage. You need at least one; you might need two if you don't have CPDLC or a qualified satellite voice system.

North Atlantic Track (NAT) Frequency Families

The North Atlantic is probably the busiest oceanic airspace in the world and hunting for the correct frequency can be a challenge if your assigned frequencies become unusable. A system of "frequency families" make it a little easier.

[ICAO Doc 003, ¶3.1.6] The NAT Families were defined utilising the frequencies allocated for the purpose of providing an AMS [Aeronautical Mobile Service] throughout the coverage area required.

NAT Family	Frequencies
A	3016, 5598, 8906, 13306 and 17946 KHz
B	2899, 5616, 8864, 13291 and 17946 kHz
C	2872, 5649, 8879, 11336, 13306 and 17946 kHz
D	2971, 4675, 8891, 11279, 13291 and 17946 kHz
E	2962, 6628, 8825, 11309, 13354 and 17946 kHz
F	3476, 6622, 8831, 13291 and 17946 kHz
H	3491, 6667

[ICAO Doc 003, ¶4.1]

The frequencies assigned to an aircraft should belong to the same sub-network, which includes all the stations that may be affected by the aircraft flight route.

If you are assigned a frequency that becomes unusable, you should attempt contact on a frequency from the same family.

Frequencies should be guarded only during the periods when they are usable, instead of maintaining the current twenty-four hour watch practice.

Do not be surprised if a frequency is completely silent; it may very well be unused.

During off-peak periods, when it is unnecessary to guard all frequencies and families, radio stations should use common families to achieve more efficient use of staff resources.

You may hear other stations on the same frequency.

Chapter 3

Voice Position Reports

A position report will normally be required in oceanic airspace unless instructed to "omit position reports" by the air traffic service (ATS) unit. There is a certain etiquette to be followed, to be sure. You can survive without it, but the radio operator on the other end and the pilots sharing HF time will appreciate your efforts if your transmissions are brief, clear, and follow the correct format.

The radio operator is typing away at a console and is ready to enter the data in a specific order and format. If you deviate from the format, the radio operator has to do a mental translation from poor to proper. If you deviate from the order, the radio operator will have to make liberal use of the TAB and DELETE keys. All of this introduces the possibility of errors.

[AC 91-70A, Appendix 2, ¶2.i.(3)] After passing over the oceanic waypoint, crews that give a position report to ATC must use the standard format.

Figure: ARINC Radio Operator
(Photo by Chris Parker)

HF Issues

- *Most of your position reporting will be made to an ARINC station which is not an ATS entity but a communications relay point. They are passing your position report to ATC and any ATC instructions to you. The radio operator may be monitoring several frequencies so you should always initiate HF radio calls with the frequency. I.e., "Shanwick, Shanwick, November Seven Seven Zero Zero, position on three, zero, one, six."*

- *HF connectivity can be problematic depending on the aircraft, the weather, and solar sun spot activity. A rule of thumb is: "the higher the sun, the higher the frequency." Pick higher frequencies in the day and lower at night.*

- *The best source of frequency information is on the en route chart. Some regions employ "frequency families" that are determined by the aircraft registration, location, and/or route of flight. If the assigned frequency is unusable, selecting another frequency in the same family would be appropriate.*

- *Satellite phones provide another option, though most regions still classify this option as a last resort. (Many international recurrent training vendors say the service providers really don't care; I've not seen evidence to back that up.) The person answering the phone is a radio operator and expects the normal position reporting format.*

Note: if the phone number on the chart is six digits long it is for an INMARSAT satellite phone. Your aircraft might be using INMARSAT satellites (most do) but it may not be an INMARSAT phone (many aren't). If you don't have an INMARSAT phone you might not be able to use that six-digit number. The G450, for example, does have INMARSAT phones and can use the six-digit number. Many of the phone numbers are standard telephone numbers that can be used on any aircraft satellite phones.

Section 1	1	Aircraft identification	*(aircraft identification)*
	2	Position	POSITION *(latitude and longitude)* OVER *(significant point)* ABEAM *(significant point)* *(significant point) (bearing) (distance)*
	3	Time	*(time)*
	4	Flight level or altitude	FLIGHT LEVEL *(number)* or *(number)* METRES or FEET CLIMBING TO FLIGHT LEVEL *(number)* or *(number)* METRES or FEET DESCENDING TO FLIGHT LEVEL *(number)* or *(number)* METRES or FEET
	5	Next position and estimated time over	*(position) (time)*
	6	Ensuing significant point	*(position)* NEXT

Figure: Model AIREP, Section 1, from ICAO Doc 4444, Appendix A, §1.

Format: Position (Section 1)

[ICAO Doc 4444, Appendix A, §1]

The person on the other end of the radio is sitting in front of a computer terminal with a form laid out in the following format. If you give your position report in this order, the radio operator will have an easier time relaying an accurate position the first time. If you skip around, it will slow things down and introduce the chance of error. So use this format.

[ICAO Doc 4444, Appendix A, §1, ¶1.1] Section 1 is obligatory, although Items 5 and 6 thereof may be omitted when prescribed in Regional Supplementary Procedures.

Item 1 — AIRCRAFT IDENTIFICATION. Report the aircraft radiotelephony call sign.

Item 2 — POSITION. Report position in latitude (degrees as 2 numerics or degrees and minutes as 4 numerics, followed by "North" or "South") and longitude (degrees as 3 numerics or degrees and minutes as 5 numerics, followed by "East" or "West"), or as a significant point identified by a coded designator (2 to 5 characters), or as a significant point followed by magnetic bearing (3 numerics) and distance in nautical miles from the point (e.g. "4620 North 07805 West", "4620 North 07800 West", "4600 North 07800 West", LN ("LIMA NOVEMBER"), "MAY", "HADDY" or "DUB 180 DEGREES 40 MILES"). Precede significant point by "ABEAM", if applicable.

Item 3 — TIME. Report time in hours and minutes UTC (4 numerics) unless reporting time in minutes past the hour (2 numerics) is prescribed on the basis of regional air navigation agreements. The time reported must be the actual time of the aircraft at the position and not the time of origination or transmission of the report. Time shall always be reported in hours and minutes UTC when making a special air-report.

Item 4 — FLIGHT LEVEL OR ALTITUDE. Report flight level by 3 numerics (e.g. "FLIGHT LEVEL 310"), when on standard pressure altimeter setting. Report altitude in metres followed by "METRES" or in feet followed by "FEET", when on QNH. Report "CLIMBING" (followed by the level) when climbing, or "DESCENDING" (followed by the level) when descending, to a new level after passing the significant point.

Item 5 — NEXT POSITION AND ESTIMATED TIME OVER. Report the next reporting point and the estimated time over such reporting point, or report the estimated position that will be reached one hour later, according to the position reporting procedures in force. Use the data conventions specified in Item 2 for position. Report the estimated time over this position. Report time in hours and minutes UTC (4 numerics) unless reporting time in minutes past the hour (2 numerics) as prescribed on the basis of regional air navigation agreements.

Item 6 — ENSUING SIGNIFICANT POINT. Report the ensuing significant point following the "next position and estimated time over".

Section 2	7	Estimated time of arrival	(aerodrome) (time)
	8	Endurance	ENDURANCE (hours and minutes)

Figure: Model AIREP, Section 2, from ICAO Doc 4444, Appendix A, §1.

Format: Company data (Section 2)

[ICAO Doc 4444, Appendix A, §1, ¶1.1] Section 2 shall be added, in whole or in part, only when so requested by the operator or its designated representative, or when deemed necessary by the pilot-in- command.

This will not apply to the vast majority of corporate aviation.

Format: Meteorology data (Section 3)

[ICAO Doc 4444, Appendix A, §1, ¶1.1] Section 3 shall be added in accordance with Annex 3 and the Regional Supplementary Procedures, Part 3 — Meteorology.

The requirement for a position report varies with region and is normally specified in the applicable en route chart or state pages. In the North Atlantic, not too long ago, the report was mandatory for aircraft not on the organized track system or upon request. These days, with so many aircraft giving real time CPDLC weather reports, the only time you will need to do this is if, for some reason, they ask you to.

If required, the Met Report is given immediately following the position report. If a mid-point report is also given, the position is given first in terms of a four-digit latitude and three digit longitude, such as 4124N 030W.

	9	Air temperature	TEMPERATURE PLUS *(degrees Celsius)* TEMPERATURE MINUS *(degrees Celsius)*	
	10	Wind direction	WIND *(number)* DEGREES	*or* CALM
	11	Wind speed	*(number)* KILOMETRES PER HOUR *or* KNOTS	
	12	Turbulence	TURBULENCE LIGHT TURBULENCE MODERATE TURBULENCE SEVERE	
	13	Aircraft icing	ICING LIGHT ICING MODERATE ICING SEVERE	
Section 3	14	Humidity (if available)	HUMIDITY *(per cent)*	
	15	Phenomenon encountered or observed, prompting a special air-report: • Severe turbulence • Severe icing • Severe mountainwave • Thunderstorms without hail • Thunderstorms with hail • Heavy dust/sandstorm • Volcanic ash cloud • Pre-eruption volcanic activity or volcanic eruption SST: • Moderate turbulence • Hail • Cumulonimbus clouds	 TURBULENCE SEVERE ICING SEVERE MOUNTAINWAVE SEVERE THUNDERSTORMS THUNDERSTORMS WITH HAIL DUSTSTORM or SANDSTORM HEAVY VOLCANIC ASH CLOUD PRE-ERUPTION VOLCANIC ACTIVITY or VOLCANIC ERUPTION TURBULENCE MODERATE HAIL CB CLOUDS	

Figure: Model AIREP, Section 3, from ICAO Doc 4444, Appendix A, §1.

Example Position Report

Item	Spoken
Aircraft identification	NOVEMBER SEVEN SEVEN ZERO ZERO
Position	CHECKS FIVE SEVEN NORTH ZERO THREE ZERO WEST
Time (ATA)	AT TWO ONE TWO ZERO ZULU
Altitude	FLIGHT LEVEL FOUR THREE ZERO
Next reporting point	ESTIMATES FIVE SIX NORTH ZERO FOUR ZERO WEST
Time (ETA)	AT TWO TWO ZERO FOUR
Next significant point	FIVE THREE NORTH ZERO FIVE ZERO WEST NEXT
Temperature (at this point)	MINUS FOUR FIVE
Wind (at this point)	TWO FOUR ZERO DIAGONAL TWO ONE
Midpoint position	FIVE SEVEN ZERO FIVE NORTH ZERO TWO FIVE WEST
Temperature (mid-point)	MINUS FOUR EIGHT
Wind (midpoint)	TWO FIVE ZERO DIAGONAL TWO FIVE
	OVER

About the met report: back in the old days you could tell a pro by the seamless transition between each item, right after the word "Next" would come "minus . . .", it was a thing of beauty. These days, however, nobody is giving weather reports and the radio operator is likely to be just as out of practice receiving met reports as you are giving them.

Chapter 4

Satellite Communications / Satellite Voice

The use of satellite voice systems for air traffic control has evolved over the years but has been made complicated by the variety of systems on aircraft versus systems that have proliferated in space. In other words, if your manufacturer guessed wrong about the way things were headed, your aircraft may not be as prepared as others.

First some terminology. We grew up with Satellite Communications (SAT-COM) to mean picking up a phone and making a call via satellite. But now we have a myriad of systems that use the same satellites to transmit and receive all sorts of data. So SATCOM includes the data and the voice; we speak of SATVOICE to denote the picking up the phone bit.

Can you use SATVOICE to make a position report? In most parts of the world: yes. Can you use SATVOICE to replace the requirement for an HF? No, you still need at least one HF. Can you plan on using SATVOICE for air traffic services with an HF as backup? If the region you are flying has made such provisions and you have a qualified system, yes. But how do you know your system qualifies? The easiest way to tell is to look at your MMEL.

Finally, just how many HF's do you need? The answer used to be just one, unless your country or the region you flew said more. Up until 2014, the U.S. only implied you needed "a" HF radio and no region specified more than that. In 2012 the ICAO implied you needed at least two long-range communications systems and one of those had to be an HF. In 2014, the FAA issued a global change to all master minimum equipment lists that codifies that. So the answer is now "at least one, perhaps two."

Historical Background

We've come a long way with satellite communications and there are changes in our near future . . .

[ICAO SVGM, pg. vi]

- In procedural airspace, aeronautical communications have historically been conducted with high frequency (HF) radios due to the advantage of being able to transmit and receive air-ground communications for thousands of miles. Most appropriate authorities hence required two independent HF sets on-board.

That statment notwithstanding, most appropriate authorities seem to be quiet on this subject. The answer depends on what other equipment you have. See "LRCS To Be Carried On Board," later in this chapter.

- The potential for improvement in efficiency resulting from the adoption of satellite technology was discussed at length during the Limited NAT Regional Air Navigation (LIM/NAT/RAN) Conference in Cascais, Portugal, in 1992. Although both data and voice communications were evaluated, it was recognised that data offered greater economic benefit and that the emphasis should be put on that form of communications. This was not seen as precluding the use of voice in abnormal circumstances but the use of SATCOM voice for routine communications was not seen as viable.

- In 1995, the initial future air navigation system (FANS 1/A) provided an integrated airborne CNS package. In addition to required navigation performance (RNP) and global navigation satellite system (GNSS) capabilities, FANS 1/A includes controller pilot data link communications (CPDLC) and automatic dependent surveillance – contract (ADS-C) capabilities using SATCOM, VHF, and HF data links. CPDLC and ADS-C were seen as the normal or preferred means of ATS communications and surveillance in procedural airspace. However, voice communications would continue to be required as an alternative means of ATS communications. At the same time, aircraft were equipped with SATVOICE capability.

- In 2008, the 44th Meeting of the NAT SPG (17-20 June 2008) agreed that authorization to use SATVOICE for all ATS communications would permit reduction in risk of communications failure, improve safety of operations, and alleviate HF channel congestion. However, guidance material would be needed to address a number of issues related to call setup times, security and system performance and capacity. It was further concluded that any decision regarding Minimum Equipment List (MEL) relief of one HF radio was subject to approval by the appropriate authority. This work resulted in NAT SPG Conclusion 45/28 endorsing a proposal for amendment to the NAT SUPPS Doc 7030 that removed the above-mentioned provision.

The only U.S. requirement for any HF radios at all used to be in AC 91-70A, ¶3-3.c. and that is simply for a functioning two-way radio capable of communications with the appropriate air traffic services unit. "A" radio means one. But all that changed in 2012 with an FAA policy letter and now the answer is "at least one." [See "LRCS to be Carried on Board," below]

SATVOICE System Overview

[14 CFR 1] Long-range communication system (LRCS). A system that uses satellite relay, data link, high frequency, or another approved communication system which extends beyond line of sight.

[ICAO SVGM, ¶2.2.2] Satellite communication systems are defined by three different altitude orbits; low earth orbit (LEO), medium earth orbit (MEO) and geosynchronous earth orbit (GEO). The altitude of the orbit determines the area illuminated by the satellite. The higher the orbit the weaker the signal is from the satellite, but it has a much larger footprint. Propagation loss is overcome by increased complexity of the antenna systems along with higher transmitter power. Conversely, a LEO satellite's footprint is much smaller requiring a higher number of satellites to provide coverage, but the antennas used are much simpler along with reduced radio frequency power requirement on the subscriber end. Also, the lifetime of a LEO satellite is less due to drag caused by the close proximity of earth.

Iridium

[ICAO SVGM, ¶2.3] Iridium uses a constellation of 66 satellites at an altitude of 780 km (450 miles) in six orbital planes, with eleven satellites in each orbital plane, providing global coverage. Additionally there are a number of spare satellites to replace any in-orbit failures. At that altitude each satellite covers a circular area of 4,700 km (2,900 miles) and is in-view to a location on the ground for approximately 9 minutes. Using a small amount of overlap in coverage between each satellite, the Iridium network hands-off the call to the next satellite coming into view to the ground location. This is similar to a GSM cellular telephone system where the subscriber moves from one cell site to another except that the satellite is the moving vehicle. The speed of the aircraft appears almost stationary compared to the speed the satellite moves.

Iridium operates in low earth orbit, which means it doesn't cost as much to get their satellites in space. The cost to install on an aircraft is also relatively cheap compared to earlier systems.

Inmarsat

[ICAO SVGM, ¶2.4]

- The Inmarsat network of satellites is in geostationary orbit directly above the earth equator at an altitude of 35,786 km (22,236 miles). At that altitude above earth, each satellite's footprint covers approximately 120 degrees of the earth at the equator and to approximately 82 degrees North and 82 degrees South latitude. The orbital period of each satellite is exactly the same as the rotation period of earth so each satellite appears to remain in the same position. Inmarsat periodically renews its satellite constellations and operates both I-3 and I-4 generation satellites.

- There are three new I-4 (Alphasat will become the 4th I-4) and four I-3 satellites providing aviation services, to include PSTN-based voice. L-band frequencies allocated for aviation AMS(R)S are split between a transmit and receive block. This allows the subscriber unit using a frequency duplexer to receive and transmit simultaneously. Inmarsat's primary transmit frequency allocation is adjacent to Iridium's allocation used for both transmit and receive; this can cause interference to the secondary Iridium receive allocation when the aircraft operator desires both satellite services to operate simultaneously and on the same aircraft.

- SwiftBroadband (SBB) is the next Safety Services technology to be introduced after Classic Aero. SBB is only available on the Inmarsat I-4 satellites providing such services as PSTN voice, but will also introduce new capabilities to properly equipped aircraft.

Public Switched Telephone Network (PSTN)

[ICAO SVGM, ¶2.6] The aeronautical SATVOICE system uses the public switched telephone network (PSTN) and/or dedicated networks to route calls between the aircraft and the appropriate ground party. Dedicated network access switches locate the aircraft anywhere in the world regardless of the satellite and ground earth station (GES) to which the aircraft is logged on.

There is a fair amount of magic going on here, but all of that was handled by the vendor who installed the equipment on your aircraft, the satellite service provider, and the person who set up your aircraft accounts. From the pilot's perspective, it is only important to remember that when you pick up the phone and the necessary connections are made, you are talking to someone on the other end who picked up a telephone. You cannot do this as a matter of making normal position reports and other air traffic services unless the air traffic services unit on the other end has made provisions to use these SATVOICE systems.

SATVOICE as a Long Range Communications System

Is SATVOICE a valid Long Range Communications System (LRCS)?

[ICAO SVGM, ¶2.1.4] SATVOICE could potentially be considered a LRCS as defined by State MMEL/MEL policies. When approving reduced carriage requirements for HF radio, States may allow aircraft to operate with only one serviceable HF radio. However, airspace requirements will take precedence over the MMEL/MEL requirements.

The answer is "It depends." It depends if your State and the airspace in which you fly allow it. If you are flying an N-numbered airplane your State does allow it, but it is more complicated than that.

Can SATVOICE replace the HF?

[ICAO SVGM, ¶2.1.4] SATVOICE is not a replacement for ADS-C/CPDLC or HF/VHF voice via a radio operator.

LRCS to be Carried on Board

[ICAO SVGM, ¶3.3.2]

The State of the Operator and/or State of Registry establish the minimum number of LRCSs to be carried on board. In principle, where two LRCSs are required, one SATVOICE system and one HF voice system could be approved for flight operations where both services are available for routine communications, as follows:

- An HF radio is considered to be LRCS; and

- Other (e.g. SATVOICE) two-way radio equipment may be used if allowed by the relevant airspace procedures.

Note 1.— EASA is considering rules and means of compliance that would allow for one SATVOICE system and one HF communication system, providing that said services are available for routine communications.

Note 2.— The FAA Policy Letter (PL)-106 provides MMEL relief that allows one HF communication system, if the SATVOICE system is approved as a LRCS.

The referenced policy letter introduces a "global change" to all existing MMEL documents, discussed below.

- When intending to use SATVOICE to satisfy requirements for communications equipage, the aircraft operator should ensure that installed equipment is operational when commencing a flight and there are no notifications of SATVOICE service outage on the route of flight. However, experience has demonstrated that temporary unserviceable equipment may be tolerated in some cases. Several ICAO Contracting States hence require aircraft manufacturers to provide a Master MEL (MMEL). The MMEL contains a list of which equipment can be tolerated as unserviceable at commencement of flight and for how long. The MMEL is approved by the authority designated by the State of Design.

Note.— For example, the State of Design is the FAA for the United States and EASA for European Union States.

- The aircraft operator should establish a Minimum Equipment List (MEL), based upon, but no less restrictive than the relevant MMEL. The aircraft operator obtains approval of the MEL from the State of the Operator or State of Registry.

Note.— For example, see rule OPS 1.030 in the EU.

• If changes to the Minimum Equipment List (MEL) are desired to allow dispatch with one SATVOICE system and only one HF radio system, the aircraft operator should obtain approval or acceptance from the State of the Operator or State of Registry. However, regardless of MEL, the aircraft operator will need to carry radio equipment required by the applicable airspace requirements as provided in AIP (or equivalent publication).

[FAA MMEL Policy Letter (PL)106]

• The regulations now address long-range communication requirements in terms of LRCS. With that as a basis, an aircraft on extended range segments unable to utilize line-of-sight systems must have at least two operational LRCSs to honor regulatory communication requirements (unless specifically excepted under the operational rules).

• While CPDLC enhances ATS communications for normal use, it is not adequate for non-routine and emergency communications and therefore not appropriate as a basis for MMEL relief of HF communication systems (ref. FAA Legal Interpretation dated 06 Dec 2011 regarding 14 CFR § 121.99 data/com in lieu of voice requirements). In addition, some ATS facility may not be capable of providing SATVOICE services as a LRCS. HF-voice is the only LRCS currently available for Air Traffic Control communications in many areas. Therefore, in areas requiring two operational LRCSs, at least one must be HF-voice when the MEL is applied. In areas requiring one LRCS, that system must be HF-voice.

This is the first document from the FAA that says you need two LRCS. You could get away with just one HF as your only means of long-range communications until this came out. Now, if you don't have a qualified SATVOICE or CPDLC, you need two HFs.

Flight Crew Procedures

[ICAO SVGM, ¶5.1]

- An aircraft operator with data link equipped aircraft (CPDLC, ADS-C, and FMC WPR) operating in airspace where data link services are provided should use data link as the normal means of communications. Some normal ATC communications and most non-normal communications will require use of voice communications. The flight crew may use SATVOICE or HF/VHF voice at their discretion, provided the use is in accordance with airspace requirements established by Regional SUPPs, AIPs (or equivalent publication) for the flight.

- Although the underlying technology lends itself to a conversational mode of communications, such use can create misunderstanding and confusion. Therefore, when using SATVOICE, the flight crew should follow RTF conventions identical to HF/VHF communications in accordance with applicable standards and regulations pertaining to aeronautical communications.

- When SATVOICE is required for the flight, such as for extended operations or to meet airspace communication requirements, then during pre-flight or prior to entry into the relevant airspace, the flight crew should ensure the aircraft SATVOICE system is operational and there are no notifications of SATVOICE service outage in that airspace.

- On initial contact with a radio station, the flight crew should provide aircraft identification and request frequency assignment and perform a successful SELCAL check on HF, when required by the appropriate ATS authority. Subsequent communications with that radio station may then be performed via SATVOICE or HF/VHF voice, in accordance with applicable airworthiness, operating and airspace requirements.

- The SATVOICE numbers (e.g. short codes) for aeronautical stations and ATSUs are published in State AIPs and some charts. SATVOICE numbers together with the appropriate priority level may be stored in an aircraft SATVOICE system for easy access by the flight crew.

ARINC SATCOM Voice Procedures

[ARINC Handbook, ¶2.6]

- ARINC Communications Centers are equipped to receive and originate SATCOM Voice calls from or to suitably equipped aircraft. It is recognized that these systems, due to cost and other requirements, are still not available to a large number of aircraft; however, ARINC has the capability to use SATCOM Voice as an alternative means of communications for either ATC or AOC communications with those aircraft that have been equipped. The medium used for communications is transparent to the end user. All ARINC services using HF/VHF are available, and SATCOM Voice messages either can be relayed by the ARINC Radio Operator or the call-in progress can be connected to other phone lines (conferenced) through the telephone control system at each ARINC Communications Center.

ARINC says the use of SATCOM is "transparent" to the end user, meaning ATC. Many of the ATC sources say you should use SATCOM in lieu of HF or CPDLC only in unusual circumstances.

Note: When using SATCOM voice, continue to use radio discipline procedures. Using the SATCOM phone like a regular telephone can cause misunderstandings and confusion.

The phone call ends up with the HF radio operator who is expecting you to use the same terminology as if on HF.

- Satellite Voice-equipped aircraft should direct calls to the appropriate ARINC Communications Center using either INMARSAT-assigned security phone numbers (ICAO short codes) or direct dial using the 10-digit PSTN phone number:

Pacific Flights	Atlantic Flights
SFO 436625	NYC 436623
1-925-371-3920	1-631-244-2492

You will be using INMARSAT satellites but your aircraft may or may not have an INMARSAT phone. To use the short codes you need an INMARSAT phone.

- Note: These six-digit numbers are converted by the Ground Earth Station (GES) receiving the aircraft call announcement to the respective PSTN dial number for connection to the appropriate ARINC Center.

This only works on the INMARSAT satellite system.

- After an answer by the ARINC Radio Operator, the parties should complete the exchange of information using the same procedures as would be used on other voice (HF/VHF) communications mediums.

Line of Sight and Curvature of the Earth Issues

Because INMARSAT satellites are in geostationary orbits over the equator, the curvature of the earth limits their use at the poles. While the G450 manual says you may have issues above 70° latitude, it is said that SATCOM is available for voice and data link up to 82°N.

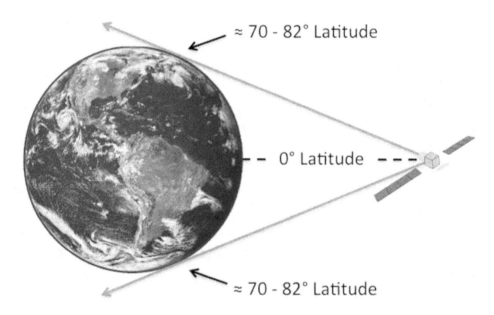

Figure: INMARSAT Line of Sight.

Chapter 5

Controller-Pilot Data Link Communications (CPDLC)

*Y*ou can think of Controller Pilot Data Link Communications as a replace-*
ment for your HF when oceanic and VHF over some domestic areas. Your
aircraft manufacturer could confuse things because before CPDLC there were
other systems. In the airline world there was Aircraft Communication Ad-
dressing and Reporting System (ACARS), which could be used for CPDLC
but usually isn't. In the Gulfstream Honeywell world, for example, CPDLC is
called Air Traffic Control Communications (ATC COM) while Aeronautical
Operational Control (AOC) is Gulfstream-speak for ACARS.

Purpose

The role CPDLC plays in the Future Air Navigation System is to reduce the
time it takes for air traffic control to issue instructions to a pilot and the pilot
to acknowledge. In a domestic environment this is rarely a problem. When
oceanic, however, it can be a factor. Reducing that time, known as Required
Communications Performance (RCP), allows ATC to reduce aircraft spacing.

[AC 120-70B, para;7.a.] The concept of RCP relates to the communications
component of the Communication, Navigation, and Surveillance / Air Traffic
System Management (CNS/ATM) framework, and complements Required
Navigation Performance (RNP) and Required Surveillance Performance
(RSP). In general, the requirements for operation in a defined airspace, or
performance of a defined procedure, include elements of CNS functionality and performance, as well as ATM functionality and performance. The
guidance provided in this AC regarding RCP is consistent with ICAO Doc
9869, Manual on RCP. RCP is a statement of the performance requirements
for operational communication in support of specific ATM functions. The
RCP is determined by cognizant authorities in consideration of air traffic
operations, target levels of safety, separation assurance, AFS and functional

hazard analysis associated with the airspace, operation or procedure. Thus, RCP is operationally derived and not based on any specific technology, or combination of technologies, that may be utilized for communications. The performance of communications is generally accepted as comprising communication transaction time, integrity, continuity, and availability.

[Guidance Material for ATS Data Link Services in NAT Airspace, ¶12.8.1.]

RCP Type	Satisfies requirements as
RCP 240	Normal means of communication for application of 30 nm lateral separation and reduced longitudinal separation minima
RCP 400	Alternative means of communication for application of 30 nm lateral separation and reduced longitudinal separation minima
RCP 400	Normal means of communication for application of lateral separation greater than or equal to 50 nm and time-based longitudinal separation

The bottom line on CPDLC is if you can reduced the round trip time between the issuing of the message from ATC and the reception of the pilot's reply to 240 seconds or less, you can reduce the lateral and longitudinal spacing.

Oceanic CPDLC versus Voice

[ICAO GOLD, ¶5.1.3.]

- When operating within airspace where CPDLC is available and local ATC procedures do not state otherwise, CPDLC should be the primary means of communication. Voice should be used as the backup communication medium (e.g. direct VHF, direct HF, third party HF, Satellite voice).

- While the CPDLC message set defined in Appendix A provides for ATC communications, voice may be a more appropriate means depending on the circumstances, e.g. some types of non-routine communications. Refer to paragraph 5.8 for guidelines on use of voice and data communications in emergency and non-routine situations.

- During an emergency, the flight crew would normally revert to voice communications. However, the flight crew may use CPDLC for emergency communications if it is either more expedient or if they are unable to establish voice contact.

- The response to a CPDLC message should be via CPDLC, and the response to a voice message should be via voice.

- If a conflicting CPDLC and voice clearance/instruction is received, the flight crew should obtain clarification using voice.

- If the intent of an uplinked message is uncertain, the flight crew should reject (UNABLE) the message. The flight crew may use either CPDLC or voice to confirm the intent of the message.

- Regardless of whether CPDLC is being used as the primary means for communication, the flight crew should continuously monitor VHF/HF/UHF guard frequency. In addition, the flight crew should continuously maintain a listening or SELCAL watch on the specified backup or secondary frequency (frequencies). On aircraft capable of two SATCOM channels, one channel may be selected to the phone number for the radio facility assigned to the current flight information region (FIR) to enable timely voice communication with ATS. The second channel may be selected to the company phone number to enable timely voice communications with company dispatch.

If you have CPDLC and you are in airspace where CPDLC is being used, you should use CPDLC as primary, voice communications as secondary. The general rule of thumb is: if contacted by CPDLC, respond with CPDLC; if contacted by voice, response with voice. When oceanic you still need to check in with HF, get a good SELCAL check, and maintain a listening watch if SELCAL fails.

Domestic CPDLC versus Voice

[FANS-1/A Operations Manual, ¶9.2.1] Implementation of CPDLC into continental airspace is intended as a supplement to the use of VHF voice and the intent is to build a single communications environment where both voice and CPDLC are considered as being normal Air Traffic Management (ATM) tools.

[FANS-1/A Operations Manual, ¶9.3]

- The following procedures only apply to normal (non-emergency) operations. While the intent of these procedures is to develop a standardised and predictable environment using a combination of voice and CPDLC, the decision on whether voice or CPDLC is the more appropriate medium for use in a given operational situation will be made by the pilots and controllers involved.

- As a supplement to VHF voice, CPDLC is intended to be restricted to the passing of strategic information. Strategic information involves routine, non-time-critical communications, and includes examples such as the passing of amended flight levels, amended routes, speed control messages, frequency changes, and SSR codes, when the speed of delivery is not critical to safety.

- Voice instructions and acknowledgments shall have precedence over CPDLC messages at all times. In the event that any ambiguity exists in a message or message exchange, then the controller/pilot shall revert to voice communication for clarification.

- Flight crews shall either comply with uplink CPDLC instructions or respond with UNABLE, and shall respond to uplink messages using CPDLC whenever possible.

Actual practice over domestic Europe:

- *Log on to CPDLC where you can.*

- *Use CPDLC for all routine issues.*

- *Confirm via voice any CPDLC instruction that changes the aircraft altitude, heading, or airspeed, adding the term "datalink" to let the controller know where the instruction came from. Example:*

- *(Via CPDLC) CLIMB TO FL 290*

- *(Via VHF) "London Control, November seven seven zero zero, data link climb flight level two niner zero."*

- *Do not use ADS-C domestically.*

Multiple CPDLC Contacts

[ICAO GOLD, ¶ 2.2.4.1.1.] An aircraft can have a maximum of two CPDLC connections established concurrently, each with a different ATSU. Only one CPDLC connection can be active at any given time; any second connection is inactive.

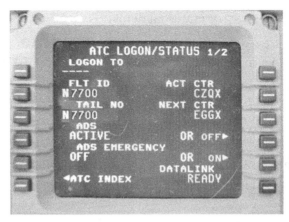

[ICAO GOLD, ¶ 2.2.6.2.2.] An ATSU system may request multiple simultaneous ADS contracts to a single aircraft, including one periodic and one event contract, which may be supplemented by any number of demand contracts. Up to five separate ground systems may request ADS contracts with a single aircraft.

You can only have one active CPDLC connection, think of it as your actual air traffic control contact. But you can have two connections, usually the active connection and the "next."

Flight Crew Response Times

[ICAO GOLD, ¶5.3.2.]

- System performance requirements have been established to support reduced separation standards. Specific latency times have been allocated to the technical performance, based on flight crew and controller response times. Regional/State monitoring agencies monitor performance to ensure the technical and operational components of the system meet required standards. To support RCP 240 operations (e.g. 30 nautical mile longitudinal separation) the flight crew should respond to an uplink message within one minute.

- Flight crew procedures should be developed to respond to uplinks as soon as practical after they are received. For most uplinks, the flight crew will have adequate time to read and respond within one minute. However, the flight crew should not be pressured to respond without taking adequate time to fully understand the uplinked message and to satisfy other higher priority operational demands.

- If the flight crew determines they will need a significant amount of time to respond to a message, they should send a STANDBY response.

It is said that if they don't hear back from you in sixty seconds, they will consider the communication lost and if a clearance was involved, that clearance is cancelled. I've not seen that in writing but the threat is clear: respond within a minute, use "STANDBY" if you must. When dealing with clearances, I usually hit the print button, send the acknowledge, and then read the contents. I figure I can always respond a second time if I have to.

Position Reports at FIR Boundaries

[ICAO GOLD, ¶5.2.3.6.] When notified that a new active CPDLC connection has been established, and if entering an FIR that requires the crew to send a CPDLC position report to confirm current data authority status (refer Appendix E, paragraph E.2.2), the flight crew should send a CPDLC position report without delay unless advised through a CONTACT or MONITOR instruction of a specific transfer point.

This is often taught this way: "Send a position report whenever entering oceanic airspace, except in the North Atlantic," meaning the North Atlantic is the only exception. In fact, the rule seems to be: "Send a position report crossing an FIR boundary if Appendix E tells you to."

Fukuoka	O	O	N	RJJJ	FUKJJYA	IPACG FIT	CPDLC voice transfer: CONTACT TOKYO CENTER [frequency] Confirm CPDLC CDA: One CPDLC position report at FIR boundary. See paragraph E.2.2.
Gander	O	O	O	CZQX	YQXE2YA	NAT CNSG	Report revised ETA: Next waypoint ETA error 3 minutes or more, use free text DM 67k REVISED ETA [position] [time]. See paragraph E.2.6.
~~Hanian~~	O	O	N	YDDD	DNICAVA		

Figure: Gander vs. Fukuoka Position Reporting Requirements under CPDLC, from ICAO Gold, Appendix E.

Section IV – Communicate

Chapter 6

CPDLC Checklist

*L*ike anything else, after you become familiar with the procedures the checklist becomes less necessary. Also like many things in aviation, if you don't do this often, you should consider using the checklist every single time because you might forget an important step. If your manufacturer or operator doesn't provide a CPDLC checklist it will be up to you to devise one. What follows is the one we've designed for our Gulfstream G450. The procedures may not work for your airplane, but they will get you started.

CPDLC Preflight Setup

1. Ensure you have the following documents in paper form, EFB, or iPad:

   a. ICAO Global Operational Data Link Document (GOLD)

   b. Any aircraft or company specific guidance

2. Review latest ICAO NAT Bulletins

3. Verify the following appears in your ICAO Flight Plan

   a. Block 7 - Aircraft ID agrees with FMS Flight ID

   b. Block 10A - Equipment Code "J3" and "J5" (Data Link System)

   c. Block 10B - Equipment Code "D1" (ADS)

4. Master Document / En Route Charts

   a. Annotate FIR boundaries

   b. Check FIRs versus GOLD Appendix E and make note of:

      i. CPDLC status

      ii. ADS-C status

      iii. AFN address

    c.   Any instructions under Remarks

5.   Confirm COM/NAV3 in Data Mode

6.   Verify Data Link works by any of the following methods:

    a.   Downlink the flight plan

    b.   Downlink D-ATIS

    c.   Downlink PDC

    d.   Downlink Terminal Wx

7.   Check VHF Datalink

    a.   DLK > SYSTEM > DATALINK MGR

        i.   If data link is GND VHF (VDL) test SATCOM (DLK > STATUS > TEST > DATALINK SEND)

        ii.   If data link is SAT check GND VHF (VDL) when airborne

8.   Confirm FMS Settings for CPDLC

    a.   Confirm Flight ID entered into TCAS details page of FMS agrees with Block 7 of Flight Plan

    b.   Confirm Data Link is Operational:

        i.   DLK > SYSTEM > DATALINK MGR

        ii.   VHF available

        iii.   SATCOM available

Switch CMF (If data link frozen)

1.   Select MENU

2.   Select MISC

3.   Toggle LSK 5L to the other CMF. It will take a few seconds, but you should see the change reflected on the screen.

Force SATCOM / Disable VHF Data Mode

1. RADIO Page 2/2

2. COM / NAV 3

3. MODE VOICE

Downlink Oceanic Clearance

1. From a DSP (Everywhere except New York Oceanic)

   Note: if you have Item 18. RMK/AGCS EQUIPPED in your flight plan, you should get an "Unsolicited clearance" from Gander.

   a. DLK > ATS > OCEANIC CLX

   b. Set ENTRY POINT, ENTRY TIME, and adjust Req Mach and Req FL if required

   c. SEND

   d. ACKNOWLEDGE on receipt

2. From NY Oceanic using CPDLC

   a. Will get the oceanic from NY Oceanic via ATC UPLINK message

   b. ACCEPT within 60 seconds

   c. REVIEW

   d. ATC CLEARANCE to interpret LLXX waypoints

   e. ACTIVATE to insert into FMS flight plan

   f. Remove extraneous waypoints at end of flight plan

CPDLC Log On

If you are on the ground at a departure airfield within 15 minutes of an OCA or FIR that supports CPDLC, you are expected to log on NET 45 minutes prior to takeoff. If you are unable to log on from the ground, wait until passing 10,000 feet. Log on to the current FIR unless you are within 15 to 25 minutes of the next FIR, then log on to the next FIR. If already airborne, log on to the next ATSU NET 45 minutes NLT 15 minutes from reaching their airspace.

1.   Log On Procedure

    a.   NAV > ATC > LOGON STATUS

    b.   Ensure FLT ID and TAIL NO are correct

    c.   Ensure ADS ARMED

    d.   Ensure ADS EMERGENCY mode is OFF

    e.   On second page, ensure ATC COMM is ARMED

    f.   On first page, enter LOGIN ID of FIR (From GOLD Appendix E, En Route Chart, or GAC-OMS-4)

    g.   SEND

2.   You should see ACCEPTED on LOGON field

3.   Once handed over to an ATSU with CPDLC you should see:

    a.   ATC COMM ESTABLISHED

    b.   LOGON TO field should go blank

    c.   The FIR's ID should be in the ACT CTR field

    d.   ATC COMM should now be ACTIVE

4.   If you are also in an ADS location, you will see ADS ESTABLISHED and the ADS will go from ARMED to ACTIVE.

CPDLC Latency Timer Message Response

1. You may get "CONFIRM MESSAGE LATENCY TIMER OFF" or "SET UPLINK DELAY VALUE TO 40 SECONDS"

2. The G-450 does not have a latency timer

3. Respond using free text "TIMER NOT AVAILABLE"

CPDLC Change Altitude Speed Heading (While Under VHF Control)

1. When receiving a CPDLC message that changes the aircraft's profile (altitude, speed, heading) when in European airspace, ATC requires voice confirmation as well as the CPDLC response.

   a. Via CPDLC send WILCO

   b. Via VHF send voice confirmation, for example: "London Control, November One Two Three Alpha Alpha, data link climb to flight level two four zero."

2. CPDLC shows Report Level "ARMED," which means it will be sent automatically upon reaching level.

CPDLC Crossing an FIR Boundary

1. Before crossing an FIR boundary, you should get a conditional clearance to contact the next ATSU.

2. Accept the clearance, send, but do not contact the next ATSU yet.

3. On the LOGON/STATUS page you will see the NEXT CTR field has the next ATSU listed.

4. When the next ATSU takes control, you will see ATC COMM ESTABLISHED

5. A check-in with the departing controller is not necessary.

6. At the waypoint listed, contact the new controller.

CPDLC Coast Out

1.   Establish log on NET 45 minutes, NLT 15 minutes prior to oceanic FIR

2.   Verify ATC COMM ESTABLISHED and ATSU in ACT CTR

3.   When sent to HF, for example:

_____ Radio, November _____, CPDLC, _____ Next,

"Shanwick Radio, November one two three alpha, CPDLC, Gander Next,

flight level _____, request SELCAL check _____

flight level four one zero, request SELCAL check alpha bravo charlie delta"

4.   If you also have ADS-C, you should hear: "November one two three alpha bravo, Shanwick Radio, SELCAL check OK, voice reports not required in Shanwick OCA, at 30 West contact Gander on three zero one six primary or five five niner eight secondary."

5.   For most ATSU's around the world, you will also send a position report. (This is not required in the North Atlantic.) Check GOLD Appendix E Remarks for the ATSU's requirements.

Crossing an Oceanic Boundary

1. You should get new ADS contracts at least 15 minutes prior to the boundary.

2. At the boundary you should get ATC COMM ESTABLISHED.

3. If you will be leaving oceanic airspace after this OCA, include the last two fixes on the cleared route, for example:

_____ Radio, November _____, CPDLC, _____, _____,

"Gander Radio, November one two three alpha, CPDLC, CARPE, REDBY,

flight level _____ request SELCAL check _____

flight level four one zero request SELCAL check alpha bravo charlie delta."

Make a SATCOM Short Code Call

1. You can contact most oceanic radio centers using SATCOM for any emergency or non-routine situation. To dial the 6-digit short code from the MCDU:

   a. Select MENU > SAT > DIRECTORY

   b. Type the number in the scratch pad

   c. Push MANUAL DIAL (5L)

   d. The system dials the number

   e. To end the call, push END CALL (2R)

2. The oceanic numbers are given on some en route charts and are reproduced here:

   a. Gander Radio: 431613

   b. New York Radio (ARINC): 436623

   c. Iceland Radio (Emergency): 425101 or 425103

   d. Iceland Radio (Com Failure): 425105

   e. Santa Maria Radio: 426305 or 426302

   f. Shanwick Radio: 425002

Constrain a Satellite

1.   Under normal operations, constraining a satellite is not necessary. If, for some reason a particular satellite drops you, this might be helpful.

2.   Before ADS-C LOGON on the MCDU:

    a.   MENU

    b.   SAT (6L)

    c.   SUBMENU (6L)

    d.   LOGON (2L)

    e.   GES (6L)

    f.   Constrain the satellite in question

    g.   LOGON (6L)

    h.   GES (6L)

    i.   Constrain the satellite in question

    j.   LOGON (6L)

Unconstrain a Satellite

1.   MENU

2.   SAT (6L)

3.   SUBMENU (6L)

4.   LOGON (2L)

5.   AUTO LOGON (2L)

Exiting CPDLC and ADS-C Airspace

1.   The CPDLC connection and the ADS contract should terminate automatically.

2.   If not, switch both off

Chapter 7

Emergency Locator Transmitter (ELT)

*T*he emergency locator transmitter is one of those things you hardly notice, almost never interact with, and may never use. In fact, unless you are responsible for certification or maintenance of your airplane, you may not think about it at all. But you really should know a few basic facts because there may come a time when your life depends on that knowledge.

History

[US AIM, ¶6-2-4.a.2.] ELTs of various types were developed as a means of locating downed aircraft. These electronic, battery operated transmitters operate on one of three frequencies. These operating frequencies are 121.5 MHz, 243.0 MHz, and the newer 406 MHz. ELTs operating on 121.5 MHz and 243.0 MHz are analog devices. The newer 406 MHz ELT is a digital transmitter that can be encoded with the owner's contact information or aircraft data. The latest 406 MHz ELT models can also be encoded with the aircraft's position data which can help SAR forces locate the aircraft much more quickly after a crash. The 406 MHz ELTs also transmits a stronger signal when activated than the older 121.5 MHz ELTs.

Requirement

[14 CFR 91 §91.207]

(a) Except as provided in paragraphs (e) and (f) of this section, no person may operate a U.S.-registered civil airplane unless—

(1) There is attached to the airplane an approved automatic type emergency locator transmitter that is in operable condition for the following operations, except that after June 21, 1995, an emergency locator transmitter that

meets the requirements of TSO-C91 may not be used for new installations:

(i) Those operations governed by the supplemental air carrier and commercial operator rules of parts 121 and 125;

(ii) Charter flights governed by the domestic and flag air carrier rules of part 121 of this chapter; and

(iii) Operations governed by part 135 of this chapter; or

(2) For operations other than those specified in paragraph (a)(1) of this section, there must be attached to the airplane an approved personal type or an approved automatic type emergency locator transmitter that is in operable condition, except that after June 21, 1995, an emergency locator transmitter that meets the requirements of TSO-C91 may not be used for new installations.

(b) Each emergency locator transmitter required by paragraph (a) of this section must be attached to the airplane in such a manner that the probability of damage to the transmitter in the event of crash impact is minimized. Fixed and deployable automatic type transmitters must be attached to the airplane as far aft as practicable.

Inspection

[14 CFR 91 §91.207(d)]

Each emergency locator transmitter required by paragraph (a) of this section must be inspected within 12 calendar months after the last inspection for—

(1) Proper installation;

(2) Battery corrosion;

(3) Operation of the controls and crash sensor; and

(4) The presence of a sufficient signal radiated from its antenna.

There are provisions in 14 CFR 91 §91.207 you will need to look up if your need to ferry the airplane with an inoperative ELT.

Registration

[US AIM, ¶6-2-4.a.2.(a)] The Federal Communications Commission (FCC) requires 406 MHz ELTs be registered with the National Oceanic and Atmospheric Administration (NOAA) as outlined in the ELT's documentation. The FAA's 406 MHz ELT Technical Standard Order (TSO) TSO–C126 also requires that each 406 MHz ELT be registered with NOAA. The reason is NOAA maintains the owner registration database for U.S. registered 406 MHz alerting devices, which includes ELTs. NOAA also operates the United States' portion of the Cospas–Sarsat satellite distress alerting system designed to detect activated ELTs and other distress alerting devices.

Activation

[AIM, ¶6-2-4.a.2.]

(b) In the event that a properly registered 406 MHz ELT activates, the Cospas–Sarsat satellite system can decode the owner's information and provide that data to the appropriate search and rescue (SAR) center. In the United States, NOAA provides the alert data to the appropriate U.S. Air Force Rescue Coordination Center (RCC) or U.S. Coast Guard Rescue Coordination Center. That RCC can then telephone or contact the owner to verify the status of the aircraft. If the aircraft is safely secured in a hangar, a costly ground or airborne search is avoided. In the case of an inadvertent 406 MHz ELT activation, the owner can deactivate the 406 MHz ELT. If the 406 MHz ELT equipped aircraft is being flown, the RCC can quickly activate a search. 406 MHz ELTs permit the Cospas–Sarsat satellite system to narrow the search area to a more confined area compared to that of a 121.5 MHz or 243.0 MHz ELT. 406 MHz ELTs also include a low–power 121.5 MHz homing transmitter to aid searchers in finding the aircraft in the terminal search phase.

(c) Each analog ELT emits a distinctive downward swept audio tone on 121.5 MHz and 243.0 MHz.

(d) If "armed" and when subject to crash–generated forces, ELTs are designed to automatically activate and continuously emit their respective signals, analog or digital. The transmitters will operate continuously for at least 48 hours over a wide temperature range. A properly installed, maintained, and functioning ELT can expedite search and rescue operations and save lives if it survives the crash and is activated.

"Legacy" Systems

[AIM, ¶6-2-4.a.2.]

(f) Because of the large number of 121.5 MHz ELT false alerts and the lack of a quick means of verifying the actual status of an activated 121.5 MHz or 243.0 MHz analog ELT through an owner registration database, U.S. SAR forces do not respond as quickly to initial 121.5/243.0 MHz ELT alerts as the SAR forces do to 406 MHz ELT alerts. Compared to the almost instantaneous detection of a 406 MHz ELT, SAR forces' normal practice is to wait for either a confirmation of a 121.5/243.0 MHz alert by additional satellite passes or through confirmation of an overdue aircraft or similar notification. In some cases, this confirmation process can take hours. SAR forces can initiate a response to 406 MHz alerts in minutes compared to the potential delay of hours for a 121.5/243.0 MHz ELT.

[AIM, ¶6-2-4.a.3.] The Cospas–Sarsat system has announced the termination of satellite monitoring and reception of the 121.5 MHz and 243.0 MHz frequencies in 2009. The Cospas–Sarsat system will continue to monitor the 406 MHz frequency. What this means for pilots is that after the termination date, those aircraft with only 121.5 MHz or 243.0 MHz ELT's onboard will have to depend upon either a nearby Air Traffic Control facility receiving the alert signal or an overflying aircraft monitoring 121.5 MHz or 243.0 MHz detecting the alert. To ensure adequate monitoring of these frequencies and timely alerts after 2009, all airborne pilots should periodically monitor these frequencies to try and detect an activated 121.5/243.0 MHz ELT.

Testing

[AIM, ¶6-2-4.a.3.b.]

1. ELTs should be tested in accordance with the manufacturer's instructions, preferably in a shielded or screened room or specially designed test container to prevent the broadcast of signals which could trigger a false alert.

2. When this cannot be done, aircraft operational testing is authorized as follows:

(a) Analog 121.5 / 243 MHz ELTs should only be tested during the first 5 minutes after any hour. If operational tests must be made outside of this period, they should be coordinated with the nearest FAA Control Tower or

FSS. Tests should be no longer than three audible sweeps. If the antenna is removable, a dummy load should be substituted during test procedures.

(b) Digital 406 MHz ELTs should only be tested in accordance with the unit's manufacturer's instructions.

(c) Airborne tests are not authorized.

Inflight Monitoring and Reporting

[AIM, ¶6-2-4.a.3.d.1.] Pilots are encouraged to monitor 121.5 MHz and/or 243.0 MHz while inflight to assist in identifying possible emergency ELT transmissions. On receiving a signal, report the following information to the nearest air traffic facility:

(a) Your position at the time the signal was first heard.

(b) Your position at the time the signal was last heard.

(c) Your position at maximum signal strength.

(d) Your flight altitudes and frequency on which the emergency signal was heard: 121.5 MHz or 243.0 MHz. If possible, positions should be given relative to a navigation aid. If the aircraft has homing equipment, provide the bearing to the emergency signal with each reported position.

Cospas-Sarsat System

[http://www.cospas-sarsat.int/en/system-overview/cospas-sarsat-system] The basic Cospas-Sarsat concept is illustrated in the adjacent figure. The System is composed of:

- distress radio beacons (ELTs for aviation use, EPIRBs for maritime use, and PLBs for personal use) which transmit signals during distress situations;

- instruments on board satellites in geostationary and low-altitude Earth orbits which detect the signals transmitted by distress radio beacons;

- ground receiving stations, referred to as Local Users Terminals (LUTs), which receive and process the satellite downlink signal to generate distress alerts; and

- Mission Control Centers (MCCs) which receive alerts produced by LUTs and forward them to Rescue Coordination Centers (RCCs), Search and Rescue Points Of Contacts (SPOCs) or other MCCs.

The Cospas-Sarsat System includes two types of satellites:

- satellites in low-altitude Earth orbit (LEO) which form the LEOSAR System

- satellites in geostationary Earth orbit (GEO) which form the GEOSAR System The future Cospas-Sarsat System will include a new type of satellite in the medium-altitude Earth orbit (MEO) which will form the MEOSAR System.

LEOSAR System.

The Cospas-Sarsat LEOSAR system uses polar-orbiting satellites and, therefore, operates with basic constraints which result from non-continuous coverage provided by LEOSAR satellites. The use of low-altitude orbiting satellites provides for a strong Doppler effect in the up-link signal thereby enabling the use of Doppler positioning techniques. The LEOSAR system operates in two coverage modes, namely local and global coverage.

GEOSAR System.

Cospas-Sarsat has demonstrated that the current generation of Cospas-Sarsat beacons could be detected using search and rescue instruments on board geostationary satellites. The GEOSAR system consists of repeaters carried on board various geostationary satellites and the associated ground facilities called GEOLUTs which process the satellite signal. Geostationary satellites orbit the Earth at an altitude of 36,000 km, with an orbit period of 24 hours, thus appearing fixed relative to the Earth at approximately 0 degrees latitude (i.e. over the equator). A single geostationary satellite provides GEOSAR uplink coverage of about one third of the globe, except for polar regions. Therefore, three geostationary satellites equally spaced in longitude can provide continuous coverage of all areas of the globe between approximately 70 degrees North and 70 degrees South latitude.

Chapter 1

Required Surveillance Performance (RSP)

*M*ost pilots who have flown internationally in the last decade or so are *well acquainted with the concept of Required Navigation Performance (RNP), the idea that where you can fly will be determined on how accurately you can fly and how well the system alerts you when things are less than promised. While it isn't a perfect statement, you can think that the XX in your RNP-XX relates to that accuracy. The same concept holds true for communications and surveillance. In the case of communications, the number attached to your Required Surveillance Performance (RSP) is the number of seconds it takes for surveillance data from the CSP interface to arrive at the ATSU flight data processing system. You won't find a lot about RSP because it is so closely related to Required Communications Performance (RCP). Does it matter? Yes, the lower the number the tighter the airspace you will be allowed to fly. Put another way: the higher the number, the more airspace around the world that will be denied you.*

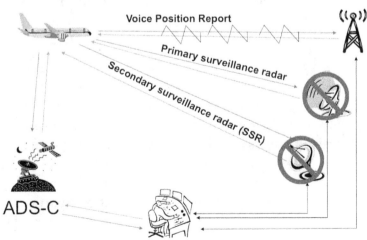

Figure: Evolution of Surveillance (FAA Presentation, 8 February 2012).

History

Surveillance before ADS-C

Surveillance, when you are in radar contact, is achieved with a transponder. if you are in oceanic or remote airspace, without radar coverage, how does air traffic control achieve surveillance? Before the advent of ADS-C surveillance was achieved by voice position reports. You told ATC where you are and ATC assumed that was true.

Surveillance after ADS-C

[ICAO Doc 9869, paragraph 1.1] The FANS concept, which came to be known as the communications, navigation, surveillance/air traffic management (CNS/ATM) systems concept, involves a complex and interrelated set of technologies, dependent largely on satellites.

[ICAO Doc 9869, paragraph 2.3]

- To enable ATM functions within a performance-based airspace, it will be necessary to characterize the performance required for the applicable communication, navigation and/or surveillance elements. RCP will be used in conjunction with RNP and other performance-based measures.

- For a particular ATM function, an increase or decrease in the required performance for any single element (i.e., C or N or S) may allow a tradeoff in required performance of some or all of the other elements, provided the target level of safety is maintained.

- It is important that the States harmonize RCP type for the same or similar ATM functions to reduce training requirements and errors resulting from confusion in operations across airspace boundaries.

[ICAO GOLD, pg 1-9] Performance-based surveillance (PBS). ATS surveillance services and capability based on performance requirements for air traffic service provision, aircraft and flight operations along an ATS route, on an instrument approach procedure or in a designated airspace. Surveillance performance requirements are allocated to system components in an RSP specification in terms of surveillance data delivery time, continuity, availability, integrity, accuracy of the surveillance data, safety and functionality needed for the proposed operation in the context of a particular airspace concept.

Concept

[ICAO Gold, pg 1-11]

- Required surveillance performance (RSP) specification. A set of requirements for air traffic service provision, aircraft capability, and operations needed to support performance-based surveillance within a defined airspace.

- The term RSP is used in the context of a specification that is applicable to the prescription of airspace requirements, qualification of ATS provision, aircraft capability, and operational use, including post-implementation monitoring (e.g. RSP 180 refers to the criteria for various components of the operational system to ensure an acceptable surveillance capability for the controller is maintained).

[ICAO Gold, Appendix D, Paragraph D.2.3.2] The analysis of actual communication performance (ASP) is based on the measurement of the transit times of the ADS-C periodic and event reports between the aircraft and the ANSP ground system. This is measured as the difference between the time extracted from the decoded ADS-C basic group timestamp when the message originated from the FMS and the time the message is received at the ANSP.

The ANSP is the Air Navigation Service Provider, "An organization responsible for the provision of air traffic services." The ICAO Gold manual seems to use Air Traffic Service Unit (ATSU) instead.

[ICAO Gold, paragraph 2.1.3.3.1 b)] RSP 180 includes an accuracy requirement on the "position at time" based on the prescribed RNP/RNAV specification and a +/- one-second accuracy on Coordinated Universal Time (UTC). It also includes a time requirement from when the aircraft is at the compulsory reporting point to when the report is received by the controlling ATS unit.

You can think of an RSP-XXX specification as referring to the end-to-end surveillance loop. An RSP-400, for example, means air traffic control asks "where are you" and the electrons come back with an answer in 400 seconds or less. You cannot attach an RSP level to methods before ADS-C. When you get right down to it, you had no surveillance at all.

Examples

The ICAO Gold Manual speaks of RSP 180, 240, and 400 in the context of reduced separation minima, which leads you to believe an airplane with nothing but an HF for communications and no automatic surveillance has an RSP greater than that.

As the technology goes up, the RSP goes down. As RSP goes down, the lateranl and longitudinal spacing goes down too.

RSP specification	Intended uses for which the RSP specification is applicable
RSP 180	When ADS-C is the normal means of surveillance supporting the application of separation minima predicated on surveillance performance (e.g. 30 NM lateral and 30 NM or 50 NM longitudinal).
RSP 400	When ADS-C or FMC WPR is the normal means of surveillance supporting the application of lateral separation greater than or equal to 50 NM and time-based longitudinal separation.
	When a technology other than HF voice radio provides an alternative means of surveillance (e.g. position reporting via satellite voice) supporting the application of separation minima predicated on surveillance performance (e.g. 30 NM lateral and 30 NM or 50 NM longitudinal).

Figure: Examples of Applying RSP Specification (From ICAO Gold, Tables 2-3 and 2-4)

Chapter 2

Automatic Dependent Surveillance – Broadcast (ADS-B Out)

Y̶ou can think of Automatic Dependent Surveillance - Broadcast Out (ADS-B Out) as a higher tech replacement for your transponder. ADS-B OUT sends your GPS position to air traffic control and other aircraft equipped with ADS-B In. It is much more accurate than a radar blip. You can think of Automatic Dependent Surveillance - Broadcast In (ADS-B In) as a more accurate version of your TCAS. While TCAS aircraft positions shown in your cockpit are approximate, ADS-B In positions are exact. ADS-B Out is already mandatory in parts of the world with timelines in most of the other parts. As of 2015 there are no mandates for ADS-B In. So we'll concentrate here on ADS-B Out.

Functional Description

Overview

[AC 20-165A, ¶1.5] ADS-B is a next generation surveillance technology incorporating both air and ground aspects that provide air traffic control (ATC) with a more accurate picture of the aircraft's three-dimensional position in the en route, terminal, approach and surface environments. The aircraft provides the airborne portion in the form of a broadcast of its identification, position, altitude, velocity, and other information. The ground portion is comprised of ADS-B ground stations which receive these broadcasts and direct them to ATC automation systems for presentation on a controller's display.

ADS-B is automatic because no external interrogation is required. It is dependent because it relies on onboard position sources and broadcast transmission systems to provide surveillance information to ATC, and other users.

ADS-B In and ADS-B Out.

ADS-B Out refers to an aircraft broadcasting own-ship information. ADS-B In refers to an aircraft's ability to receive ADS-B information.

System Description

[AC 90-114, ¶2.2] The ADS-B system architecture is composed of aircraft avionics and a ground infrastructure. Onboard avionics determine the position of the aircraft, typically by using the Global Navigation Satellite Systems (GNSS) and transmitting this and additional information about the aircraft to ground stations for use by ATC; to ADS-B-equipped aircraft; and to other aviation service providers.

In the United States, the ADS-B system operates on two frequencies:

- 1090 MHz Frequency. The 1090 MHz frequency is associated with current Mode A, C, and S transponder operations.

- 978 MHz Frequency. ADS-B equipment operating on 978 MHz are referred to as Universal Access Transceivers (UAT) in this AC.

ADS-B avionics can have the ability to both transmit and receive.

- The transmission of ADS-B information from aircraft is known as ADS-B OUT.

- The receipt of ADS-B information by an aircraft is known as ADS-B IN.

Broadcast Services

[AC 90-114, ¶2-3] ADS-R. Because the ADS-B system operates on two separate frequencies, there is a need to translate, reformat, and rebroadcast the information from each frequency to enable aircraft operating on the alternate frequency to process and use the other's information. This process is referred to as ADS-R and occurs within the ADS-B ground station.

TIS-B is the broadcast of transponder-based traffic information derived from ATC surveillance systems. TIS-B provides ADS-B-IN-equipped aircraft with a more complete picture of surrounding traffic in situations where not all aircraft are equipped with ADS-B.

The FIS-B operates on UAT only and provides ADS-B-IN-equipped aircraft with a suite of advisory-only aeronautical and weather information products to enhance the user's SA.

Mandates

January 15, 2009, Hudson Bay

NAV CANADA implemented the use of Automatic Dependent Surveillance Broadcast (ADS-B Out) on January 15, 2009 in the Hudson Bay area between FL350 and FL400 inclusive. Because not all aircraft were equipped with ADS-B avionics ADS-B based application of surveillance separation standards is being applied tactically to eligible aircraft. The current application area can be found in the Canada Aeronautical Information Publication.

How do I get a copy of this? As of late 2015, the Canada AIP is available at: http://www.navcanada.ca/EN/products-and-services/Pages/AIP.aspx

December 12, 2013, Australia

[Australia Aeronautical Information Service H09/11 ¶1.5] The regulatory changes effectively establish mandatory aircraft fitment of GNSS and ADS-B avionics equipment for the operation of any aircraft in airspace at or above FL290 after the compliance date of 12 December 2013.

How do I get a copy of this? As of late 2015, this publication was available a: http://www.airservicesaustralia.com

December 12, 2013, Singapore

[Singapore AIC 14/10 ¶2.1] On and after 12th December 2013, if an aircraft operates on Airways L642, M771, N891, M753, L644 and N892 bounded within 073605N 1090045E 040713N 1063543E 041717N 1061247E (MAB-LI) 044841N 1052247E (DOLOX) 045223N 1041442E (ENREP) 045000N 1034400E thence north along the Singapore FIR Boundary to 070000N 1080000E (see Attachment B) at or above FL290: the aircraft must carry serviceable ADS-B transmitting equipment that has been certified as meeting EASA AMC 20-24, or meets the equipment configuration standards in Appendix XI of Civil Aviation Order 20.18 of the Civil Aviation Safety Authority of Australia; and the aircraft operator must have the relevant operational approval from the State of Registry.

[Singapore AIC 14/10 ¶2.2] Aircraft that does not have the relevant ADS-B operational approval from the State of Registry will be assigned a flight level below FL290.

Singapore has been showing some flexibility but, as of this manual's publication, AIC 14/10 is still the most current guidance.

*H*ow do I get a copy of this? As of late 2015, the Singapore CASA website maintains a copy here: http://www.caas.gov.sg/caas/en/Regulations/ Aeronautical_Information/AIC/index.html. You should search for the latest ADS-B guidance.

December 7, 2017, Eurocontrol

Finding definitive information about Eurocontrol mandates is difficult. The official Eurocontrol website is often years out of date. The current mandates, according to news reports, are years beyond what the official website claims. As of late 2015, the mandates are as follows: Newly manufactured aircraft with a certificate of airworthiness issued on or after January 8, 2016 must be equipped with ADS-B out. All other aircraft must be so equipped by June 8, 2020.

*H*ow do I get a copy of this? As of late 2015, Europe's Single European Sky ATM Research (SESAR) information is available at http://www.eurocontrol.int. You may be better off looking for the dates on aviation news sites.

January 1, 2020, United States

[14 CFR 91 §91.225]

(a) After January 1, 2020, and unless otherwise authorized by ATC, no person may operate an aircraft in Class A airspace unless the aircraft has equipment installed that—

(1) Meets the requirements in TSO-C166b, Extended Squitter Automatic Dependent Surveillance-Broadcast (ADS-B) and Traffic Information Service-Broadcast (TIS-B) Equipment Operating on the Radio Frequency of 1090 Megahertz (MHz); and

(2) Meets the requirements of §91.227.

(b) After January 1, 2020, and unless otherwise authorized by ATC, no person may operate an aircraft below 18,000 feet MSL and in airspace described in paragraph (d) of this section unless the aircraft has equipment installed that—

(1) Meets the requirements in—

(i) TSO-C166b; or

(ii) TSO-C154c, Universal Access Transceiver (UAT) Automatic Dependent Surveillance-Broadcast (ADS-B) Equipment Operating on the Frequency of 978 MHz;

(2) Meets the requirements of §91.227.

(c) Operators with equipment installed with an approved deviation under §21.618 of this chapter also are in compliance with this section.

(d) After January 1, 2020, and unless otherwise authorized by ATC, no person may operate an aircraft in the following airspace unless the aircraft has equipment installed that meets the requirements in paragraph (b) of this section:

(1) Class B and Class C airspace areas;

(2) Except as provided for in paragraph (e) of this section, within 30 nautical miles of an airport listed in appendix D, section 1 to this part from the surface upward to 10,000 feet MSL;

(3) Above the ceiling and within the lateral boundaries of a Class B or Class C airspace area designated for an airport upward to 10,000 feet MSL;

(4) Except as provided in paragraph (e) of this section, Class E airspace within the 48 contiguous states and the District of Columbia at and above 10,000 feet MSL, excluding the airspace at and below 2,500 feet above the surface; and

(5) Class E airspace at and above 3,000 feet MSL over the Gulf of Mexico from the coastline of the United States out to 12 nautical miles.

You will need ADS-B Out in the United States starting January 1, 2020 in most airspace: Class A, Class B, Class C, Within 30 nm of Class D airports, Class E above 10,000' MSL except below 2,500' AGL, and in the Gulf of Mexico above 3,000' MSL 12 nm beyond the shoreline.

Required Authorizations

Australia

[Information for Operators (InFO) 13009] The following information identifies FAA approval requirements for U.S. aircraft operators in foreign ADS-B airspace: Australia: A153 not required. Approved ADS-B avionics will be required on, and from, December 12, 2013, for all operations at or above flight level (FL) 290.

[Australia Advisory Circular 21-45(1) ¶10.1.1] CAO 82.1 Paragraph 5.8, CAO 82.3 Paragraph 10.8 and CAO 82.5 Paragraph 10.8 detail the requirements for ADS-B that foreign registered aircraft must comply with if intending to utilise ADS-B services operations within Australian FIR.

[Australian Civil Aviation Order 82.3, ¶10.8] The operator of a foreign registered aircraft must ensure that it complies with the requirements (Directions) in Appendices 6 and 6A. The definitions in Appendix 6 also apply for Appendices 6A and 7.

[Australian Civil Aviation Order 82.3, Appendix 6 and 7] Directions relating to carriage and use of automatic dependent surveillance – broadcast equipment

- FAA means the Federal Aviation Administration of the United States.

- ADS-B transmitting equipment must be of a type that: (a) is authorised by: (i) the FAA in accordance with TSO-C166 as in force on 20 September 2004, or a later version as in force from time to time; or (ii) CASA, in writing

The Australians have 3 regulations, depending on if you are flying charter (Australian Civil Aviation Order 82.1), small cabin (Australian Civil Aviation Order 82.3), or large cabin (Australian Civil Aviation Order 82.5) aircraft. Each of these say if the U.S. FAA says you are good to go, you are good to go.

Canada

[Information for Operators (InFO) 13009] Authorization, per A153, is required only when an operator seeks operational benefit from ADS-B Out equipage in the airspace defined in Nav Canada Aeronautical Information Circulars (AICs) 31/11 and 44/11.

[Nav Canada Aeronautical Information Circular 31/11] Domestic operators and those foreign operators holding a Foreign Air Carrier Operations Certificate are required to apply to Transport Canada for Operations Specifications 609 or 610 to be eligible to have a separation standard applied based on ADS-B Out. Transport Canada has provided guidance in Advisory Circular AC700-009 revision 2 as to how operators can achieve this specification. Operators who do not fall into these categories are required to provide NAV CANADA with proof from the civil aviation authority of their aircraft's state of registry of compliance with the European Aviation Safety Agency's (EASA) Acceptable Means of Compliance (AMC) 20-24. In addition, in all cases operators must complete an aircraft equipment survey and provide NAV CANADA with each aircraft's unique 24-bit transponder address in order to be entered onto the list of eligible aircraft.

[Nav Canada Aeronautical Information Circular 44/11]Operators must meet the conditions of operational specification No. 609 or No. 610, as appropriate, outlined in Transport Canada, Advisory Circular (AC) 700-009, Issue No. 2. Operators must also complete an aircraft equipment survey and provide NAV CANADA with each aircraft's unique 24-bit transponder address in order to be entered onto the list of eligible aircraft.

[Transport Canada AC 700-009 ¶6.2] A foreign air operator must meet the conditions of operational specification No. 610, provided in Appendix B of this document, to obtain operational approval for ADS-B operations. The conditions are as follows:

(a) the aircraft, the equipment and the installation must:

(i) meet the airworthiness requirements of the State of the Foreign Air Operator; and

(ii) meet the certification considerations of the European Aviation Safety Agency (EASA) AMC 20-24 -- Certification Considerations for the Enhanced ATS in Non-Radar Areas using ADS-B Surveillance (ADS-B-NRA) Application.

(b) Company Operations Manual— The air operator must establish procedures in its Company Operations Manual for the guidance of its personnel and any other procedures related to ADS-B that are necessary for safe operations.

(c) Training—The air operator must provide training to each flight crew member involved with ADS-B operations that address at least the items listed at sections 10.3.2 and 10.4 of EASA document AMC 20-24.

Hong Kong

[Information for Operators (InFO) 13009] Authorization, per A153, is required for all U.S. aircraft operators flying over performance-based navigation routes L642 or M771 at or above FL290 within Hong Kong flight information region (FIR) on and after December 12, 2013. Additionally, A153 will be required on and after December 31, 2014 for all U.S. aircraft flying within the entire Hong Kong FIR at or above FL290. For further information regarding ADS-B operations within the Hong Kong FIR, refer to Hong Kong AIC 09/11, Automatic Dependent Surveillance Broadcast (ADS-B) Out Operations.

[Hong Kong Aeronautical Information Circular (AIC) 09/11, ¶4] The aircraft operator must have the relevant ADS-B operational approval from the State of Registry.

Singapore

[Information for Operators (InFO) 13009] The following information identifies FAA approval requirements for U.S. aircraft operators in foreign ADS-B airspace: Singapore: A153 required. Authorization, per A153, is required for U.S. aircraft operators operating on ATS routes N891, M753, L642, M771, L644, and N892 at FL290 and above within the Singapore FIR on and after December 12, 2013. For additional information regarding ADS-B operations within the Singapore FIR, refer to Singapore AIC 14/10, Introduction of Automatic Dependent Surveillance Broadcast (ADS-B) Out Services within parts of the Singapore FIR.

[Singapore AIP Supplement 254 ¶2.1] The aircraft must carry serviceable ADS-B transmitting equipment that has been certified as meeting EASA AMC 20-24, or meets the equipment configuration standards of the Civil Aviation Safety Authority of Australia; and the aircraft operator must have the relevant operational approval from the State of Registry.

United States

[AC 90-114 Ch. 1 ¶ 1-3.b.] There is no authorization required by the Federal Aviation Administration (FAA) to conduct ADS-B OUT operations in the airspace defined by 14 CFR §91.225 (U.S.-designated airspace).

Outside of U.S.-Designated Airspace

[AC 90-114 App. 1. ¶2.] FAA authorization is required for all U.S. operators to conduct ADS-B OUT operations outside of U.S.-designated airspace. This appendix provides guidance to operators on the process and documentation required when requesting issuance of this authorization.

NOTE: As applicable, authorization under FAA Order 8900.1, Flight Standards Information Management System (FSIMS), Volume 3, Chapter 18, Section 3, Part A Operations Specifications—General, operations specification (OpSpec) A153 and a regional authorization (e.g., OpSpec B050) may be necessary to conduct ADS-B operations in areas outside of U.S.-designated airspace.

Instructions for how to request an authorization, LOA or OpSpec, are contained in AC 90-114, Appendix 1.

Equipment Requirements

EASA (and much of the world)

European Aviation Safety Agency (EASA) Acceptable Means of Compliance (AMC) 20-24 ¶9 provides several methods to demonstrate ADS-B equipment qualification. In the G450, we have a specific statement in ASC 079.

United States

U.S. equipment requirements are contained in Advisory Circular 20-165A.

[AC 90-114 ¶ 1-3.c.]

- NOTE: Outside the U.S. National Airspace System (NAS), many worldwide air traffic service providers (ATSP) allow the use of ADS-B equipment certified to the European Aviation Safety Agency (EASA) Acceptable Means of Compliance (AMC) 20-24, Certification Considerations for the Enhanced ATS in Non-Radar Areas using ADS-B Surveillance (ADS-B-NRA) Application via 1090 MHz Extended Squitter, dated February 5, 2008.

- NOTE: ADS-B equipment installed in accordance with AC 20-165 (TSO-C166b and TSO-C154c) meets the equipment requirements of AMC 20-24. However, AMC 20-24 equipment does not comply with § 91.225.

Operating Rules

[14 CFR 91 §91.225]

(f) Each person operating an aircraft equipped with ADS-B Out must operate this equipment in the transmit mode at all times.

(g) Requests for ATC authorized deviations from the requirements of this section must be made to the ATC facility having jurisdiction over the concerned airspace within the time periods specified as follows:

(1) For operation of an aircraft with an inoperative ADS-B Out, to the airport of ultimate destination, including any intermediate stops, or to proceed to a place where suitable repairs can be made or both, the request may be made at any time.

(2) For operation of an aircraft that is not equipped with ADS-B Out, the request must be made at least 1 hour before the proposed operation.

[AC 90-114 Ch. 1 ¶ 4-4.] When operating aircraft equipped with ADS-B OUT, operators should indicate their ADS-B capability on the flight plan as "RMK/ADSB."

Pilot Training

[AC 90-114 Appendix 1, ¶2.c.(7)] Pilots conducting operations under this authorization must be trained in the use and limitations of the installed ADS-B system, unless one of the crewmembers is an ADS-B-trained check airman, as appropriate. Operators must submit documentation that details the method and content of the pilot training to be conducted. Pilot training must address the following:

- ADS-B operating procedures;

- Flight planning;

- MEL procedures;

- Human factors;

- ADS-B phraseology applicable to specific regions of operation (see Table 1, Canadian-Specific Surveillance Phraseology, and Table 2, Australian-Specific Surveillance Phraseology);

- ADS-B system operation, including normal/abnormal procedures;

- Correct entry of ICAO aircraft ID as applicable to the flight;

- Operational procedures regarding the transmission of the generic emergency code (i.e., 7700) in cases when the flightcrew actually selected a discrete emergency code (e.g., 7500, 7600);

- Handling of data source errors (e.g., discrepancies between navigation data sources); and

- Incident reporting procedures.

Automatic Dependent Surveillance – Contract (ADS-C)

*Y*ou can think of ADS-C as a replacement for Air Traffic Control radar contact. When you log on on to an Air Traffic Service Unit with ADS-C, you
agree to contracts that send information to the ATSU on a regular basis.

Functional Description

Overview

[AC 91-70A, ¶5-4] Automatic Dependent Surveillance-Contract (ADS-C).
ADS-C is an Air Traffic Service (ATS) application established by contract
in which aircraft automatically transmit, via data link, data derived from
onboard navigation systems. As a minimum, the data includes a 3-D position, the corresponding time of the position data, and a Figure of Merit that
characterizes the accuracy of the position data. You may provide additional
data as appropriate.

It uses the various systems aboard the aircraft to provide aircraft position,
velocity, intent, and meteorological data. The aircraft can transmit this data
to the ATS provider system for estimating and predicting aircraft position.

The ATS provider applies a contract request to an aircraft. ADS-C reports
are issued by the aircraft per the contract request. The contract identifies the
types of information and the conditions that the aircraft transmit.

An ADS Contract is an agreement from the pilot to the ATSU, to provide in-
formation. You can provide information through various types of contracts
and you can do this with up to four different ATSUs. The data is extracted
automatically from electronics in your aircraft. In exchange they grant you
access to the airspace you are in, or coordinate with nearby airspace. ADS-C
will take the place of voice position reports in many regions of the world. You
need special equipment and authorization to use ADS-C.

Benefit

[ICAO GOLD, ¶2.1.3.1] The Safety and Performance Standard for Air Traffic Data Link Services in Oceanic and Remote Airspace (Oceanic SPR Standard, RTCA DO-306/EUROCAE ED-122), provides operational, safety and performance criteria for data link services that are applicable in airspace, where procedural separation is being applied, for normal ATC communication and surveillance to support separation assurance, route conformance monitoring, re-routes, and weather deviation management. These criteria include specifications for required communication performance (RCP) and required surveillance performance (RSP), taking into consideration the following data link applications:

1.   Data link initiation capability (DLIC);

2.   CPDLC for ATC communication;

3.   ADS-C for surveillance - automatic position reporting;

ADS-C gives you a better Required Surveillance Performance (RSP) and CPDLC gives you better Required Communication Performance (RCP). Combined, they allow you to fly in airspace with tighter separation minima which means you have a greater selection of airspace available to you.

Contract Types

Periodic Contracts

[ICAO GOLD, ¶2.2.6.3] A periodic contract allows an ATSU to specify:

- The time interval at which the aircraft system sends an ADS-C report; and

- The optional ADS-C groups that are to be included in the periodic report.

The ATSU can also specify how often the reports are sent, anywhere from 1 to 4,096 seconds. (64 seconds is the usual minimum interval.)

Photo: G450 MCDU, ADS Periodic Contract

An ATSU can establish only one periodic contract with an aircraft at any one time. A number of ATSUs can each establish their own periodic contract and specify their own conditions for the report with the same aircraft at the same time.

The ATSU determines what information it wants and how often it wants it. From the flight crew standpoint, you will see differing numbers of items on the periodic contract. The example photo shows the contract from YQXE2YA wants FLIGHT ID and METEORO information every 1088 seconds.

Event Contracts

[ICAO GOLD, ¶2.2.6.3.6] An event contract allows an ATSU to request an ADS-C report whenever a specific event occurs. An ATSU can establish only one event contract with an aircraft at any one time. However, the event contract can contain multiple event types. These types of optional events include:

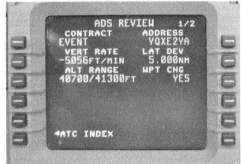

Photo: G450 MCDU, Event Contract

- Waypoint change event (WCE);

- Level range deviation event (LRDE);

- Lateral deviation event (LDE);

- Vertical rate change event (VRE).

In the example photo, the ATS will be notified automatically if the aircraft's vertical velocity exceeds 5,056 fpm, lateral deviation exceeds 5 nm, the altitude goes below 40,700 or above 41,300 feet, and at every waypoint change. The waypoint change is determined by the FMS so anything you do to the FMS that affects the next waypoint and the waypoint one after that will be reported. For example, if you were to insert your ETP before the next waypoint, that gets reported.

Demand Contracts

[ICAO GOLD, ¶2.2.6.3.4] A demand contract allows an ATSU to request a single ADS-C periodic report. A demand contract does not cancel or modify any other ADS contracts that may be in effect with the aircraft.

Log On

[ICAO GOLD, ¶2.2.3.1] A logon, initiated either by the flight crew or by another ATSU, is performed prior to the ATSU establishing a CPDLC and/or ADS-C connection. The purpose of the logon is to:

1. Provide the ATSU with the data link application "context" of the aircraft, namely:

    a. The ATS data link applications supported by the aircraft system (e.g. CPDLC, ADS-C) and the associated version numbers of these applications; and

    b. The unique identification of the aircraft;

2. Provide the ATSU with the relevant aircraft information required to allow the ATSU to correlate the logon information with the aircraft's corresponding flight plan.

3. On receipt of a logon request, the ATSU correlates the logon information with the relevant information in the flight plan held by the ATSU. This ensures that messages are sent to the correct aircraft and that automation associated with ADS-C reports or CPDLC messages updates the correct flight plan.

4. When making this correlation, the ground system ensures that the aircraft identification in the logon request matches that in Item 7 of the associated flight plan and at least one of the aircraft registration or aircraft address provided match the corresponding descriptors (following the REG and/or CODE indicators, respectively) in Item 18 of the flight plan;

The log on procedure varies with aircraft. In the case of a Gulfstream 550, the ADS-C log on takes places as a consequence of the CPDLC log on. The CPDLC FIR region code is entered into the ATC LOGON STATUS page of the MCDU after ensuring all other items are correct. The information is sent and once accepted the MCDU scratch pad will show "ADS ESTABLISHED" and the ADS ARMED entry will change to ADS ACTIVE.

Photo: G450 MCDU, ADS Armed.

Position Reporting

Position Reporting in an ADS-C Environment

[ICAO Gold, ¶5.6.3] In an ADS-C environment, the flight crew should not provide position reports or revised waypoint estimates by CPDLC or voice, unless otherwise instructed or under conditions in certain airspace as stipulated in Regional Supplementary Procedures or AIP (or other appropriate publication).

Appendix E of the ICAO GOLD manual lists which regions require and which do not require the additional position report.

If required by regional supplementary procedures or AIP (or other appropriate publication), the flight crew should provide a CPDLC position report when either of the following events occurs:

- An initial CPDLC connection is established; or

- The CPDLC connection transfer has been completed (i.e. at the associated boundary entry position).

The flight crew should maintain the active route in the aircraft system to be the same as the ATC cleared route of flight.

Note.— If the flight crew activates a non-ATC cleared route into the aircraft system, the ADS-C reports will include information that will indicate the aircraft is flying a route that is deviating from the cleared route.

You should never insert your equal time points as FMS waypoints.

When reporting by ADS-C only, the flight crew should include ATC waypoints in the aircraft active flight plan even if they are not compulsory reporting points.

Position Reporting in a non-ADS-C Environment

[ICAO Gold, ¶5.6.2] When ADS-C is not available, the flight crew should conduct position reporting by voice or CPDLC. When using CPDLC, the flight crew should send DM 48 POSITION REPORT [position report] whenever an ATC waypoint is sequenced, (or passed abeam when offset flight is in progress).

When using CPDLC for position reporting, the flight crew should send position reports only at compulsory reporting points and ensure that the position and next position information applies to compulsory reporting points, unless requested otherwise by ATC. The ensuing significant point after the next position may be either a compulsory or non-compulsory reporting point.

The Importance of FMS Waypoint Sequencing

You don't have to worry about flying a Strategic Lateral Offset because your FMS will sequence the waypoints even if you are two miles away from the intended course. But if you are further than the tolerance allowed by your FMS, it may not sequence. If that happens, the position report will not be made.

[ICAO Gold, ¶5.6.1] The flight crew should ensure that waypoints are sequenced correctly. If an aircraft passes abeam a waypoint by more than the aircraft FMS waypoint sequencing parameter, the flight crew should sequence the waypoints in the FMS, as appropriate.

As shown in [the figure], when an aircraft passes abeam a waypoint in excess of the defined sequencing parameter for specific aircraft types), the FMS will not sequence the active waypoint. If the flight crew does not sequence the waypoint, incorrect information will be contained in ADS-C reports, CPDLC position reports and FMC waypoint position reports – the next waypoint in these reports will actually be the waypoint that the aircraft has already passed.

When using CPDLC or FMC WPR to provide position information, the flight crew should use latitudes and longitudes encoded as waypoint names in the ICAO format.

The point here is do not use ARINC-424 format. The ATSU doesn't understand "3030N" but wants to see the full latitude and longitude.

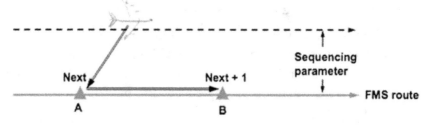

Figure: Waypoint sequencing anomaly, from ICAO Gold, figure 5-2.

Exiting CPDLC and ADS-C Service Areas

[ICAO GOLD, ¶5.2.5] The flight crew should consult the current ATSU prior to the manual termination of any ADS contract with the aircraft, even if it is suspected to be unnecessary or that its termination has failed.

Note.— ADS contracts are managed (e.g. established and terminated) by ATSUs.

Approximately 15 minutes after exiting CPDLC and/or ADS-C service areas, the flight crew should ensure there are no active CPDLC or ADS-C connections. Ensuring that connections are not active eliminates the possibility of inadvertent or inappropriate use of the connections, and reduces operating costs and loading of the system.

Note.— Some ATSUs may maintain ADS contracts with an aircraft for a period of time (e.g. 15 minutes) after the aircraft has left the airspace.

Transfer of ADS-C Services Between ATSUs

[ICAO GOLD, ¶5.2.3] Under normal circumstances, the current and next ATSUs automatically transfer CPDLC and ADS-C services. The transfer is seamless to the flight crew.

Note.— The flight crew should not need to reinitiate a logon.

The flight crew should promptly respond to CPDLC uplinks to minimize the risk of an open CPDLC uplink message when transferring to the next ATSU.

When entering the next ATSU's airspace, the flight crew should confirm the successful transfer from the current ATSU to the next ATSU by observing the change in the active center indication provided by the aircraft system.

When required by local procedures, the flight crew should send DM 48 POSITION REPORT [position report]. Alternatively, the flight crew may be required to respond to a CPDLC message exchange initiated by the ATSU.

ADS-C Reports

[ICAO GOLD, ¶2.2.6.4] The aircraft system sends specific aircraft data in different groups of an ADS-C report. Each group contains different types of data. An ADS-C event report contains only some of the groups, which are fixed. The ADS-C periodic report can contain any of the ADS-C groups, which the ATSU specifies in the contract request.

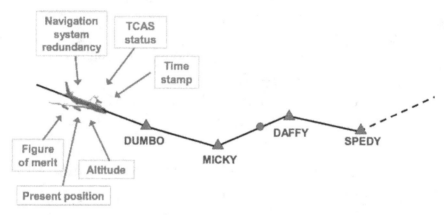

Figure: ADS-C Basic Group, from ICAO Gold, figure 2-38.

Figure: ADS-C Flight Identification Group, from ICAO Gold, figure 2-39.

Figure: ADS-C Earth Reference Group, from ICAO Gold, figure 2-40.

Figure: ADS-C Air Reference Group, from ICAO Gold, figure 2-41.

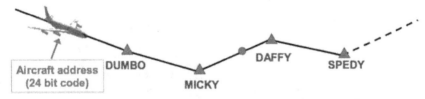

Figure: ADS-C Airframe Identification Group, from ICAO Gold, figure 2-42.

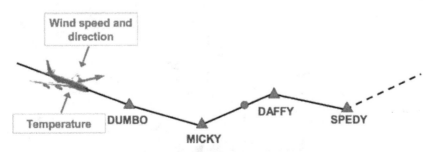

Figure: ADS-C Meteorological Group, from ICAO Gold, figure 2-43.

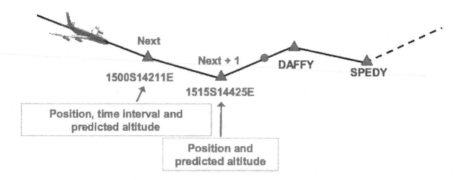

Figure: ADS-C Predicted Route Group, from ICAO Gold, figure 2-44.

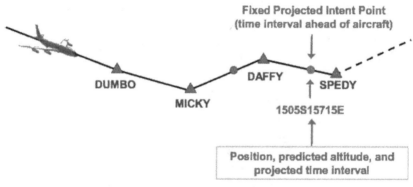

Figure: ADS-C Fixed Projected Intent Group, from ICAO Gold, figure 2-45.

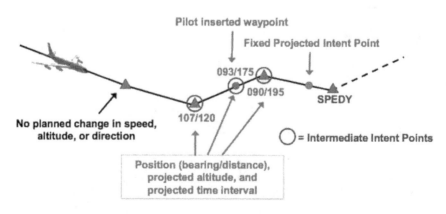

Figure: ADS-C Intermediate Projected Intent Group, from ICAO Gold, figure 2-46.

Chapter 4

Transponder Modes and Codes

*M*ost *of this stuff is common knowledge, perhaps we miss a few things here and there. When exactly do you squawk 2000? What does that former Air Force guy mean when he says IFF? What is a secondary target?*

History

IFF

[DoD Dictionary of Military and Associated Terms, pg. 123] Identification, friend or foe — A device that emits a signal positively identifying it as a friendly.

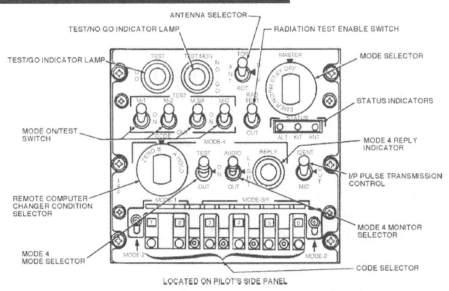

Figure: AN/APX-100 IFF Transponder, from an old Air Force flight manual.

You will often hear "IFF" from ex-military types when what they mean to say is "transponder." While the IFF found in many military aircraft are much more than just transponders, for our purposes the terms can be considered synonymous.

ATC: Primary versus Secondary Radar

[Air Traffic Organization Policy Order JO 7110.65U, pg. PCG P-4] PRIMARY RADAR TARGET– An analog or digital target, exclusive of a secondary radar target, presented on a radar display.

[Air Traffic Organization Policy Order JO 7110.65U, pg. PCG S-2] SECONDARY RADAR TARGET– A target derived from a transponder return presented on a radar display.

The primary target is the "blip" on the controllers radar screen that is nothing more than the aircraft's radar return, while the secondary target is the signal and information beamed from the aircraft's transponder to the radar.

Modes

Mode 1 (Military)

This was a two digit code we could set depending on mission.

Mode 2 (Military)

I've heard this code told the good guys what your mission is and was set for each aircraft, though aircraft I've flown allowed us to change this in flight.

Mode 3 (Military) / Mode A (Civilian)

This is the 4-digit code we set in the cockpit as assigned by ATC or what we are doing at the time, often called "Mode 3/A" and usually combined with Mode C to provide altitude information.

Mode 3 (Military) / Mode C (Civilian)

Provides the aircraft's pressure altitude, sometimes called "Mode 3C."

Mode 4 (Military)

Provides a 3-pulse reply to crypto coded challenge.

Mode 5 (Military)

Provides a cryptographically secured version of Mode S and ADS-B GPS position.

Mode S (Military and Civilian)

Provides multiple information formats to a selective interrogation. Each aircraft is assigned a fixed 24-bit address.

The code is simply a hexadecimal conversion from your registration. You can check this at: http://www.avionictools.com/.

Codes

1200 — VFR

[Aeronautical Information Manual, ¶4-1-17.g.] Transponder Operation Under Visual Flight Rules (VFR): Unless otherwise instructed by an ATC facility, adjust transponder to reply on Mode 3/A Code 1200 regardless of altitude.

[Transport Canada Aeronautical Information Manual, ¶1.9.4] During VFR flight in low-level airspace, adjust your transponder to reply on the following unless otherwise assigned by an ATS unit: (a) Mode A, Code 1200, for operation at or below 12 500 ft ASL; or (b) Mode A, Code 1400, for operation above 12 500 ft ASL

There may be other examples, but for at least in the U.S. and in Canada below 12,500 feet, squawk 1200 when VFR.

2000 — Oceanic

[ICAO Doc 8168, Vol I, §III-3-1-1, ¶1.1.2] Except in case of emergency, communication failure or unlawful interference (see 1.4, 1.5 and 1.6), the pilot shall:

a) operate the transponder and select Mode A codes as directed by the ATC unit with which contact is being made; or

b) operate the transponder on Mode A codes as prescribed on the basis of regional air navigation agreements; or

c) in the absence of any ATC directions or regional air navigation agreements, operate the transponder on Mode A Code 2000.

[ICAO Doc 7030, §AFI, ¶5.1.1.2.] Africa-Indian Ocean Regional Supplementary Procedures. Unless otherwise directed by air traffic control, the last assigned SSR (Mode A) code shall be retained. If no SSR code has been assigned, Mode A code 2000 shall be selected and retained.

[ICAO NAT Doc 007, ¶6.8.1] All aircraft operating as IFR flights in the NAT Region shall be equipped with a pressure- altitude reporting SSR transponder. Unless otherwise directed by ATC, pilots flying in the NAT FIRs will operate transponders continuously in Mode A/C Code 2000, except that the last assigned code will be retained for a period of 30 min after entry into NAT airspace or after leaving a radar service area. Pilots should note that it is important to change from the last assigned domestic code to the Mode A/C Code 2000 since the original domestic code may not be recognised by the subsequent Domestic Radar Service on exit from the oceanic airspace.

[AC 91-70A ¶5-5.b.] In airspace controlled by Oakland Center or Honolulu Center, accomplish normal VHF communication. In airspace controlled by Oakland Oceanic (KZAK), CPDLC or HF voice backup accomplishes ATC communication (including en route requests) and position reporting. You can also use HF as primary communication for the aircraft not equipped with data link. When reaching oceanic airspace, squawk 2000 and monitor VHF 121.5 and the pacific air-to-air frequency 123.45.

[AC 91-70A ¶8-16.b.] In South America, there are no alternate instructions in the AIP. Therefore, use code 2000 when beyond radar coverage if there is no specification for another code.

[AC 91-70A ¶13-9.b.] Special Requirements For Flights Transiting Iceland. Pilots will operate SSR transponders continuously on Mode A, Code 2000, except that departing aircraft will retain the last assigned code for 30 minutes after entry into NAT oceanic airspace unless otherwise instructed by ATC.

[AC 91-70A ¶14-2.d.] On polar routes beyond areas of radar coverage, squawk 2000.

[AC 91-70A Appendix 2, ¶2.g.] Thirty minutes after oceanic entry, crews should Squawk 2000, if applicable. There may be regional differences such as Squawking 2100 in Bermuda's airspace or maintaining last assigned Squawk in the West Atlantic Route System (WATRS). Crews transiting Reykjavik's airspace must maintain last assigned Squawk.

In general you are going to squawk 2000 when oceanic, waiting 30 minutes after the entry waypoint is required over the North Atlantic and doesn't hurt elsewhere. There are exceptions so make sure you view the regional pages before entry.

7500 — Hijacking

[ICAO Doc 4444, ¶8.5.2.1] Code 7500 shall be reserved internationally for use by pilots encountering unlawful interference.

[ICAO Doc 8168, Vol I, §III-3-1-2, ¶1.6]

- If there is unlawful interference with an aircraft in flight, the pilot-in-command shall attempt to set the transponder to Mode A Code 7500 in order to indicate the situation. If circumstances so warrant, Code 7700 should be used instead.

- If a pilot has selected Mode A Code 7500 and has been requested to confirm this code by ATC (in accordance with 1.1.5), the pilot shall, according to circumstances, either confirm this or not reply at all.

Note.— If the pilot does not reply, ATC will take this as confirmation that the use of Code 7500 is not an inadvertent false code selection.

[ICAO Doc 8168, Vol I, §III-3-1-1, ¶1.1.5] When requested by ATC to CONFIRM SQUAWK (code), the pilot shall:

a) verify the Mode A code setting on the transponder;

b) reselect the assigned code if necessary; and

c) confirm to ATC the setting displayed on the controls of the transponder.

7600 — Lost Comm

[ICAO Doc 4444, ¶8.5.2.1] Code 7600 shall be reserved internationally for use by pilots encountering a state of radio communication failure.

[ICAO Doc 8168, Vol I, §III-3-1-2, ¶1.5] The pilot of an aircraft losing two-way communications shall set the transponder to Mode A Code 7600. Note.— A controller who observes an SSR response indicating selection of the communications failure code will determine the extent of the failure by instructing the pilot to SQUAWK IDENT or to change code. If it is determined that the aircraft receiver is functioning, further control of the aircraft will be continued using code changes or IDENT transmission to acknowledge receipt of clearances. Different procedures may be applied to Mode S equipped aircraft in areas of Mode S coverage.

7700 — Emergency

[ICAO Doc 4444, ¶8.5.2.1] Code 7700 shall be reserved internationally for use by pilots encountering a state of emergency.

[ICAO Doc 8168, Vol I, §III-3-1-2, ¶1.4] The pilot of an aircraft in a state of emergency shall set the transponder to Mode A Code 7700 unless ATC has previously directed the pilot to operate the transponder on a specified code. In the latter case, the pilot shall continue to use the specified code unless otherwise advised by ATC. However, a pilot may select Mode A Code 7700 whenever there is a specific reason to believe that this would be the best course of action.

Chapter 1

Inflight Contingencies in Oceanic Airspace

The ICAO cleaned up the disparate procedures for oceanic contingencies nicely about 2007, so what follows below, word-for-word, is ICAO Doc 4444, Procedures for Air Navigations Services, Amendment 2 §15.2.

Introduction

[ICAO Doc 4444, Procedures for Air Navigations Services, Amendment 2]

15.2.1.1. Although all possible contingencies cannot be covered, the procedures in 15.2.2 and 15.2.3 provide the more frequent cases such as:

a.   inability to comply with assigned clearance due to meteorological conditions, aircraft performance, or pressurization failure;

b.   en route diversion across the prevailing traffic flow; and

c.   loss of, or significant reduction in, the required navigation capability when operating in an airspace where the navigation performance accuracy is a prerequisite to the safe conduct of flight operations.

15.2.1.2. With regard to 15.2.1.1 a) and b), the procedures are applicable primarily when descent and/or turn back or diversion is required. The pilot shall take action as necessary to ensure the safety of the aircraft, and the pilot's judgement shall determine the sequence of actions to be taken, having regard to the prevailing circumstances. Air traffic control shall render all possible assistance.

General Procedures

[ICAO Doc 4444, Procedures for Air Navigations Services, Amendment 2]

15.2.2.1. If an aircraft is unable to continue the flight in accordance with its ATC clearance, and/or an aircraft is unable to maintain the navigation performance accuracy specified for the airspace, a revised clearance shall be obtained, whenever possible, prior to initiating any action.

15.2.2.2. The radiotelephony distress signal (MAYDAY) or urgency signal (PAN PAN) preferably spoken three times shall be used as appropriate. Subsequent ATC action with respect to that aircraft shall be based on the intentions of the pilot and the overall air traffic situation.

Declaring an emergency is a game changer just about anywhere in the world and using "Mayday" or "Pan Pan" is the only way to change the rules of the game in some parts of the world. You shouldn't be shy about using it if you need traffic priority. I've done this eighteen times in my short life and there has never been anything negative as a result.

15.2.2.3. If prior clearance cannot be obtained, until a revised clearance is received the following contingency procedures should be employed and the pilot shall advise air traffic control as soon as practicable, reminding them of the type of aircraft involved and the nature of the problem. In general terms, the aircraft should be flown at a flight level and on an offset track where other aircraft are least likely to be encountered. Specifically, the pilot shall:

a. leave the assigned route or track by initially turning at least 45 degrees to the right or to the left, in order to acquire a same or opposite direction track offset 15 nm (28 km) from the assigned track centreline. When possible, the direction of the turn should be determined by the position of the aircraft relative to any organized route or track system. Other factors which may affect the direction of the turn are:

   1. the direction to an alternate airport;

   2. terrain clearance;

   3. any strategic lateral offset being flown; and

   4. the flight levels allocated on adjacent routes or tracks;

b.   having initiated the turn:

    1.   if unable to maintain the assigned flight level, initially minimize the rate of descent to the extent that is operationally feasible (pilots should take into account the possibility that aircraft below on the same track may be flying a 1 or 2 nm strategic lateral offset procedure (SLOP)) and select a final altitude which differs from those normally used by 150 m (500 ft) if at or below FL 410, or by 300 m (1,000 ft) if above FL 410; or

    2.   if able to maintain the assigned flight level, once the aircraft has deviated 19 km (10 nm) from the assigned track centreline, climb or descend to select a flight level which differs from those normally used by by 150 m (500 ft) if at or below FL 410, or by 300 m (1,000 ft) if above FL 410;

c.   establish communications with and alert nearby aircraft by broadcasting, at suitable intervals on 121.5 MHz (or, as a backup, on the inter-pilot air-to-air frequency 123.45 MHz) and where appropriate on the frequency in use: aircraft identification, flight level, position (including the ATS route designator or the track code, as appropriate) and intentions;

d.   maintain a watch for conflicting traffic both visually and by reference to ACAS (if equipped);

e.   turn on all aircraft exterior lights (commensurate with appropriate operating limitations); and

f.   keep the SSR transponder on at all times.

15.2.2.3.1. When leaving the assigned track:

a.   if the intention is to acquire a same direction offset track, the pilot should consider limiting the turn to a 45 degree heading change, in order not to overshoot the offset contingency track; or

b.   if the intention is to acquire and maintain an opposite direction offset track, then:

    1.   operational limitations on bank angles at cruising altitudes will normally result in overshooting the track to be acquired. In such cases a continuous turn should be extended beyond

180 degrees heading change, in order to re-intercept the offset contingency track as soon as operationally feasible; and

2.   furthermore, if executing such a turn back in a 56 km (30 nm) lateral separation route structure, extreme caution pertaining to opposite direction traffic on adjacent routes must be exercised and any climb or descent, as specified in 15.2.2.3 b) 2), should be completed preferably before approaching within 19 km (10 nm) of any adjacent ATS route.

Some people call this the "Quad Four Maneuver" since it came from ICAO Doc 4444; it is as good a name as any, I suppose. Regardless of what you call it, you should have it memorized:

- *Turn 45° away from track,*
- *Pick a direction based on alternates, nearby tracks, SLOP, and desired altitude,*
- *Obtain a 15 nm offset,*
- *Pick an altitude 500 ft off if at or below FL 410, 1000 ft if above,*
- *Broadcast to ATC and nearby aircraft*
- *Light up the airplane.*

What about a 180° turn back to where you started? You can do that, but which way you going to turn? Here is some food for thought. We tried this in the G-550 simulator: M0.83, FL 430, lose an engine, reverse course. It took 4 minutes to turn 180° and 22 miles turn diameter.

Chapter 2

Lost Communications

If you are a U.S. pilot who never leaves the confines of the United States and Canada, you should be aware that the lost communications you grew up with are an exception to International Procedures. When you do leave the U.S., you will have some studying to do.

If you have a copy of a Jeppesen Airway Manual you should have all you need to learn about individual country lost communications procedures, but you need to understand International Standard Procedures first. If you don't have a current Jeppesen Airway Manual you will have some digging to do. Each country is required to post their differences from the ICAO standard in their individual Aeronautical Information Publication (AIP), but few of these are in English and fewer still are easily obtainable. ICAO Doc 7030 - Regional Supplementary Procedures was supposed to have fixed all this, but it did not. Be careful out there.

International Standard Procedures

[ICAO Annex 2]

3.6.5.1 An aircraft operated as a controlled flight shall maintain continuous air-ground voice communication watch on the appropriate communication channel of, and establish two-way communication as necessary with, the appropriate air traffic control unit, except as may be prescribed by the appropriate ATS authority in respect of aircraft forming part of aerodrome traffic at a controlled aerodrome.

Note 1.— SELCAL or similar automatic signaling devices satisfy the requirement to maintain an air-ground voice communication watch.

Note 2.— The requirement for an aircraft to maintain an air-ground voice communication watch remains in effect after CPDLC has been established.

3.6.5.2 Communication failure. If a communication failure precludes compliance with 3.6.5.1, the aircraft shall comply with the voice communication failure procedures of Annex 10, Volume II, and with such of the following procedures as are appropriate. The aircraft shall attempt to establish communications with the appropriate air traffic control unit using all other available means. In addition, the aircraft, when forming part of the aerodrome traffic at a controlled aerodrome, shall keep a watch for such instructions as may be issued by visual signals.

The relevant portion of Annex 10, Volume II are shown below.

3.6.5.2.1 If in visual meteorological conditions, the aircraft shall:

a) continue to fly in visual meteorological conditions; land at the nearest suitable aerodrome; and report its arrival by the most expeditious means to the appropriate air traffic services unit;

b) if considered advisable, complete an IFR flight in accordance with 3.6.5.2.2.

3.6.5.2.2 If in instrument meteorological conditions or when the pilot of an IFR flight considers it inadvisable to complete the flight in accordance with 3.6.5.2.1 a), the aircraft shall:

a) unless otherwise prescribed on the basis of regional air navigation agreement, in airspace where radar is not used in the provision of air traffic control, maintain the last assigned speed and level, or minimum flight altitude if higher, for a period of 20 minutes following the aircraft's failure to report its position over a compulsory reporting point and thereafter adjust level and speed in accordance with the filed flight plan;

b) in airspace where radar is used in the provision of air traffic control, maintain the last assigned speed and level, or minimum flight altitude if higher, for a period of 7 minutes following:

1) the time the last assigned level or minimum flight altitude is reached; or

2) the time the transponder is set to Code 7600; or

3) the aircraft's failure to report its position over a compulsory reporting point;

whichever is later, and thereafter adjust level and speed in accordance with the filed flight plan;

c) when being radar vectored or having been directed by ATC to proceed offset using area navigation (RNAV) without a specified limit, rejoin the current flight plan route no later than the next significant point, taking into consideration the applicable minimum flight altitude;

d) proceed according to the current flight plan route to the appropriate designated navigation aid or fix serving the destination aerodrome and, when required to ensure compliance with e) below, hold over this aid or fix until commencement of descent;

e) commence descent from the navigation aid or fix specified in d) at, or as close as possible to, the expected approach time last received and acknowledged; or, if no expected approach time has been received and acknowledged, at, or as close as possible to, the estimated time of arrival resulting from the current flight plan;

f) complete a normal instrument approach procedure as specified for the designated navigation aid or fix; and

g) land, if possible, within 30 minutes after the estimated time of arrival specified in e) or the last acknowledged expected approach time, whichever is later.

Note 1.— The provision of air traffic control service to other flights operating in the airspace concerned will be based on the premise that an aircraft experiencing communication failure will comply with the rules in 3.6.5.2.2.

Note 2. — See also 5.1.2.

[ICAO Annex 2, ¶5.1.2]

Except when necessary for takeoff or landing, or except when specifically authorized by the appropriate authority, an IFR flight shall be flown at a level which is not below the minimum flight altitude established by the State whose territory is overflown, or, where no such minimum flight altitude has been established:

a) over high terrain or in mountainous areas, at a level which is at least 600 m (2,000 ft) above the highest obstacle located within 8 km of the estimated position of the aircraft;

b) elsewhere than as specified in a), at a level which is at least 300 m (1,000 ft) above the highest obstacle located within 8 km of the estimated position of the aircraft.

Note 1.— The estimated position of the aircraft will take account of the navigational accuracy which can be achieved on the relevant route segment, having regard to the navigational facilities available on the ground and in the aircraft.

Note 2.— See also 3.1.2.

[ICAO Annex 2, ¶3.1.2] Minimum heights

Except when necessary for takeoff or landing, or except by permission from the appropriate authority, aircraft shall not be flown over the congested areas of cities, towns or settlements or over an open-air assembly of persons, unless at such a height as will permit, in the event of an emergency arising, a landing to be made without undue hazard to persons or property on the surface.

[ICAO Annex 10]

5.2.2.7. Communications Failure

5.2.2.7.1 Air-ground

5.2.2.7.1.1 When an aircraft station fails to establish contact with the aeronautical station on the designated frequency, it shall attempt to establish contact on another frequency appropriate to the route. If this attempt fails, the aircraft station shall attempt to establish communication with other aircraft or other aeronautical stations on frequencies appropriate to the route. In addition, an aircraft operating within a network shall monitor the appropriate VHF frequency for calls from nearby aircraft.

5.2.2.7.1.2 If the attempts specified under 5.2.2.7.1.1 fail, the aircraft station shall transmit its message twice on the designated frequency(ies), preceded by the phrase "TRANSMITTING BLIND" and, if necessary, include the addressee(s) for which the message is intended.

5.2.2.7.1.2.1 PANS.— In network operation, a message which is transmitted blind should be transmitted twice on both primary and secondary frequencies. Before changing frequency, the aircraft station should announce the frequency to which it is changing.

Canadian Exceptions

Two-way Radio Communication Failure in IFR Flight

[Canadian Aviation Regulations, §602.137]

(1) Where there is a two-way radio communication failure between the controlling air traffic control unit and an IFR aircraft that is in or has received a clearance to enter controlled airspace, the pilot-in-command shall

(a) maintain a listening watch on the appropriate frequency for control messages or further clearance and acknowledge receipt of any such messages, if possible, by any means available;

(b) set the transponder to code 7600; and

(c) attempt to establish communications with any air traffic services facility or other aircraft, inform the facility or aircraft of the difficulty and request it to relay the information to the last air traffic control unit with which communications had been established.

(2) Where communications cannot be established with any air traffic services facility, either directly or by relay through an intermediary, the pilot-in-command shall, except where specific instructions to cover an anticipated communications failure have been received from an air traffic control unit, comply with the procedures specified by the Minister in the Canada Air Pilot and the Canada Flight Supplement.

Two-way Radio Communication Failure in VFR Flight

[Canadian Aviation Regulations, §602.138]

Where there is a two-way radio communication failure between the controlling air traffic control unit and a VFR aircraft while operating in Class B, Class C or Class D airspace, the pilot-in-command shall

(a) leave the airspace

(i) where the airspace is a control zone, by landing at the aerodrome for which the control zone is established, and

(ii) in any other case, by the shortest route;

(b) where the aircraft is equipped with a transponder, set the transponder to code 7600; and

(c) inform an air traffic control unit as soon as possible of the actions taken pursuant to paragraph (a).

The references to "procedures specified by the Minister in the Canada Air Pilot and the Canada Flight Supplement" appear to refer to the "Rules of the Air" (RAC) section of the Transport Canada Aeronautical Information Manual, and closely mirror procedures in the United States. Canadian pilots flying in the United States are provided with this caution:

[Transport Canada Aeronautical Information Manual, §RAC, ¶6.3.2.]

For flights to the United States, communications failure procedures are essentially the same, but it is the pilot's responsibility to consult the appropriate American publications. Some instrument procedures do not include a procedure turn but include the statement "RADAR OR RNAV REQUIRED" as part of the procedure. The initial approach segment of these instrument procedures is being provided by ATC radar vectors. Without ATC radar vectoring, the instrument procedure may not have a published initial approach segment.

Should an aircraft communications failure occur while the aircraft is being vectored on one of these approaches, separately or as part of a STAR, the pilot is expected to comply with the communications failure procedure by selecting the transponder to Mode A/3 Code 7600 immediately. Pilots should always be aware of the traffic situation. For example, ATC may have indicated that your aircraft was second for an approach to Runway 06L; under these circumstances, the flight should be continued along the route that normally would have been expected under radar vectoring. In some cases of communications failure, pilots may need to revert to dead reckoning navigation (DR) to the final approach course. It is important to other aircraft and ATC for the aircraft experiencing a communications failure to continue the flight along a route that would permit the aircraft to conduct a straight-in approach and landing without unexpected manoeuvring. Pilots are expected to exercise good judgment in these cases. Unexpected manoeuvres, such as turns away from the final approach course, may cause traffic disruptions and conflicts.

If the communications failure occurs while being vectored at a radar vectoring altitude that is lower than a published IFR altitude (e.g., minimum sector altitude 25 nm), the pilot shall immediately climb to and maintain the appropriate minimum IFR altitude until arrival at a fix associated with the instrument procedure.

North Atlantic Exceptions

[ICAO NAT Doc 007, ¶6.6.]

Operational Procedures following Loss of HF Communications Prior to Entry into the NAT

On-Board HF Communications Equipment Failure

6.6.20 Due to the potential length of time in oceanic airspace, it is strongly recommended that a pilot, experiencing an HF communications equipment failure prior to entering the NAT, whilst still in domestic airspace and still in VHF contact with the domestic ATC Unit, does not enter NAT airspace but adopts the procedure specified in the appropriate domestic AIP and lands at a suitable airport. Should the pilot, nevertheless, elect to continue the flight then every effort must be made to obtain an oceanic clearance and the routing, initial level and speed contained in that clearance must be maintained throughout the entire oceanic segment. Any level or speed changes required to comply with the Oceanic Clearance must be completed within the vicinity of the oceanic entry point.

6.6.21 If, however, an oceanic clearance cannot be obtained, the individual aircraft suffering radio communications equipment failure should enter oceanic airspace at the first oceanic entry point, level and speed contained in the filed flight plan and proceed via the filed flight plan route to landfall. The initial oceanic level and speed included in the filed flight plan must be maintained until landfall. Any subsequent step-climbs included in the filed flight plan must not be executed.

HF Blackout

6.6.22 In the case of aircraft that lose ATC communications as a result of poor propagation conditions (HF Blackouts) when approaching NAT airspace through domestic airspace where ATC communications are also conducted via HF (e.g. entering the NAT through Northern Canadian airspace into the Reykjavik OCA), it is probably less advisable to execute unscheduled landings. These poor propagation conditions are very likely to affect many aircraft simultaneously and multiple diversions of "lost comms" aircraft might create further difficulties and risks.

6.6.23 As with the equipment failure situation, aircraft approaching the NAT and losing ATC communications as a result of poor HF radio propagation conditions should, if already in receipt of an oceanic clearance, follow the routing specified in that clearance and maintain the initial cleared level and speed throughout the oceanic segment i.e. through to landfall.

6.6.24 However, in these HF Blackout circumstances, if no oceanic clearance has been received, the aircraft must remain at the last cleared domestic flight level, not only to the ocean entry point but also throughout the whole subsequent oceanic segment (i.e. until final landfall). This is in stark contrast to the equipment failure case. In such HF Blackouts, pilots must not effect level changes to comply with filed flight plans. Such aircraft should, maintain the last cleared level and, enter oceanic airspace at the first oceanic entry point and speed contained in the filed flight plan, then proceed via the filed flight plan route to landfall.

6.6.25 The rationale here must be appreciated. In such circumstances it is likely that ATC will have simultaneously lost HF communications with multiple aircraft in the same vicinity. Should pilots then wrongly apply the "normal" radio failure procedures and "fly the flight plan", there is a possibility that two such aircraft may have filed conflicting flight paths/levels through the subsequent oceanic airspace, and without communications with either aircraft, ATC would then be unable to intervene to resolve the conflict. Since safe aircraft level separation assurance has already been incorporated into the current domestic clearances, it is consequently imperative that under such (Domestic and Oceanic) HF-blackout circumstances, all aircraft electing to continue flight into NAT oceanic airspace without a received and acknowledged oceanic clearance, should adhere to the flight level in the last received domestic clearance. No level changes should be made to comply with a filed oceanic level that is different from that of the domestic clearance in effect at the time that ATC air-ground communications were lost.

Operational Procedures following Loss of HF Communications after Entering the NAT

6.6.26 If the HF communications equipment failure occurs or HF Blackout conditions are encountered after entering the NAT then:

The pilot must proceed in accordance with the last received and acknowledged Oceanic Clearance, including level and speed, to the last specified oceanic route point (normally landfall). After passing this point, the pilot should conform with the relevant AIP specified State procedures/regulations and if necessary rejoin the filed flight plan route by proceeding, via the published ATS route structure where possible, to the next significant point contained in the filed flight plan. Note: the relevant State procedures/regulations to be followed by an aircraft in order to rejoin its filed Flight Plan route are specified in detail in the appropriate State AIP.

6.6.27 Aircraft with a destination within the NAT Region should proceed to their clearance limit and follow the ICAO standard procedure to commence descent from the appropriate designated navigation aid serving the destination aerodrome at, or as close as possible to, the expected approach time. Detailed procedures are promulgated in relevant State AIPs.

Summary of Operational Procedures Required following Loss of Air/ Ground ATS Communications in the NAT Region

6.6.28 The foregoing detailed operational procedures can be simply summarised as follows:

- Equipment Failure before receiving an Oceanic Clearance:- Divert or fly the Flight Plan route, speed and initial planned oceanic level to landfall.

- Blackout encountered (in an HF comms Domestic ATC environment) before receiving an Oceanic Clearance:- Continue at Domestic cleared level and follow flight planned route and speed to landfall.

- Equipment Failure or Blackout after receiving an Oceanic Clearance:- Fly that clearance to landfall.

In all cases, after landfall rejoin, or continue on, the flight planned route, using appropriate State AIP specified procedures for the domestic airspace entered.

Pacific Exceptions

[ICAO Doc 7030, PAC 9.3)

In the event of total loss of communication, an aircraft shall:

a) try to re-establish communication by all other means;

b) if all attempts to re-establish communication with ATC are unsuccessful:

1) squawk 7600;

2) if able, broadcast in the blind at suitable intervals: flight identification, flight level, aircraft position (including the ATS route designator or the track code) and intentions on the frequency in use, as well as on frequency 121.5 MHz (or, as a back-up, the VHF inter-pilot air-to-air frequency 123.45 MHz);

3) watch for conflicting traffic both visually and by reference to airborne collision avoidance systems or traffic displays (if equipped);

4) turn on all aircraft exterior lights (commensurate with appropriate operating limitations);

5) maintain the last assigned speed and level for a period of 60 minutes following the aircraft's failure to report its position over a compulsory reporting point (including ADS-C flights), and thereafter adjust speed and altitude in accordance with the filed flight plan;

Note.— In airspace where the strategic lateral offset procedure (SLOP) has been authorized, aircraft experiencing communication failure may also elect to initiate SLOP in accordance with State AIP, including an offset of 1.8 or 3.7 km (1 nm or 2 nm) right of track.

6) Upon exiting oceanic airspace, conform to the relevant State procedures and regulations.

United States Exceptions

[14 CFR 91, §91.185]

(a) General. Unless otherwise authorized by ATC, each pilot who has two-way radio communications failure when operating under IFR shall comply with the rules of this section.

(b) VFR conditions. If the failure occurs in VFR conditions, or if VFR conditions are encountered after the failure, each pilot shall continue the flight under VFR and land as soon as practicable.

(c) IFR conditions. If the failure occurs in IFR conditions, or if paragraph (b) of this section cannot be complied with, each pilot shall continue the flight according to the following:

(1) Route.

(i) By the route assigned in the last ATC clearance received;

(ii) If being radar vectored, by the direct route from the point of radio failure to the fix, route, or airway specified in the vector clearance;

(iii) In the absence of an assigned route, by the route that ATC has advised may be expected in a further clearance; or

(iv) In the absence of an assigned route or a route that ATC has advised may be expected in a further clearance, by the route filed in the flight plan.

(2) Altitude. At the highest of the following altitudes or flight levels for the route segment being flown:

(i) The altitude or flight level assigned in the last ATC clearance received;

(ii) The minimum altitude (converted, if appropriate, to minimum flight level as prescribed in §91.121(c)) for IFR operations; or

(iii) The altitude or flight level ATC has advised may be expected in a further clearance.

(3) Leave clearance limit.

(i) When the clearance limit is a fix from which an approach begins, commence descent or descent and approach as close as possible to the expect-further-clearance time if one has been received, or if one has not been received, as close as possible to the estimated time of arrival as calculated from the filed or amended (with ATC) estimated time en route.

(ii) If the clearance limit is not a fix from which an approach begins, leave the clearance limit at the expect-further-clearance time if one has been received, or if none has been received, upon arrival over the clearance limit, and proceed to a fix from which an approach begins and commence descent or descent and approach as close as possible to the estimated time of arrival as calculated from the filed or amended (with ATC) estimated time en route.

Country and Airport Exceptions

Individual countries and even airports within the country may have their own peculiar routings and procedures to be used in the event of lost communications. Your Jeppesen manuals are your best source for this information but the location of the lost communications information is not consistent. You may find it on the individual airport briefing pages, the arrival/ departure pages, the approach charts, or in the text pages. Among the text pages, you need to look at the ATC and Emergency pages.

Chapter 3

Loss of Long Range Navigation

*T*he *ICAO rules for what you need to navigate are given in ICAO Annex 6 - Operation of Aircraft and are summarized below. The ICAO procedures for "loss of, or significant reduction in, the required navigation capability when operating in an airspace where the navigation performance accuracy is prerequisite to the safe conduct of flight operations" are contained in ICAO Document 4444, Amendment 2 § 15.2.1 and summarized in Book VI, Chapter 1.*

North Atlantic exceptions to these procedures are contained in ICAO Document 7030 for various regions and in the ICAO NAT Doc 007, North Atlantic Operations and Airspace Manual for MNPS airspace. The North Atlantic exceptions are also provided, below. There are also other exceptions throughout the world that you can theoretically get from ICAO Doc 7030, but that document is rarely up-to-date. A snapshot of what the most recent version, as of 2015, is included below. You should also make liberal use of your Jeppesen Airway Manual state pages and NOTAMS.

ICAO Operation of Aircraft Rules

[ICAO Annex 6 - Operation of Aircraft - Part 1]

7.2.1 An aeroplane shall be provided with navigation equipment which will enable it to proceed:

a.   in accordance with its operational flight plan; and

b.   in accordance with the requirements of air traffic services;

except when, if not so precluded by the appropriate authority, navigation for flights under the visual flight rules is accomplished by visual reference to landmarks.

7.2.2 For operations where a navigation specification for performance-based navigation has been prescribed, an aeroplane shall, in addition to the requirements specified in 7.2.1:

a.   be provided with navigation equipment which will enable it to operate in accordance with the prescribed navigation specification(s); and

b.   be authorized by the State of the Operator for such operations.

Note.— Information on performance-based navigation, and guidance concerning the implementation and operational approval process, are contained in the Performance-based Navigation (PBN) Manual (Doc 9613). This document also contains a comprehensive list of references to other documents produced by States and international bodies concerning navigation systems.

7.2.3 For flights in defined portions of airspace where, based on Regional Air Navigation Agreement, minimum navigation performance specifications (MNPS) are prescribed, an aeroplane shall be provided with navigation equipment which:

a.   continuously provides indications to the flight crew of adherence to or departure from track to the required degree of accuracy at any point along that track; and

b.   has been authorized by the State of the Operator for the MNPS operations concerned.

Note.— The prescribed minimum navigation performance specifications and the procedures governing their application are published in the Regional Supplementary Procedures (Doc 7030).

7.2.4 For flights in defined portions of airspace where, based on Regional Air Navigation Agreement, a reduced vertical separation minimum (RVSM) of 300 m (1,000 ft) is applied between FL 290 and FL 410 inclusive, an aeroplane:

a.   shall be provided with equipment which is capable of:

    1.   indicating to the flight crew the flight level being flown;

    2.   automatically maintaining a selected flight level;

    3.   providing an alert to the flight crew when a deviation occurs from the selected flight level. The threshold for the alert shall not exceed ± 90 m (300 ft); and

    4.   automatically reporting pressure-altitude;

b.   shall be authorized by the State of the Operator for operation in the airspace concerned; and

c.   shall demonstrate a vertical navigation performance in accordance with Appendix 4.

7.2.9 The aeroplane shall be sufficiently provided with navigation equipment to ensure that, in the event of the failure of one item of equipment at any stage of the flight, the remaining equipment will enable the aeroplane to navigate in accordance with 7.2.1 and, where applicable, 7.2.2, 7.2.3 and 7.2.4.

Note.— Guidance material relating to aircraft equipment necessary for flight in airspace where RVSM is applied is contained in the Manual on Implementation of a 300 m (1,000 ft) Vertical Separation Minimum Between FL 290 and FL 410 Inclusive (Doc 9574).

Exceptions: MNPS Airspace

[ICAO NAT Doc 007, ¶12.1.2] For unrestricted operation in MNPS Airspace an approved aircraft must be equipped with a minimum of two fully serviceable LRNSs. MNPS approved aircraft which have suffered any equipment failures prior to NAT entry that result in only a single LRNS remaining serviceable may still be flight planned and flown through the MNPS Airspace but only on specified routes established for this purpose.

[ICAO NAT Doc 007, ¶12.1.3] If after takeoff, abnormal navigation indications relating to INS or IRS systems occur, they should be analysed to discover their cause. Unless the flight can proceed safely using alternative approved navigation sources only, the pilot should consider landing at the nearest appropriate airfield to allow the problem to be fully investigated, using technical assistance if necessary. Under no circumstances should a flight continue into oceanic (MNPS) Airspace with unresolved navigation system errors, or with errors which have been established to have been caused by inertial platform misalignment or initial position insertion error.

Methods of Determining which System is Faulty

[ICAO NAT Doc 007, ¶12.1.6] With only two systems on board, identifying the defective unit can be difficult. If such a situation does arise in oceanic airspace any or all of the following actions should be considered:

a.   checking malfunction codes for indication of unserviceability

b.   obtaining a fix. It may be possible to use the following:

1. the weather radar (range marks and relative bearing lines) to determine the position relative to an identifiable landmark such as an island; or

2. the ADF to obtain bearings from a suitable long-range NDB, in which case magnetic variation at the position of the aircraft should be used to convert the RMI bearings to true; or

3. if within range, a VOR, in which case the magnetic variation at the VOR location should be used to convert the radial to a true bearing (except when flying in the Canadian Northern Domestic Airspace where VOR bearings may be oriented with reference to true as opposed to magnetic north).

c. contacting a nearby aircraft on VHF, and comparing information on spot wind, or ground speed and drift.

d. if such assistance is not available, and as a last resort, the flight plan wind speed and direction for the current DR position of the aircraft, can be compared with that from navigation system outputs.

Action if the Faulty System Cannot be Identified

[ICAO NAT Doc 007, ¶12.1.7] Occasions may still arise when distance or cross track differences develop between systems, but the crew cannot determine which system is at fault. The majority of operators feel that the procedure most likely to limit gross tracking errors under such circumstances is to fly the aircraft half way between the cross track differences as long as the uncertainty exists. In such instances, ATC should be advised that the flight is experiencing navigation difficulties so that appropriate separation can be effected if necessary.

Guidance on What Constitutes a Failed System

[ICAO NAT Doc 007, ¶12.1.8] Operations or navigation manuals should include guidelines on how to decide when a navigation system should be considered to have failed, e.g. failures may be indicated by a red warning light, or by self diagnosis indications, or by an error over a known position exceeding the value agreed between an operator and its certifying authority. As a generalisation, if there is a difference greater than 15 nm between two aircraft navigation systems (or between the three systems if it is not possible to detect which are the most reliable) it is advisable to split the difference between the readings when determining the aircraft's position. However, if the disparity exceeds 25 nm one or more of the navigation systems should be regarded as having failed, in which case ATC should be notified.

Loss of Navigation/FMS Capability

[ICAO NAT Doc 007, ¶12.2.1] Some aircraft carry triplex equipment (3 LRNSs) and hence if one system fails, even before takeoff, the two basic requirements for MNPS Airspace operations may still be met and the flight can proceed normally. The following guidance is offered for aircraft having state approval for unrestricted operations in MNPS airspace and which are equipped with only two operational LRNSs.

One System Fails Before Takeoff [With only one system remaining]

[ICAO NAT Doc 007, ¶12.2.2] The pilot must consider:

a. delaying departure until repair is possible;

b. obtaining a clearance above or below MNPS Airspace;

c. planning on the special routes known as the 'Blue Spruce' Routes, which have been established for use by aircraft suffering partial loss of navigation capability (Note: As indicated in Chapter 1, these routes may also be flown by aircraft approved for NAT MNPSA operations but equipped with only a single LRNS).

These Blue Spruce Routes are listed in ICAO NAT Doc 007 and your Jeppesen Airway Manual Atlantic Planning Charts.

d. The following special routes may also be flown without an LRNS (i.e. with only short-range navigation equipment such as VOR, DME, ADF), but it must be noted that State approval for operation within MNPS Airspace via these routes is still necessary:

    1. VALDI - MY (Myggenes) - ING – KEF (G3)

    2. GONUT - MY (Myggenes) (G11)

e. Such use of the foregoing routes is subject to the following conditions:

    1. sufficient navigation capability remains to ensure that MNPS accuracy and the ICAO Annex 6 (Part I para 7.2.9 and Part II para 2.5.2.9) requirements for redundancy can be met by relying on short-range navaids;

    2. a revised flight plan is filed with the appropriate ATS unit;

3.　　an appropriate ATC clearance is obtained.

One System Fails Before the OCA Boundary is Reached [With only one system remaining]

[ICAO NAT Doc 007, ¶12.2.4] The pilot must consider:

- landing at a suitable aerodrome before the boundary or returning to the aerodrome of departure;
- diverting via one of the special routes described previously;
- obtaining a re-clearance above or below MNPS airspace.

One System Fails After the OCA Boundary is Crossed [With only one system remaining]

[ICAO NAT Doc 007, ¶12.2.5] Once the aircraft has entered oceanic airspace, the pilot should normally continue to operate the aircraft in accordance with the Oceanic Clearance already received, appreciating that the reliability of the total navigation system has been significantly reduced.

1.　　The pilot should however,

　　a.　　assess the prevailing circumstances (e.g. performance of the remaining system, remaining portion of the flight in MNPS Airspace, etc.);

　　b.　　prepare a proposal to ATC with respect to the prevailing circumstances (e.g. request clearance above or below MNPS Airspace, turn-back, obtain clearance to fly along one of the special routes, etc.);

　　c.　　advise and consult with ATC as to the most suitable action;

　　d.　　obtain appropriate re-clearance prior to any deviation from the last acknowledged Oceanic Clearance.

2.　　When the flight continues in accordance with its original clearance (especially if the distance ahead within MNPS Airspace is significant), the pilot should begin a careful monitoring programme:

　　a.　　to take special care in the operation of the remaining system bearing in mind that routine methods of error checking are no longer available;

　　b.　　to check the main and standby compass systems frequently against the information which is still available;

c.   to check the performance record of the remaining equipment and if doubt arises regarding its performance and/or reliability, the following procedures should be considered:

i.   attempting visual sighting of other aircraft or their contrails, which may provide a track indication;

ii.   calling the appropriate OAC for information on other aircraft adjacent to the aircraft's estimated position and/or calling on VHF to establish contact with such aircraft (preferably same track/level) to obtain from them information which could be useful. e.g. drift, groundspeed, wind details.

The Remaining System Fails After Entering MNPS Airspace

[ICAO NAT Doc 007, ¶12.2.8 The pilot should:

a.   immediately notify ATC;

b.   make best use of procedures specified above relating to attempting visual sightings and establishing contact on VHF with adjacent aircraft for useful information;

c.   keep a special look-out for possible conflicting aircraft, and make maximum use of exterior lights;

d.   if no instructions are received from ATC within a reasonable period consider climbing or descending 500 feet, broadcasting action on 121.5 MHz and advising ATC as soon as possible.

Note: This procedure also applies when a single remaining system gives an indication of degradation of performance, or neither system fails completely but the system indications diverge widely and the defective system cannot be determined.

Complete Failure of Navigation Systems Computers

[ICAO NAT Doc 007, ¶12.2.9] A characteristic of the navigation computer system is that the computer element might fail, and thus deprive the aircraft of steering guidance and the indication of position relative to cleared track, but the basic outputs of the IRS (LAT/LONG, Drift and Groundspeed) are left unimpaired. A typical drill to minimise the effects of a total navigation computer system failure is suggested below. It requires comprehensive use of the plotting chart.

a.   use the basic IRS/GPS outputs to adjust heading to maintain mean track and to calculate ETAs.

b.   draw the cleared route on a chart and extract mean true tracks between waypoints.

c.   at intervals of not more than 15 minutes plot position (LAT/LONG) on the chart and adjust heading to regain track.

Exceptions (Other)

Theoretically, you should be able to examine ICAO Doc 7030 to come up with regional differences and call it good. Unfortunately this document is rarely up to date and you should closely study the state pages in your Jeppesen Airway Manual as well as any NOTAMS. If you do examine "Chapter 9. Special Procedures" for each region in ICAO Doc 7030 as of 2015, here is a summary of what you will find:

- *EUR (European) — If the aircraft cannot meet the navigation route or procedure requirements, a revised clearance should be obtained using conventional navigation aids or radar vectors. If still on the ground, the aircraft may be permitted to fly to the nearest suitable aerodrome where repairs can be made.*

- *MID/ASIA (Middle East/Asia) — If the aircraft has a failure to below RNP 5 or is unable to continue in accordance with its current clearance, a revised clearance shall be requested.*

- *NAT (North Atlantic) — An aircraft compelled to descend through MNPS airspace should plan on descending below FL280, should descend through the tracks on a course midway between parallel tracks, and contact ATC as soon as practicable.*

Chapter 4

Loss of RVSM Capability in Oceanic Airspace

L osing your ability to keep the airplane precisely on altitude is becoming a bigger deal every day, as the skies are becoming more tightly packed. Because each situation is likely to be unique, there are no cut and dried rules that always apply. ICAO contingency procedures are given in ICAO Doc 9574, North Atlantic procedures are given in ICAO Nat Doc 001, and other regional differences are given in ICAO Doc 7030. Everything is summarized here. You should also refer to the Special Procedures for In-flight Contingencies in Oceanic Airspace, given in Part VI, Chapter 1.

ICAO Contingency Procedures

[ICAO Doc 9574, ¶5.1.1 h)] The following contingency procedures should be adhered to after entering RVSM airspace:

1. the pilot should notify ATC of contingencies (equipment failures, weather conditions) in which the ability to maintain CFL is affected and coordinate a plan of action;

2. equipment failures should be notified to ATC. Some examples are:

    a. failure of all automatic altitude-keeping devices on board the aircraft;

    b. loss of redundancy of altimetry systems, or any part of these, on board the aircraft;

    c. failure of all altitude-reporting transponders;

    d. loss of thrust on an engine necessitating descent; and

    e. any other equipment failure affecting the ability to maintain CFL;

3. the pilot should notify ATC when encountering severe turbulence; and

4. if unable to notify ATC and obtain an ATC clearance prior to deviating from the assigned CFL, the pilot should follow established contingency procedures as defined by the region of operation and obtain ATC clearance as soon as possible.

North Atlantic Procedures

Contingencies Within MNPS Airspace

[ICAO Nat Doc 001, ¶3.10] This guidance material should enable the pilot and the air traffic controller to better understand what actions to take under certain conditions of equipment failure and during encounters with turbulence. A pilot should notify ATC of any contingency that affects the ability of the aircraft to maintain the CFL (particularly in RVSM Airspace). Together they should coordinate a plan of action. Examples of notifiable equipment failures are:

- failure of all automatic AKDs [Altitude Keeping Devices] onboard the aircraft;
- full or partial loss of redundancy of altimetry systems aboard the aircraft;
- loss of thrust on an engine necessitating descent; or
- any other equipment failure affecting the ability to maintain CFL;

However, it is recognized that both a pilot and controller will use their judgement to determine the action most appropriate to any given situation. For certain equipment failures, the safest course of action may be for the aircraft to continue in MNPS Airspace while the pilot and controller take precautionary action to protect separation. For extreme cases of equipment failure, the safest course of action may be for the aircraft to leave MNPS Airspace after obtaining a revised ATC clearance. If unable to obtain such prior clearance then the pilot should execute a contingency manoeuvre and leave the assigned route or track, as specified in the 'NAT' Section, of the ICAO "Regional Supplementary Procedures" (Doc.7030).

Contingencies Within RVSM Airspace

[ICAO Nat Doc 001, ¶3.11] The following guidance on contingency procedures to adopt when encountering loss of height keeping equipment, should not be interpreted in any way that prejudices the final authority and responsibility of the pilot-in-command for the safe operation of the aeroplane.

All Automatic Altitude Keeping Devices Fail

1. If all automatic AKDs fail (e.g. autopilot altitude hold) then the pilot should:

    a. maintain CFL - if necessary through manual control;

    b. watch for conflicting traffic;

    c. if applicable, alert nearby aircraft by:

        i. making maximum use of exterior lights; and

        ii. broadcasting position, flight level, and immediate intentions, on frequency 121.5 MHz; and

    d. notify ATC of the failure and state the intended course of action. Possible courses of action include:

        i. continuing in RVSM Airspace provided that the aircraft can maintain the CFL; or

        ii. requesting ATC clearance to climb above or descend below RVSM Airspace, if the aircraft cannot maintain the assigned flight level and ATC cannot establish increased vertical, longitudinal or lateral separation; or

        iii. executing the appropriate contingency manoeuvre specified in ICAO Doc.7030 to leave the assigned route or track if prior ATC clearance cannot be obtained and the aircraft cannot maintain the assigned flight level.

2. ATC should take the following action:

    a. obtain the pilot's intentions;

    b. if the pilot intends to continue in RVSM Airspace, consider establishing increased vertical, longitudinal or lateral separation;

    c. pass traffic information to the pilot;

    d. if the pilot requests clearance to exit RVSM Airspace, accommodate that request as expeditiously as possible;

     e.   if increased vertical, longitudinal or lateral separation cannot be established and it is not possible to comply with the pilot's request for clearance to exit MNPS Airspace, then to notify other aircraft in the vicinity and continue to monitor the situation; and

     f.   advise adjacent ATC facilities/sectors, of the situation.

Loss of Redundancy in the Primary Altimetry Systems

1.   The pilot should take the following action, if the remaining altimetry system is functioning normally:

     a.   couple that system to the AKD;

     b.   notify ATC of the loss of redundancy; and

     c.   maintain increased vigilance regarding altitude-keeping.

2.   If the pilot reports that the remaining system is functioning normally the ATC controller should acknowledge the situation and continue to monitor progress.

All Primary Altimetry Systems Fail or are Considered Unreliable

1.   The pilot should:

     a.   maintain altitude - if necessary by reference to the standby altimeter (should the aircraft be so equipped);

     b.   alert nearby aircraft by:

          i.   making maximum use of exterior lights;

          ii.   broadcasting position, flight level and intentions on frequency 121.5 MHz.

     c.   notify ATC of the inability to meet RVSM performance requirements, consider declaring an emergency and request clearance to exit MNPS Airspace.

     d.   if unable to obtain ATC clearance in a timely manner, to execute appropriate contingency procedures, as specified in ICAO Doc.7030, for leaving the assigned route or track and descending below MNPS Airspace (if operationally feasible); or

     e.   if not operationally feasible to execute the appropriate contingency procedures and then continue to alert nearby aircraft and coordinate with ATC.

2.   ATC should take the following action:

    a.   when notified by the pilot that the aircraft cannot meet RVSM performance requirements, attempt to establish increased vertical, longitudinal or lateral separation;

    b.   pass traffic information to the pilot;

    c.   if unable to establish increased separation, to consider other options, such as advising the pilot of traffic information and requesting the pilot's intentions;

    d.   if the pilot requests clearance to exit RVSM Airspace, then to accommodate the request as expeditiously as possible; and

    e.   if notified by the pilot of the loss of all acceptable altimetry systems, to notify the pilot of traffic information, advise aircraft in the vicinity and monitor the situation.

Primary Altimeters Diverge by More than 60 m (200 ft)

1.   The pilot should:

    a.   attempt to determine the defective system through established trouble-shooting procedures and/or compare primary altimeter displays with those of the standby altimeter (as corrected from correction cards, if applicable);

    b.   if the defective system can be determined, couple the functioning altimetry system to the AKD; or

    c.   if the defective system cannot be determined, follow the guidance above regarding failure or unreliable altimeter indications of all primary altimeters, in conjunction as appropriate with ATC.

Other Regional Differences

The basic general procedures are outlined below. Consult AIPs, Jeppesen State Pages, and ICAO Document 7030.

[AC 91-85, Appendix 5]

- Africa / Indian Ocean: standard contingency procedures [ICAO Document 7030, AFI, Paragraph 9.5]

- Caribbean: standard contingency procedures [ICAO Document 7030, CAR, Paragraph 9.5]

- Europe: If vertical navigation performance requirements cannot be maintained, pilots must obtain a revised ATC clearance prior to initiating and deviation from the cleared route and/or flight level, whenever possible. Pilots will inform ATC if severe turbulence impacts an aircraft's ability to maintain its cleared flight level, ATC will either establish horizontal separation or an increased vertical separation. [ICAO Document 7030, EUR, Paragraph 9.5]

- Middle East / Asia: Pilots will inform ATC if severe turbulence impacts an aircraft's ability to maintain its cleared flight level, ATC will either establish horizontal separation or an increased vertical separation. [ICAO Document 7030, MID/ASIA, Paragraph 9.5]

- North America: standard contingency procedures [ICAO Document 7030, NAM, Paragraph 9.5]

- North Atlantic: standard contingency procedures [ICAO Document 7030, NAT, Paragraph 9.5] as well as the specific instructions given in ICAO Nat Doc 001, and summarized above.

- Pacific: standard contingency procedures [ICAO Document 7030, PAC, Paragraph 9.5]

- South America: standard contingency procedures [ICAO Document 7030, SAM, Paragraph 9.5]

Example Scenarios

Appendix 5 of AC 91-85 Authorization of Aircraft and Operators for Flight in Reduced Vertical Separation Minimum Airspace provides several scenarios to summarize pilot actions to mitigate the potential for conflict with other aircraft in certain contingency situations.

Scenario 1 — "Unsure"

[AC 91-85, Appendix 5, ¶5.b.(1)]

The pilot is: 1) unsure of the vertical position of the aircraft due to the loss or degradation of all primary altimetry systems, or 2) unsure of the capability to maintain CFL due to turbulence or loss of all automatic altitude control systems.

1. Maintain CFL while evaluating the situation;

2. Watch for conflicting traffic both visually and by ACAS;

3. If considered necessary, alert nearby aircraft by:

    a. Making maximum use of exterior lights;

    b. Broadcasting position, FL, and intentions on 121.5 MHz (as a back-up, the VHF inter-pilot air-to-air frequency may be used).

4. Notify ATC of the situation and intended course of action. Possible courses of action include:

    a. Maintaining the CFL and route provided that ATC can provide lateral, longitudinal or conventional vertical separation.

    b. Requesting ATC clearance to climb above or descend below RVSM airspace if the aircraft cannot maintain CFL and ATC cannot establish adequate separation from other aircraft.

    c. Executing the ICAO Doc. 4444 contingency maneuver to offset from the assigned track and FL, if ATC clearance cannot be obtained and the aircraft cannot maintain CFL. ["Quad Four Maneuver" shown below]

Scenario 2 — Bad Altimeter

[AC 91-85, Appendix 5, ¶5.b.(2)] There is a failure or loss of accuracy of one primary altimetry system (e.g., greater than 200 ft difference between primary altimeters).

The pilot should cross check standby altimeter, confirm the accuracy of a primary altimeter system and notify ATC of the loss of redundancy. If unable to confirm primary altimeter system accuracy, follow pilot actions listed in the preceding scenario.

Scenario 3 — All Altitude Control Systems Fail

[AC 91-85, Appendix 5, ¶6.a.(1)] If all automatic altitude control systems fail, the pilot should:

1. Maintain CFL while evaluating the situation;

2. Evaluate the aircraft's capability to maintain altitude through manual control;

3. Watch for conflicting traffic both visually and by ACAS;

4. If considered necessary, alert nearby aircraft by:

   a. Making maximum use of exterior lights;

   b. Broadcasting position, FL, and intentions on 121.5 MHz (as a back-up, the VHF inter-pilot air-to-air frequency may be used).

5. Notify ATC of the situation and intended course of action. Possible courses of action include:

   a. Maintaining the CFL and route provided that ATC can provide lateral, longitudinal or conventional vertical separation.

   b. Requesting ATC clearance to climb above or descend below RVSM airspace if the aircraft cannot maintain CFL and ATC cannot establish adequate separation from other aircraft.

   c. Executing the ICAO Doc. 4444 contingency maneuver to offset from the assigned track and FL, if ATC clearance cannot be obtained and the aircraft cannot maintain CFL. ["Quad Four Maneuver" shown below]

Scenario 4 — Loss of Redundancy in Primary Altimetry Systems

[AC 91-85, Appendix 5, ¶6.b.(2)] If there is a loss of accuracy in primary altimetry systems and the remaining altimetry system is functioning normally, the pilot should couple that system to the automatic altitude control system, notify ATC of the loss of redundancy and maintain vigilance of altitude keeping.

Scenario 5 — All Primary Altimetry Systems are Considered Unreliable or Fail

[AC 91-85, Appendix 5, ¶6.b.(3)] If all primary altimetry systems fail, the pilot should:

1. Maintain CFL by reference to the standby altimeter;

2. Alert nearby aircraft by:

   a. Making maximum use of exterior lights;

232

b. Broadcasting position, FL, and intentions on 121.5 MHz (as a back-up, the VHF inter-pilot air-to-air frequency may be used).

3. Consider declaring an emergency. Notify ATC of the situation and intended course of action. Possible courses of action include:

a. Maintaining CFL and route provided that ATC can provide lateral, longitudinal or conventional vertical separation.

b. Requesting ATC clearance to climb above or descend below RVSM airspace if the aircraft cannot maintain CFL and ATC cannot establish adequate separation from other aircraft.

c. Executing the ICAO Doc. 4444 contingency maneuver to off-set from the assigned track and FL, if ATC clearance cannot be obtained and the aircraft cannot maintain CFL. ["Quad Four Maneuver" shown below]

Scenario 6 — Divergence

[AC 91-85, Appendix 5, ¶6.d.] If the primary altimeters diverge by more than 200 ft (60 m), the pilot should:

1. Attempt to determine the defective system through established trouble-shooting procedures and/or comparing the primary altimeter display to the standby altimeter (as corrected by the correction cards, if required).

2. If the defective system can be determined, couple the functioning altimeter system to the altitude keeping device.

3. If the defective system cannot be determined, follow the guidance in Scenario 5 for failure or unreliable altimeter indications of all primary altimeters.

Scenario 7 — Turbulence

[AC 91-85, Appendix 5, ¶6.e.]

In the event of turbulence (greater than moderate) which the pilot believes will impact the aircraft's capability to maintain FL, the pilot should:

1. Watch for conflicting traffic both visually and by ACAS;

2. If considered necessary, alert nearby aircraft by:

a. Making maximum use of exterior lights;

      b.   Broadcasting position, FL, and intentions on 121.5 MHz (as a back-up, the VHF inter-pilot air-to-air frequency may be used).

3.   Notify ATC of the situation and intended course of action. Possible courses of action include:

      a.   Maintaining the CFL and route provided that ATC can provide lateral, longitudinal or conventional vertical separation.

      b.   Requesting ATC clearance to climb above or descend below RVSM airspace if the aircraft cannot maintain CFL and ATC cannot establish adequate separation from other aircraft.

      c.   Executing the ICAO Doc. 4444 contingency maneuver to offset from the assigned track and FL, if ATC clearance cannot be obtained and the aircraft cannot maintain CFL. ["Quad Four Maneuver" shown below]

The "Quad Four Maneuver"

Some people call this the "Quad Four Maneuver" since it came from ICAO Doc 4444; it is as good a name as any, I suppose. (The exact language is shown in Part VI, Chapter 1)

Regardless of what you call it, you should have it memorized:

- *Turn 45° away from track,*

- *Pick a direction based on alternates, nearby tracks, SLOP, and desired altitude,*

- *Obtain a 15 nm offset,*

- *Pick an altitude 500 ft off if at or below FL 410, 1000 ft if above,*

- *Broadcast to ATC and nearby aircraft*

- *Light up the airplane.*

What about a 180° turn back to where you started? You can do that, but which way you going to turn? Here is some food for thought. We tried this in the G-550 simulator: M0.83, FL 430, lose an engine, reverse course. It took 4 minutes to turn 180° and 22 miles turn diameter.

Chapter 5

Volcanic Ash

In 1982, when British Airways 9 flew through a volcanic ash cloud and flamed out all four engines, the dangers of volcanic ash were undocumented. Seven years later, when KLM 867 repeated the incident, it was clear more work was needed to detect and avoid volcanic ash. The ash is dry so does not show up on radar. It is also fine, so when it comes in contact with the airplane the static electricity makes radio communications difficult. It is abrasive and can damage windshields to the point visibility is impaired. Once the particles go through the hot section of the engine they become molten and finally they recool and collect on engine turbine blades, solidifying to the point where air flow is fouled and the engines shut down. Fortunately, in every recorded case once the aircraft descends and the engines cool, the solidified ash tends to break away and the engines can be relit.

I like the Alaska Airlines Procedures for Operating in Volcanic Ash Conditions:

- *When in doubt, don't fly.*
- *Use facts and data.*
- *Identify the location of both the ash and clear areas.*
- *Stay focused.*

Gulfstream adds this cheerful note: "Has significant financial implications, may not be known until major inspection, usually considered an Act of God and is not covered by insurance."

An Overview of the Threat

[Aeronautical Information Manual, ¶7-5-9]

a.   Severe volcanic eruptions which send ash and sulphur dioxide (SO2) gas into the upper atmosphere occur somewhere around the world several times each year. Flying into a volcanic ash cloud can be exceedingly dangerous. A B747–200 lost all four engines after such an encounter and a B747–400 had the same nearly catastrophic experience. Piston–powered aircraft are less likely to lose power but severe damage is almost certain to ensue after an encounter with a volcanic ash cloud which is only a few hours old.

b.   Most important is to avoid any encounter with volcanic ash. The ash plume may not be visible, especially in instrument conditions or at night; and even if visible, it is difficult to distinguish visually between an ash cloud and an ordinary weather cloud. Volcanic ash clouds are not displayed on airborne or ATC radar. The pilot must rely on reports from air traffic controllers and other pilots to determine the location of the ash cloud and use that information to remain well clear of the area. Additionally, the presence of a sulphur-like odor throughout the cabin may indicate the presence of SO2 emitted by volcanic activity, but may or may not indicate the presence of volcanic ash. Every attempt should be made to remain on the upwind side of the volcano.

History of Mishaps

There have been nine encounters with Volcanic Ash of transport category aircraft between 1953 and 2009, according to the USGS:

1980 May 25 — L-100, 2 of 4 engines shut down, Mount St. Helens, USA

1982 Jun 24 — B-747 (British Airways 9), 4 of 4 engines failed, Galunggung, Indonesia

1982 Jul 13 — B-747, 3 of 4 engines failed, Galunggung, Indonesia

1989 Dec 15 — B-747, 4 of 4 engines failed, Redoubt, USA

1991 Jun 17 — B-747, 2 of 4 engines failed, Pinatubo, Philippines

1991 Jun 17 — DC-10, 1 of 3 engines failed, Pinatubo, Philippines

1991 Jun 27 — DC-10, 2 of 3 engines failed, Unzen, Japan

2001 Jul 29 — B-767, 1 of 2 engines failed, Soufriere Hilles, Lesser Antilles

2006 Jul 17 — Gulfstream II, 2 of 2 engines failed, Papua New Guinea

The USGS report acknowledges that this list comprises a minimum number, since these reports are not made consistently.

Severity of the Threat

[USGS, Table 1]

Class 0	Sulfur odor noted in cabin. Anomalous atmospheric haze observed. Electrostatic discharge (St. Elmo's fire) on windshield, nose, or engine cowls. Ash reported or suspected by flight crew but no other effects or damage noted.
Class 1	Light dust observed in cabin. Ash deposits on exterior of aircraft. Fluctuations in exhaust gas temperature with return to normal values.
Class 2	Heavy cabin dust. Contamination of air handling and air conditioning systems requiring use of oxygen. Abrasion damage to exterior surfaces, engine inlet, and compressor fan blades. Pitting, frosting, or breaking of windscreen or windows. Minor plugging of pitot-static system, insufficient to affect instrument readings. Deposition of ash in engine.
Class 3	Vibration or surging of engine(s). Plugging of pitot-static system to give erroneous instrument readings. Contamination of engine oil or hydraulic system fluids. Damage to electrical or computer systems. Engine damage.
Class 4	Temporary engine failure requiring in-flight restart of engine.
Class 5	Engine failure or other damage leading to crash.

The USGS estimates there have been 94 known ash encounters of severity 1 to 4. Three were severe enough to involve the loss of all engines and 26 created severe damage.

Engine Failures

[USGS, pg. 3] Melting and resolidification of ash within jet turbine engines has been identified as the primary mechanism responsible for engine failure in an ash encounter. The melting temperature of the magmatic silicate glass in ash is lower than the operating temperatures of modern turbine engines; consequently, ingested ash particles can melt in hot sections and then accumulate as re-solidified deposits in cooler parts of the engine, causing ignition flame-out and engine shutdown. In two encounters, climb out from the cloud at maximum thrust was identified as a key operational condition for engine shutdown. When engine power increased, more ash-laden air was ingested by the jet turbines and combustion temperatures were raised; thus, conditions favorable for substantial melting of ash particles were met. This lesson has been incorporated into guidance to pilots about recommended actions to take during an encounter.

[USGS, pg. 5] [The 17 June 1991 incident] is notable in that prolonged exposure to dilute ash may have contributed to significant damage. That incident involved the same aircraft (a B747–200B) as incident 1991–14; both flights were operating between South Africa and Southeast Asia in the aftermath of the June 1991 eruption of Mount Pinatubo. In both encounters, the aircraft was operating in airspace at distances in excess of 500 km from the volcano. In [the 15 June 1991 incident], the crew noted static discharge lasting approximately an hour, but all engine parameters were normal during flight, and no problems were experienced with any of the aircraft systems. Two days later, the aircraft flew for several hours through an area coincident with remote-sensing evidence of an ash cloud before one engine lost power and a second engine was shut down by the crew. During descent, the engine that had been shut down was restarted, and the aircraft made a successful landing. These events raise the possibility of significant damage from cumulative exposure to dilute ash.

[USGS, pg. 5] The 2006 Gulfstream II incident is notable for involving a different mechanism for engine shutdown than melted ash. The aircraft was flying over Papua New Guinea at 11.9 km (39,000 ft) in apparently clear air with no ash or sulfurous odors noted by the cockpit crew. Between 39,000 ft and descent to 24,000, both engines failed and then were restarted; the aircraft landed safely. The operator and engine manufacturer conducted a thorough investigation, including borescope analysis of the engine and fuel analysis. The manufacturer concluded that a cylindrical filter in each fuel-flow regulator may have become blocked by volcanic ash, which at that altitude could have caused loss of fuel flow and thus engine shutdown; on descent, the increasing pressure would have substantially cleared the filter and allowed the engine to restart. The likely source of the ash was an eruption of Manam Volcano in Papua New Guinea.

Threat Areas

[ICAO Doc 9691, pg. I-i_1] The highest concentration of active volcanoes lies around the rim of the Pacific Ocean, the so-called "ring of fire", which stretches northwards, more or less continuously, along the western edge of South and North America, across the Aleutian and Kurile Island chains, down through Kamchatka, Japan and the Philippines and across Indonesia, Papua New Guinea and New Zealand to the islands of the South Pacific. Other active regions are to be found in Iceland, along the great rift valley in Central and East Africa, and in countries around the Mediterranean.

Volcanic Ash Characteristics

The Clouds

[ICAO Doc 9691, ¶2.2.1

The eruption column which results is usually divided into three dynamic regimes: "gas thrust", "convective thrust" and "umbrella region" (or "mushroom").

The gas thrust region is produced by the sudden decompression of superheated volatile constituents dissolved in the ascending magma. This produces a jet of fluids and pulverized rock material of extremely high kinetic energy at the mouth of the volcano vent, the speed of which in extreme cases could exceed 500 kt. Such exit vent speeds may reach supersonic speed depending on the ambient conditions at the time.

If insufficient air is entrained in the gas thrust region, the column remains denser than the surrounding atmosphere and, as the initial kinetic energy dissipates, the column collapses due to gravitation without forming a convective thrust region. The convective thrust region largely controls the ultimate height of the column and hence is critical to the eruption's potential concern to aviation. It is clear from the foregoing that the hotter the original jet of fluidized material at its

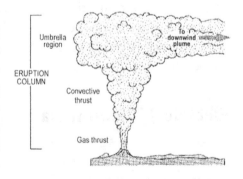

Figure: Three parts or regions from an eruption column, from ICAO Doc 9691, Figure 2-4.

239

release form the vent, the higher the thermal energy which can be carried through to the convective thrust region and the higher the column top.

The third dynamic region of the volcanic ash column is the "umbrella region," to top of the mushroom-like ash cloud as its ascent begins to slow in response to gravity and the temperature inversions at the tropopause, with the top spreading radially to begin and then predominantly in one or more particular directions in response to the upper winds at different levels of the atmosphere. This region of most concern to aviation because vast volumes of airspace at normal jet aircraft cruising level of 10 to 14 km (30,000 to 45,000 ft) become contaminated with high concentrations of volcanic ash.

The Ash

[ICAO Doc 9691, ¶4.1] Volcanic ash is mostly glass shards and pulverized rock, very abrasive and, being largely composed of siliceous materials, with a melting temperature below the operating temperature of jet engines at cruise thrust. The ash is accompanied by gaseous solutions of sulphur dioxide (sulphuric acid) and chlorine (hydrochloric acid). Given these stark facts, it is easy to imagine the serious hazard that volcanic ash poses to an aircraft which encounters it in the atmosphere. Volcanic ash damages the jet turbine engines, abrades cockpit windows, airframe and flight surfaces, clogs the pitot-static system, penetrates into air conditioning and equipment cooling systems and contaminates electrical and avionics units, fuel and hydraulic systems and cargo-hold smoke-detection systems. Moreover, the first two or three days following an explosive eruption are especially critical because high concentrations of ash comprising particles up to ~10 μm diameter could be encountered at cruise levels some considerable distance from the volcano. Beyond three days, it is assumed that if the ash is still visible by eye or from satellite data, it still presents a hazard to aircraft.

Electrical Phenomena

[ICAO Doc 9691, ¶2.3.1] The occurrence of lightning in volcanic ash columns has been reported since antiquity. Moreover, one of the prime means of recognizing that an aircraft has encountered volcanic ash is the static electricity discharge exhibited by St. Elmo's fire at point on the airframe and the glow inside the jet engines. The static electric charge on the aircraft also creates a "cocoon" effect which may cause a temporary deterioration, or even complete loss, of VHF or HF communications.

Effect on Jet Engines

[ICAO Doc 9691, ¶4.2]

There are basically three effects which contribute to the overall engine damage. The first, and most critical, is the fact that volcanic ash has a melting point below jet engine operating temperatures with thrust settings above idle. The ash is made up predominantly of silicates with a melting temperature of 1,100°C, while at normal thrust the operating temperature of jet engines is 1,400°C. The ash melts in the hot section of the engine and fuses on the high pressure nozzle guide vanes and turbine blades. This drastically reduces the high pressure turbine inlet guide-vane throat area causing the static burner pressure and compressor discharge pressure to increase rapidly which, in turn, causes engine surge. This effect alone can cause immediate thrust loss and possible engine flame-out.

During the strip-down inspections, the fused volcanic ash deposits on the high pressure nozzle guide vanes were found to be very brittle at room temperature and easily broke up and fell off the nozzle guide vanes. It seems clear that this can also happen when contaminated engines are shut down in flight and then restarted. The sudden thermal and pressure shocks of the ram air during the restart process, coupled with the cooling of the fused ash deposit when the engine is reduced to idle, seem to break off much of the deposit. Moreover, subsequent operation of the engines after restart, in the clearer air outside the ash cloud, also seems to further dislodge and evacuate some of the fused ash deposits.

The volcanic ash being abrasive also erodes compressor rotor paths and rotor blade tips (mostly high pressure section), causing loss of high pressure turbine efficiency and engine thrust. The erosion also results in a decrease in the engine stall margin. The main factors that affect the extent of the erosion of the compressor blades are the hardness of the volcanic ash, particle size and concentration, the ash particle impact velocity, and thrust setting and core protection. Although this abrasion effect takes longer than the melting fusion of volcanic ash to shut down an engine, the abrasion damage is permanent and irreversible. Reduction of engine thrust to idle slows the rate of erosion of the compressor blades but cannot eliminate it entirely while the engine is still ingesting air contaminated by volcanic ash.

In addition to the melting/fusing of the volcanic ash and the blade erosion problems referred to above, the ash can clog flow holes in the fuel and cooling systems, although these particular effects appear to be rather variable. In ground tests of jet engines subjected to forced volcanic ash ingestion, a deposition of black carbon-like material was found on the fuel nozzles. Analysis confirmed that the contaminating material was predominantly carbon, and although the main fuel nozzle appeared to remain clear, the swirl vanes which atomize the fuel were clogged. Such a condition would render engine restart very difficult if not impossible, because there seems to be no tendency for the material to break off during restart attempts.

Aviation Color Codes

GREEN	Volcano is in typical background, noneruptive state.
	Or, after a change from a higher level:
	Volcanic activity has ceased and volcano has returned to noneruptive background state
YELLOW	Volcano is exhibiting signs of elevated unrest above known background level.
	Or, after a change from a higher level:
	Volcanic activity has decreased significantly but continues to be closely monitored for possible renewed increase.
ORANGE	Volcano is exhibiting heightened or escalating unrest with increased potential of eruption, timeframe uncertain.
	Or:
	Eruption is underway with no or minor ash emissions [ash-plume height specified, if possible].
RED	Eruption is imminent with significant emission of volcanic ash into the atmosphere likely.
	Or:
	Eruption is underway or suspected with significant emission of volcanic ash into the atmosphere [ash-plume height specified, if possible].

Figure: Aviation color codes, from Alaska Volcano Plan, pg. 15.

Ash Encounter Indicators

[ICAO Doc 9974, ¶1.3 and 1.4]

In day visual meteorological conditions (VMC) a precursor to a volcanic ash encounter will likely be a visual indication of a volcanic ash cloud or haze. If a flight crew observes a cloud or haze suspected of containing volcanic ash they should be aware that a volcanic ash encounter is imminent and they should take action to avoid the contaminated airspace.

Indicators that an aircraft is encountering volcanic ash are related principally to the following:

- Odour. When encountering volcanic ash, flight crews usually notice a smoky or acrid odour that can smell like electrical smoke, burnt dust or sulphur.

- Haze. Most flight crews, as well as cabin crew or passengers, see a haze develop within the aircraft cockpit and/or cabin. Dust can settle on surfaces.

- Changing engine conditions. Surging, torching from the tailpipe, and flameouts can occur. Engine temperatures can change unexpectedly, and a white glow can appear at the engine inlet.

- Airspeed. If volcanic ash fouls the pitot tube, the indicated airspeed can decrease or fluctuate erratically.

- Pressurization. Cabin pressure can change, including possible loss of cabin pressurization.

- Static discharges. A phenomenon similar to St. Elmo's fire or glow can occur. In these instances, blue-coloured sparks can appear to flow up the outside of the windshield or a white glow can appear at the leading edges of the wings or at the front of the engine inlets.

Any of these indicators should suffice to alert the flight crew of an ash encounter, and appropriate action should be taken to vacate the contaminated airspace as safely and expeditiously as possible.

Pilot Procedures

[ICAO Doc 9691, ¶4.4]

1.   The foregoing analysis of the effect of volcanic ash on aircraft forms the basis for the procedures recommended for use by pilots whose aircraft inadvertently encounter a volcanic ash cloud.

    a.   In such circumstance, the following general procedures have been recommended:

        i.   immediately reduce thrust to idle. This will lower the exhaust-gas temperature (EGT), which in turn will reduce the fused ash build-up on the turbine blades and hot-section components. Volcanic ash can also cause rapid erosion and damage to the internal components of the engines;

        ii.   turn autothrottles off (if engaged). The autothrottles should be turned off to prevent the system from increasing thrust above idle. Due to the reduced surge margins, limit the number of thrust adjustments and make changes with slow and smooth thrust-lever movements;

        iii.   exit volcanic ash cloud as quickly as possible. Volcanic ash may extend for several hundred miles. The shortest distance/time out of the ash may require an immediate, descending 180-degree turn, terrain permitting. Setting climb thrust and attempting to climb above the volcanic ash cloud is not recommended due to accelerated engine damage/flame-out at high thrust settings;

        iv.   turn engine and wing anti-ice on. All air conditioning packs on. Turn on the engine and wing anti-ice systems and place all air conditioning packs to "on", in order to further improve the engine stall margin by increasing the bleed-air flow. It may be possible to stabilize one or more engines at the idle thrust setting where the EGT will remain within limits. An attempt should be made to keep at least one engine operating at idle and within limits to provide electrical power and bleed air for cabin pressurization until clear of the volcanic ash;

v.   start the auxiliary power unit (APU), if available. The APU can be used to power the electrical system in the event of a multiple-engine power loss. The APU may also provide a pneumatic air source for improved engine starting, depending on the aircraft model; and

vi.   put oxygen mask on at 100 percent, if required. If a significant amount of volcanic ash fills the cockpit or if there is a strong smell of sulphur, don an oxygen mask and select 100 percent. Manual deployment of passenger oxygen masks is not recommended if cabin pressure is normal because the passenger oxygen supply will be diluted with volcanic ash-filled cabin air. If the cabin altitude exceeds 4,250 m (14,000 ft), the passenger oxygen masks will deploy automatically.

b.   In the event of engine flame-out:

i.   turn ignition on. Place ignition switches to "on" as appropriate for the engine model (position normally used for in-flight engine start). Cycling of fuel levers (switches) is not required. For aircraft equipped with autostart systems, the autostart selector should be in the "on" position. The autostart system was designed and certified with a "hands-off" philosophy for emergency air starts in recognition of crew workload during this type of event;

ii.   monitor EGT. If necessary, shut down and then restart engines to keep from exceeding EGT limits;

iii.   close the outflow valves, if not already closed;

iv.   do not pull the fire switches;

v.   leave fuel boost pump switches "on" and open crossfeed valves;

vi.   do not use fuel heat — this would be undesirable if on suction fuel feed;

vii.   restart engine. If an engine fails to start, try again immediately. Successful engine start may not be possible until airspeed and altitude are within the air-start envelope. Monitor EGT carefully. If a hung start occurs, the EGT will increase rapidly. If the engine is just slow in accelerating, the EGT will increase slowly. Engines are very slow to accelerate to idle at high altitude, especially in volcanic ash — this may be interpreted as a failure to start or as a failure of the engine to accelerate to idle or as an engine malfunction;

viii.   monitor airspeed and pitch attitude. If unreliable, or if a complete loss of airspeed indication occurs (volcanic ash may block the pitot system), establish the appropriate pitch attitude dictated by the operations manual for "flight with unreliable airspeed." If airspeed indicators are unreliable, or if loss of airspeed indication occurs simultaneously with an all-engine thrust loss, shutdown or flame-out, use the attitude indicator to establish a minus-one degree pitch attitude. Inertial ground speed may be used for reference if the indicated airspeed is unreliable or lost. Ground speed may also be available from approach control during landing;

ix.   land at the nearest suitable airport. A precautionary landing should be made at the nearest suitable airport if aircraft damage or abnormal engine operation occurs due to volcanic ash penetration; and

x.   because of the abrasive effects of volcanic ash on windshields and landing lights, visibility for approach and landing may be markedly reduced. Forward visibility may be limited to that which is available through the side windows. Should this condition occur, and if the autopilot system is operating satisfactorily, a diversion to an airport where an autolanding can be accomplished should be considered. After landing, if forward visibility is restricted, consider having the aircraft towed to the parking gate.

2. The foregoing general procedures should be supplemented by specific procedures in the aircraft operations manual — developed by aircraft operators for each aircraft type in their fleet — dealing with the particular aircraft engine combination concerned.

3. Given that the most serious threat to an aircraft from volcanic ash is the risk of multiple-engine flame-out, it is extremely important to consider the ways and means of improving the success of engine restarts in air contaminated by volcanic ash. In the United States in 1991, the Aerospace Industries Association of America (AIA) ad hoc Propulsion Committee was formed comprising AIA members and representatives from international aircraft and engine manufacturers and the U.S. Geological Survey (USGS). The mandate of the Committee was to evaluate the threat of multiple-engine flameout due to volcanic ash and to make appropriate recommendations to the aviation industry and responsible government agencies. The Committee made a number of recommendations but, in particular, the following bear directly on the problem of engine restart, after flame-out:

   a. "Aircraft manufacturers, with assistance from the engine manufacturers, should define maximum engine power levels (expressed in engine pressure ratio (EPR), fan speed (N1), and (or) exhaust-gas temperature (EGT) levels) that will minimize buildup of melted and resolidified ash on HPT nozzle guide vanes. These values should be added to flight-manual procedures and should be used only when the recommended flight idle power will not assure adequate terrain clearance.

   b. Aircraft manufacturers, with assistance from engine manufacturers, should consider addition of a time-delay circuit to allow an air-started engine to reach stabilized idle speed before the electrical or generator load is applied. This would facilitate engine restarts under less-than-ideal conditions.

   c. FAA and other equivalent government agencies should require that air crews practice engine air-restart procedures in a simulator on recurring basis. Normal and deteriorated engine start characteristics should be simulated."

The prime importance of the last recommendation cannot be overestimated. Engine shut-downs or flame-outs in flight are rare events which many pilots will never be called upon to deal with in their whole careers. This is further complicated by the different procedures used for air-start as compared to normal ground-start. The only solution is for pilots to be provided with a set of air-start procedures which also cover procedures in volcanic ash contaminated air and for simulator air-starts to be part of basic and recurrent pilot training.

Resources to Avoid Ash Encounters

- Volcanic Ash Advisory Centers. There are nine volcanic ash advisory centers established by the ICAO to forecast volcanic activity and to inform aviators of potential hazards.

http://www.ssd.noaa.gov/VAAC/vaac.html

- UK Met Office provides volcanic activity forecasts when applicable.

http://www.metoffice.gov.uk/public/weather

- Smithsonian / USGC Weekly Volcanic Activity Report is updated at 2300 UTC every Wednesday with recently volcanic activity.

http://volcano.si.edu/reports_weekly.cfm

Chapter 6

Weather Deviation in Oceanic Airspace

*M*ost of these procedures are given in ICAO Doc 4444 §15.2, and are re-peated below. The basic concepts for contingencies are given in Part VI, Chapter 1.*

Weather Deviation Procedures

[ICAO Doc 4444 §15.2]

15.2.3.1 General

Note.— The following procedures are intended for deviations around adverse meteorological conditions.

15.2.3.1.1 When the pilot initiates communications with ATC, a rapid response may be obtained by stating "WEATHER DEVIATION REQUIRED" to indicate that priority is desired on the frequency and for ATC response. When necessary, the pilot should initiate the communications using the urgency call "PAN PAN" (preferably spoken three times).

15.2.3.1.2 The pilot shall inform ATC when weather deviation is no longer required, or when a weather deviation has been completed and the aircraft has returned to its cleared route.

15.2.3.2 Actions to be taken when controller-pilot communications are established

15.2.3.2.1 The pilot should notify ATC and request clearance to deviate from track, advising, when possible, the extent of the deviation expected.

15.2.3.2.2 ATC should take one of the following actions:

a.   when appropriate separation can be applied, issue clearance to deviate from track; or

b.   if there is conflicting traffic and ATC is unable to establish appropriate separation, ATC shall:

    1.   advise the pilot of inability to issue clearance for the requested deviation;

    2.   advise the pilot of the conflicting traffic; and

    3.   request the pilot's intentions.

15.2.3.2.3 The pilot should take the following actions:

a.   comply with the ATC clearance issued; or

b.   advise ATC of intentions and execute the procedures listed in 15.2.3.3.

15.2.3.3. Actions to be taken if a revised ATC clearance cannot be obtained

Note.— The provisions of this section apply to situations where a pilot needs to exercise the authority of a pilot-in-command under the provisions of Annex 2, 2.3.1.

If the aircraft is required to deviate from track to avoid adverse meteorological conditions and prior clearance cannot be obtained, an ATC clearance shall be obtained at the earliest possible time. Until an ATC clearance is received, the pilot shall take the following actions:

a.   if possible, deviate away from an organized track or route system;

b.   establish communications with and alert nearby aircraft by broadcasting, at suitable intervals: aircraft identification, flight level, position (including the ATS route designator or the track code, as appropriate) and intentions, on the frequency in use and on 121.5 MHz (or, as a backup, on the inter-pilot air-to-air frequency 123.45 MHz);

c.   watch for conflicting traffic both visually and by reference to ACAS (if equipped);

Note.— If, as a result of actions taken under the provisions of 15.2.3.3.1 b) and c), the pilot determines that there is another aircraft at or near the same flight level with which a conflict may occur, then the pilot is expected to adjust the path of the aircraft, as necessary, to avoid conflict.

a.   turn on all aircraft exterior lights (commensurate with appropriate operating limitations);

b.   for deviations of less than 19 km (10 nm) remain at a level assigned by ATC;

c. for deviations greater than 19 km (10 nm), when the aircraft is approximately 19 km (10 nm) from track, initiate a level change in accordance with Table 15-1;

d. when returning to track, be at its assigned flight level when the aircraft is within approximately 19 km (10 nm) of the centre line; and

e. if contact was not established prior to deviating, continue to attempt to contact ATC to obtain a clearance. If contact was established, continue to keep ATC advised of intentions and obtain essential traffic information.

Table 15-1

Route centerline / track	Deviations > 10 nm	Level Change
East 000 - 179 magnetic	Left of course Right of course	Descend 300 ft. Climb 300 ft.
West 180 - 359 magnetic	Left of course Right of course	Climb300 ft. Descend 300 ft.

Turning north descend, turning south climb.

Figure: Example routing as requested.

Chapter 1

Trip Preparation

*P*reparation is the key to a successful international trip. With experience the process becomes easier, but preparation is still necessary. Much of the "leg work" is taken care of by handling agents and flight planning services, but the pilot remains responsible for their completion.

It really pays to be diligent about this, even if you are a seasoned pro. I once flew into China with a veteran international ops pilot that hadn't been in a few years. He was stunned to find the Flight Level Allocation Scheme in China was unique to the world. I thought he was an idiot. Years later I flew into London, Luton for the one-hundredth time and was stunned to find every single approach into EGGW was deleted from the database. I felt like an idiot. Just because you've been doesn't make you an expert; if you haven't been recently, you need to study up.

This chapter begins an example G450 trip from Bedford, Massachusetts (KBED) to Geneva, Switzerland (LSGG), to Tokyo, Japan (RJAA), back to Bedford. It continues through the following chapters to show how the first oceanic departure, en route, and arrival portions are flown.

Example: Trip Set Up

From	To	Distance
KBED	LSGG	3203 nm
LSGG	RJAA	5312 nm
RJAA	KBED	5812 nm
	Total	14328 nm

For the purpose of example, we have been asked by our lead passenger to set up a trip from Bedford, Massachusetts (KBED) to Geneva, Switzerland (LSGG), then Tokyo, Japan (RJAA), finally returning home. The trip was originally planned in a G550 which could have made the first two legs without a doubt, but was questionable on the third leg because of past performance reports saying RJAA to KBED for some reason was problematic. The G550 dropped out and the trip has come to you, in a shorter range G450.

Aircraft Range / Crew Duty Limits

While aircraft range changes with passenger / cargo load, temperature, winds, and the vagaries of air traffic control, it helps to know what your airplane can do in generic conditions. In the case of the G450: a 4,000 nm trip at Mach 0.80, ISA conditions, no wind, and about a 43,000 lbs. operating weight will leave the airplane with 5,000 lbs. of fuel remaining at the destination. Based on this we know the last two destinations will require a fuel stop and possibly a crew change:

KBED LSGG 3203 nm – non-stop okay, single crew okay

LSGG RJAA 5312 nm – fuel stop required, augmented crew or crew swap needed

RJAA KBED 5812 nm – fuel stop required, augmented crew or crew swap needed

Crew duty limits will vary by operation and that will determine the need for crew augmentation or replacement. We will save that decision after looking for two refueling stops, what many call "technical stops."

Adding Technical Stops

It appears we will have no range issues with the first leg, from KBED to LSGG, but the remaining two legs will both require fuel stops.

We can take a chart and draw 4,000 nm circles around the two airports involved in the search for the first technical stop. We need to be careful about the

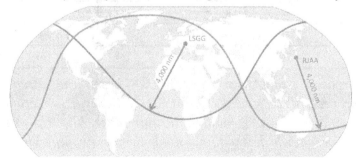

projection of the chart, a circle isn't a circle on most charts because the chart is usually distorted near the poles, the chart ends before the projected distance, or a combination of both factors. Automatic software, such as the excellent free resource available at http://gc.kls2.com/, can simplify this chore and identify the areas that are within 4,000 nm of both LSGG and RJAA. In the example chart, we see LSGG surrounded by one arc and RJAA by another. The area between the two arcs north of India identifies those points within 4,000 miles of both airports.

As much of this part of the world is troubled, we offer Moscow (UUEE) to our passengers as somewhat along the great circle route, an easy location for a crew swap, and a bit more reliable than many of the other options. Our passengers express an interest in spending a day in Mumbai, India (VABB) which is within the 4,000 nm range of both LSGG and RJAA. So we add VABB to our itinerary.

We run a similar exercise with the RJAA to KBED leg and determine that adding Anchorage, Alaska (PANC) could easily get the trip home in a day with a simple crew swap. Once again the passengers have a better idea and ask about spending a few days in Hawaii. From the standpoint of aircraft range and crew duty days, our itinerary becomes:

From	To	Distance
KBED	LSGG	3203 nm
LSGG	VABB	3630 nm
VABB	RJAA	3669 nm
RJAA	PHNL	3318 nm
PHNL	KSFO	2084 nm
KSFO	KBED	2336 nm
	Total	18241 nm

Since each of these legs are well within the airplane's range and the passengers have asked to spend the night in each location, we will not need an augmented crew or crew swaps.

Aircraft Performance

Aircraft performance should be considered for each airport and each en route leg.

Aircraft takeoff performance for the expected conditions

Can the aircraft make it off the ground?

When considering maximizing the range of your aircraft, it helps to have a general idea about how much runway is needed under most conditions at maximum weight. A G450, for example, can takeoff fully loaded up to 105°F at sea level in less than 7,000 feet of pavement.

Our example trip will take place in late March and there may be weather to consider when departing and arriving at KBED. We let our passengers know that if the runway is likely to be contaminated, we may need to reposition the airplane to KBOS to take advantage of the longer runways and the greater number of runways which will minimize the impact of crosswinds on contaminated surfaces. The other airports do not appear to have takeoff and landing performance issues.

Airport obstacle analysis

Can the aircraft out climb the obstacles near the airport?

Obstacles between the airport and your en route altitude can be a factor and should be considered. Simply ensuring your AFM performance numbers are satisfied by meeting SID requirements might be good enough, but it could needlessly reduce your payload (and therefore your range).

Of the selected airports, Geneva can pose problems. In fact, the common practice of using AFM engine-out climb data when assessing all-engine Standard Instrument Departure (SID) procedures will make the LSGG - VABB leg impossible because the G450 cannot make SID climb requirements engine-out. Using only the data available in the cockpit, a knowledgeable pilot can plan a safe takeoff at maximum gross weight by planning to shuttle between two VORs away from mountainous terrain in the event of an engine failure during takeoff or the initial climb.

Aircraft en route performance

Can the aircraft make it to a divert airport if an engine is lost at any point along the way?

You have minimum en route altitude restrictions to meet in the event of an engine failure which could be a factor, especially in mountainous terrain. Unfortunately many aircraft manufacturers do not provide easily understood data to make this determination. Nevertheless, you need to consider this.

Since we plan on performance to beat close-in obstacles, keeping minimum safe en route altitudes is rarely an issue. So too with this trip, only the obstacles in Switzerland pose a risk and we have ensured these are beaten early in the flight.

Aircraft landing performance for the expected conditions

Can the aircraft stop in the available runway distance?

You should know the absolute minimum amount of pavement your airplane needs to safely stop, the minimum your company requires, and the minimum you require. In the case of the G450, the book says the aircraft must have at least 2,500' to stop in absolutely ideal conditions. In my opinion you would be crazy to try anything less than 4,000' and I rarely venture to a runway less than 5,000'.

Only the runways at Bedford pose a risk at this time of year, so we make a note to include an alternate for our return home.

Airspace Considerations

Theoretically, ICAO Doc 7030, Regional Supplementary Procedures, is your best source of airspace requirements throughout the world. Unfortunately, it is rarely updated. Airspace rules are changing every year and it pays to have a good international trip planning service to keep on top of this.

You should consider any special airspace requirements for each leg of the trip:

Automatic Dependent Surveillance-Broadcast (ADS-B) Out

ADS-B Out is becoming required in parts of the world, but workarounds are readily available. You can expect delays and reroutes if you are not equipped and authorized. See Part V, Chapter 2.

Basic Area Navigation (B-RNAV)

B-RNAV is required in most of Europe. See Part III, Chapter 6.

Extended Operations of Multi-engine Airplanes (ETOPS)

ETOPS does not apply to 14 CFR 91 operators and only constrains 14 CFR 135 operators from flying in the most remote regions of the world. It only applies when flying beyond 3 hours of a suitable airport with an engine failed. See the Appendices, Chapter 19.

High Latitude and Northern Domestic Airspace

Operating in what many simply call "polar ops" requires special certification under 14 CFR 135 and special procedures for anyone venturing the high latitude regions. High latitude operations occur in areas above 78°N, below 60°S, the northern and southern poles, and the Canadian Northern Domestic Area (NDA). The NDA includes the Northern Control Area (NCA), the Arctic Control Area (ACA) and the Area of Magnetic Unreliability (AMU). The NDA, NCA and ACA are depicted on Canadian HI en route charts and encompass the northernmost Canadian airspace. See the Appendices, Chapter 23.

Minimum Navigation Performance Specifications (MNPS)

MNPS applies to most of the North Atlantic and the Canadian Arctic Control Area. See Part III, Chapter 7.

Overflight Permits

You may need permission to overfly some countries, some countries may have rules that permit specific nations, restrict some, and ban still others. You need to check every country you overfly and in some cases you need to be wary of who has claim to the airspace you are using. The Jeppesen State pages are a great place to start. Having an international trip planner who knows the area is an even better way to go.

Precision Area Navigation (P-RNAV)

P-RNAV is used to fly RNAV departure and arrival procedures in European Civil Aviation Conference countries (most of Europe). Terminal procedures will have "P-RNAV Required" annotated. See Part III, Chapter 8.

Reduced Vertical Separation Minimum (RVSM)

While RVSM is now the standard just about everywhere, there are country-specific rules for flight level selection and contingency procedures. See Part II, Chapter 6.

Required Navigation Performance-4 (RNP-4)

The Required Navigation Performance-4 (RNP-4) applies to parts of Australia, New Zealand, and Japan, but all of these still allow RNP-10 as a substitute. In theory, ATS can monitor aircraft with RNP-4 more closely and will have traffic priority. See Part III, Chapter 9.

Required Navigation Performance-10 (RNP-10)

RNP-10 is required in the Central East Pacific (CEP) between Hawaii and the west coast of the United States, and portions of the North Pacific (NOPAC) require RNP-10. There are other areas of the world that have adopted RNP-10, such as parts of Africa, the Indian Ocean, Australia, New Zealand, Tahiti, and some parts of South America near Recife. See Part III, Chapter 10.

Our trip takes us through the NAM, NAT, EUR, MID/ASIA, and PAC regions. A review of ICAO Doc 7030 reveals:

- *Europe: our routes of flight will take us over regions where B-RNAV, P-RNAV, RVSM, and 8.33 kHz spacing are termed "mandatory," though some exceptions are allowed. If you don't have any of these capabilities, you may be restricted to non-optimal altitudes or routes, or you may not be able to fly the routes at all. See ICAO Doc 7030, $EUR, for more details.*

- *Middle East / Asia: our routes of flight will take us over regions where RNP-4, RNP-5, RNP-10, and RVSM are either "mandatory" or recommended. You may be restricted to non-optimal altitudes or routes, or you may not be able to fly the routes at all. See ICAO Doc 7030, $MID/ASIA, for more details.*

- *North America: the only airspace requirement listed for us here is RVSM. See ICAO Doc 7030, $NAM, for more details.*

- *North Atlantic: our route of flight will take us over regions where MNPS, RVSM, as well as ACAS II are mandatory, though exceptions are allowed. See ICAO Doc 7030, $NAT, for more details.*

- *Pacific: our routes of flight will take us over regions where RNP-4, RNP-10, and RVSM are either "mandatory" or recommended. You may be restricted to non-optimal altitudes or routes, or you may not be able to fly the routes at all. See ICAO Doc 7030, $PAC, for more details.*

Note that some of these requirements are changing back and forth rapidly. RNP-4, for example, was supposed to be mandatory over much of the ASIA region by December 2013, but many countries are showing increasing flexibility as their air traffic has been slow to equip. You need to ask yourself (or your flight planning service provider) prior to every trip if you are lacking a requirement they classify as mandatory.

Note also that ICAO Doc 7030 is quiet on the subject of ADS-B Out, which is becoming required in parts of the world. As of 2015, ADS-B Out not yet required for our routes of flight, but that will change.

Airport Suitability

Each ICAO member is free to make exceptions to ICAO rules but they must post these exceptions in their individual Aeronautical Information Publications. These are usually issued in host nation languages and rarely available in English.

The Jeppesen State pages attempt to compile the notable differences and are your best "go to" source of these individual country differences. The Airport Directory for each destination airport and likely alternates are good places to start when researching airport suitability. A legend and explanation appears in the Jeppesen Airway Manual text pages under Airport Directory, Airport Data General, Legend and Explanation. Note: these pages often have errors and you should double check on anything critical or anything that just doesn't make sense. For example, I've found they don't do a good job of keeping up with WGS-84 status on these pages, though their web site on the issue is excellent.

Airport of Entry

The first and last airports visited in a foreign country must normally be designated as "Apt of Entry" in the Jeppesen Airport Directory and AIP. In some countries, any declared alternates must also be airports of entry. You need to check each country's pages to be sure.

Airport Hours of Operation

Will the airport be open at the necessary times for arrival and departure? The Airport Directory provides UTC-to-local time conversions, the airport hours of operation, and other items of interest.

Having a trip handler with a presence at the airport will be helpful, as the times in the JeppView pages may not be up-to-date. If you do not have anyone with local knowledge, the page does provide phone numbers you can call.

Runway Suitability

Are the runways long and strong enough? Are the ramps adequately stressed? The Airport Directory Pages are a good source of the following information:

- Runway Data. This is more than just the length of the runway: the Airport Directory provides runway length, TORA, LDA, TODA, and ASDA when available. It could be that you have far less than the published distances available to you.

- Runway Load Bearing. Runway strength is given in a variety of systems. Common methods, such as LCN/PCN may be explained in individual AFM or POH, as well as the Jeppesen Airport Directory, Legend. The airport directory does not always list runway load bearing information and it never lists data for associated taxiways and parking areas. If you are taking a large aircraft into an airport you aren't familiar with, it may be worth the phone call to find out if they've had aircraft of your type land and park where you intend to put your airplane.

- Lighting. Given in a variety of systems, each explained in the Jeppesen Airport Directory, Legend.

- Don't forget to consider fuel loading when computing ACNs. I was once scheduled into Maun, Botswana as the last stop in Africa and then on to Paris. A fully loaded GV exceeded the only suitable runway's PCN so we had to reorder the trip so Maun wasn't our last stop in the area.

Fuel

Does the airport offer the required grade of fuel, if refueling is necessary? If you are planning on a full load of fuel, remember fuel densities often preclude that in some parts of the world. A G-450's fuel capacity, for example, can vary over 2,000 lbs from the highest allowed fuel density to the lowest. The best place to put on a full load of fuel is the west coast of the United States. The worst? Southeast Asia. See the Appendices, Chapter 22.

Rescue and Fire Fighting System

When given a choice of airports in a city, it may be advantageous to select the airport with appropriate airport rescue and fire fighting capability. See the Appendices, Chapter 2.

Other Considerations

You should also consider the following:

- Landing Permit. Is a landing permit needed? The country's Airport Information Publication and the Jeppesen Entry Requirements pages may be consulted to determine if a landing permit is required. Your flight handling services should be consulted to ensure you have the best, up-to-date, information about landing permits. [Jeppesen Entry Requirements]

- Aircraft and Crew Support. Can the airport and the handling agent adequately support the aircraft and crew? Your familiarity with each airport will determine your need for a ground-handling agent. In many cases language difficulties and coordination between stops will make a ground-handling agent a necessity.

- Ramp space. Can the airport provide space for the aircraft for the duration?

- Hangar space. If needed, is hangar space available? You should consider the possibility of needing aircraft hangar facilities, battery and freezable liquids removal, and other overnight issues.

- Fueling, oxygen, potable water, de-icing, lavatory service, catering needs. Do the handler or other agents on the airport provide these necessary services?

- Aircraft security. State Department notices and the Jeppesen Airway Manual State pages may suggest the level of security needed for the aircraft during its stay at each location.

- Hours of operation. You should insure the airport, FBO, and handlers will be open for business during planned arrival and departure times.

- Payment methods. You should know what forms of payment are accepted by each agency you will be dealing with at each airport.

- Maintenance availability. It may be beneficial to identify authorized repair facilities near your routing as well as know what services are available at each airport.

- Ground transportation. The handler may be able to provide adequate transportation to and from the hotel or recommend rental car and taxi options.

- Hotel Reservations. Overnight accommodations should be secured.

- Special Airport Qualification. Does the applicable State require special airport qualification? These may be found in the country's Airport Information Publication, the International Flight Information Manual, and the Airport Briefing page in the Jeppesen Airway Manual terminal chart series. For example, Innsbruck, Austria considers previous experience in VMC essential prior to IMC approaches at LOWI. The Airport Briefing details training requirements and simulator options. [Jeppesen Airway Manual, Terminal Charts, Innsbruck, Austria, Page 10-1P]

Example: Airport Suitability

Airports of Entry (AOE) — The JeppView pages do not list PHNL or KSFO as airports of entry, but they are. Each of the other destinations are listed as AOE's. When we flight plan, we should ensure that any declared weather and ETP alternates are also AOE's While this isn't always a requirement, it simplifies trip planning in case a particular country does mandate it.

Hours of Operation — Each of our airports is listed as H24 but LSGG is PPR, so that merits a phone call by you or your handler.

Runways — Each airport on our itinerary has runways of adequate length, load bearing strength, and lighting.

Fuel — Each airport has the correct type of fuel but Japanese fuel is notoriously weak in terms of fuel density. We know from a Gulfstream study that a G450's total fuel capacity can be reduced from 29,500 lbs to just 28,230 lbs at the lowest available densities. Contrary to popular belief, jet engines derive thrust from the fuel in terms of weight, not volume. So warned, we run flight plans for the RJAA to PHNL range and find our worst case winds requires only 23,000 lbs of fuel, including reserves.

Rescue and Fire Fighting System — Each airport has good rescue and fire fighting capability. Note that this is rarely a show stopper for most operators.

Other Considerations — On our example trip we could run into problems with getting adequate ramp space for the aircraft, hotels for the crew, and we may want to consider hiring aircraft security at one of the locations. I recommend having a good trip planner who has recent experience with each airport. Failing that, call upon your network of pilot associates to get up-to-date intel.

Country-Specific Concerns

There are a lot of things to consider here and if you don't spend a lot of time in the areas you will be visiting, you may miss something. It helps to have someone with local and recent knowledge, a good trip planner can be invaluable. But you should be aware of at least the following issues.

Routing

[AC 91-70A, ¶3-1.i.] En route airports-determine the suitability of alternate airports.

- Oxygen requirements.

- Terrain clearance.

- Passenger requirements.

- Turnaround capability.

- Crew rest requirements, if applicable.

The anticipated routing should be checked for security concerns and any special airspace requirements.

Are there any US State Department Warning regarding the routing? International Notice to Airmen are available biweekly and provide international information and special notices which could affect a pilot's decision to enter or use certain areas of foreign or international airspace. International NOTAMs are available from flight planning providers and from http://www.faa.gov/airports_airtraffic/air_traffic/publications/notices/

Agriculture

There are quite often restrictions on what food, plants, and animal products you can bring into a country, including the United States. Within the United States, there are also restrictions into and out of the State of Hawaii.

- Entry into Other Countries. Check the Jeppesen Airway Manual Entry Requirements pages for a primer on any restrictions.

- Entry into the United States. The best source of information is available in the United States Department of Agriculture's Traveler's Page, http://www.aphis.usda.gov/wps/portal/aphis/resources/travelers-int.

- Insecticide. Some countries, Australia for example, may require the aircraft interior be sprayed with a suitable insecticide and a suitable time interval allowed prior to allowing anyone to deplane. If you have the spray before already, some countries will allow you to spray prior to landing, getting you and your passengers off the airplane earlier.

- Entry into the State of Hawaii. In general, foods that are cooked, canned, frozen, or commercially processed and/or packaged can be brought into the state as long as the product originates from the U.S. There are strict importing regulations for all animals. Refer to the State of Hawaii Department of Agriculture web site for more details, at http://www.hawaii.gov/hdoa/.

- Export from the State of Hawaii. The best source of information is available in the United States Department of Agriculture's Traveler's Page, http://www.aphis.usda.gov/wps/portal/aphis/resources/travelers-int.

Cabotage

[AC 91-70A, ¶3-1.n.] Private pilots and commercial operators should understand cabotage, formally defined as "Air transport of passengers and goods within the same national territory." The definition adopted by ICAO at the Chicago Convention is as follows: "Each state shall have the right to refuse permission to the aircraft of other contracting states to take on its territory passengers, mail, and cargo destined for another point within its territory." Although cabotage rules are different in various countries and usually incorporate the term "for hire," some countries do not allow foreign aircraft within their boundaries to carry even non-revenue passengers. The restrictions range from no restrictions to not allowed. The fines for cabotage can be extremely high; therefore, pilots and flight departments should be absolutely sure of a country's cabotage rules before carrying passengers.

Generally speaking, you cannot fly to some foreign countries, pick up local citizens and transport them within that country. Not all countries have cabotage restrictions and many that do will allow exceptions if the citizens are employees of a company associated with the airplane. The rules vary by country and you need to ensure you follow them. AC 91-70A, ¶3-1.n. offers an FAA web page that was very helpful in determining country-specific cabotage rules but that service is no longer offered. You are left to ask your flight planning service provider or looking for the country's AIP.

Customs and Immigration Requirements

Customs requirements vary by country of departure and arrival. You should check with your handler, and the Jeppesen Airway Manual Entry Requirements pages. It may be helpful to have customs and immigration phone numbers available. See the Appendices, Chapter 16.

Passport & Visa. Is a passport and entry Visa required? Rules can vary between passengers and crewmembers, can depend on the duration of stay, and in some cases can be waived. The Jeppesen Entry Requirements pages will summarize the rules. If you need a quick passport or visa, your best resource may be http://www.g3visas.com.

Entry Airports. Do the first landing and final departure airports have to be from airports of entry, international airports, or certain gateway airports? The Jeppesen Airway Manual Entry Requirements pages will summarize the rules and the Airport Directory will list which airports qualify.

Forms for Entry and Exit. Are special forms required upon arrival and departure? Your handler may have an up-to-date list of what is needed at each country.

APIS. The U.S. requires APIS for all trips leaving and returning to the U.S.

Emissions Standards

The so-called European Union Emissions Trading System (ETS), formally known as the Emission Trading Scheme, is an on-again, off-again effort to tax aviation. The system, as of 2015, is on-again. While compliance is mandatory, enforcement is less than clear. Most business aviation qualifies for "small emitter" status and may not have to pay for "cap and trade" credits. But payment is required for registration. If you fly to Europe, even infrequently, you should keep up with the news on this topic or pay an international trip planner to do that for you.

(There are also plans from other countries, including the United States, to initiate their own emissions schemes. Once again, you need to keep up with the news on this.)

Immunizations and Vaccinations

Some countries will not allow you off the airplane unless you have proof of immunizations and/or vaccinations against specific conditions. The Jeppesen State pages contain some immunization and vaccination information.

An even better resource is www.medaire.com.

Return to the U.S. From Areas South of the U.S.

All private aircraft arriving in the Continental U.S. via the U.S./Mexican border or the Pacific Coast from a foreign place in the Western Hemisphere south of 33°N latitude, or from the Gulf of Mexico and Atlantic Coasts from a place in the Western Hemisphere south of 30°N latitude, from any place in Mexico, from the U.S. Virgin Islands, and from Puerto Rico (in some cases) may be required to land only at certain specially designated airports. Exemptions are given, depending on crew and passengers.

Special restrictions cover flight to and from Cuba.

If the trip does return from one of these locations, check the requirements covered in the "US Customs and Border Protection Guide for Private Flyers," [19 CFR 122.23 - 122.27]

Import Concerns

Are there aircraft import or other taxation issues? In some cases, these duties and taxes can make the planned trip prohibitively expensive. The solution once available in Europe to plan a free import no longer exists, you need to talk to your international planner about this prior to every trip.

Destination Security

[AC 91-70A, ¶3-1.h.] Does a State Department warning exist for health, security, or other precautions?

This information could prevent travel to the country or limit access to the airport only. International Notice to Airmen are available biweekly and provide international information and special notices which could affect a pilot's decision to enter or use certain areas of foreign or international airspace. International NOTAMs are available from flight planning providers and from http://www.faa.gov/airports_airtraffic/air_traffic/publications/notices/.

Aircraft Security

You may wish to invest in aircraft security tape seals that you can apply to all doors, hatches, or other access points that will allow you to detect unauthorized access. Make sure you have all necessary locks and pins to secure doors and hatches.

Cash

Some countries restrict the amount of cash you can bring in or leave with. Generally speaking, transporting more than $10,000 in U.S. currency may require a Currency Transaction Report, such as the FinCen Form 105. Information is available at https://www.fincen.gov.

Our example trip will be concerned with multiple country-specific concerns:

Local support will depend on a handler who speaks the language and can negotiate on our behalf with agriculture, immigration, customs, air traffic control officials in Switzerland, India, and Japan.

Agriculture concerns are expressed in the States pages for India and Japan, as well as unique issues in Hawaii.

Cabotage will not be an issue, since all crew and passengers are U.S. citizens. It would not be a concern even if we had foreign nationals on board, since we are not making flights within any one particular foreign country's borders.

Customs and Immigration requirements apply to all our foreign stops. A good handler will either have the paperwork completed for us when we arrive, or will forward the necessary forms ahead of time to speed our arrivals.

Import issues are problematic in Europe, though Switzerland hasn't been a problem area. Our handler assures us that they have not been pressing the issues.

Security concerns exist in India so we have our handler contract a local security company to provide guards for the aircraft during our stay.

VII – Tutorial

Chapter 2

Oceanic Departure

*W*hen departing from a domestic to an oceanic area, pilots will have a few extra steps prior to and during the oceanic crossing. While procedures worldwide have become much more standardized, there are differences in various regions. The basic procedures are covered here, with regional differences noted. Of course these procedures are changing every day and you should check prior to every trip.

This section continues an example G450 trip from Bedford, Massachusetts (KBED) to Geneva, Switzerland (LSGG), to Mumbai, India (VABB), to Tokyo, Japan (RJAA), to Honolulu, Hawaii (PHNL), to San Francisco, California (KSFO), back to Bedford. For the purpose of covering an oceanic departure, this section will focus on the KBED to LSGG leg.

Preflight

A clear delineation of preflight tasks can ensure all duties are accomplished and a good level of crosscheck exists between pilots. A possible technique is to have the PIC accomplish all plotting and master document work while the SIC completes the aircraft exterior inspection. Once the interior inspection begins, the PF programs the FMS while the PM accomplishes the aircraft interior inspection checklist. Once that is done, the PM checks the FMS entries while the PF turns his or her attention to other airplane related matters.

Master Document

[AC 91-70A, ¶3-5.a.] ICAO Annex 2 requires the use of a journey logbook, also known as the "master" document. This "master" document is typically a computer flight plan (CFP). Operator procedures must include a designated "master" document for use on the flight deck. This document must include information that sequentially lists the waypoints that define the routes, distances between the waypoints, and any other navigation information pertinent to the cleared route.

The flight deck can have multiple copies of the electronic flight plan but only one of these can be used as a "master document."

Our example master document includes a cover page, pages on equal time point information, NOTAMS, weather, airport information, and a track message. For the sake of organization, we staple these together and label the cover page "Master Document." While some crews like to have a copy for each pilot, I discourage the practice to avoid recording required items on the wrong copy. If we have an extra copy, I store it outside the cockpit.

Master Document

```
FLIGHTPLAN N7700    KBED TO LSGG  GLF4  M80 /F  IFR   29DEC13   -- AB
COMPUTED 2024Z FOR ETD 1700Z   PROGS 281200Z              WGT IN LBS

              FUEL   TIME   DIST ARRIVE TAKEOFF  LAND   AV PLD  OPNLWT
DEST LSGG  019340 06:22  3261  2322Z  073508  054168 000500  043908
RESV       001931 00:45
ALTN       000000 00:00  0000  0000Z
HOLD       000000 00:00
REQD       029100 10:10                            ES ZFW   MX ZFW
TAXI       000400                                     44408    49000
XTRA       007829 03:03                            ES LNDG  MX LNDG
TOTL        29500 10:10                               54168   058500

KBED DCT LBSTA ENE J581 YJT CYMON DENDU 5150N 5240N 5230N 5220N
DINIM ELSOX GAPLI UL739 LIZAD UN160 PIGOP UN491 RESMI UM975 LUSAR
DCT LSGG

WIND P062    MXSH 10/LUSAR   AVG WIND 268/071
TAS 451      FL 410 YJT 390 5240N 410

CLIMB SCHED:300/M80     CRUISE SCHED:M80      DESCENT SCHED:M80/300

CLEARANCE_____

CPT    FLT T   WIND  S TAS AWY    MH   DST ETE ETR  FU    FR    FF/E
FREQ   TRO TDV COMP    GRS        MCRS DSTR ATE ATR AFU   AFR
LAT    LONG

LBSTA  CLB            DCT       005  0036 006 0616 1103 27997
                                016  3225
N42480 W070368

ENE    CLB            J581      048  0037 005 0611 518  27479
117.1                           058  3188
N43255 W070368

TOC    410            J581      047  0099 011 0600 1065 26414
                                060  3089
N44398 W069059

ODIKE  410 -64 260133 2 451 J581 049  0000 000 0600 2    26413 1517
       39  M08  P095   546       060  3088
N44401 W069056

BGR    410 -64 264130 3 451 J581 069  0014 002 0558 78   26334 1512
114.8  39  M08  P089   540       077  3074
N44505 W068524
```

Flight Plan Entry

You have several options for getting the flight plan from the master document to the FMS, each with its own set of challenges. Among the options:

- Manual entry — If you are diligent and careful, you can get every single point in the flight plan into the FMS. Make sure you don't input any extra points not on the filed flight plan, such as the TOC (Top of Climb) or TOD (Top of Descent). Some flight plans will include FIR boundaries, don't put those in. If the flight plan shows any ETPs (equal time points), leave those out as well. This method risks entry errors due to reading and typing mistakes.

- Disk, Punch Card, or Memory Stick — Some FMS have provision for saving a flight plan to a memory device which can be read by the FMS. While this method eliminates the chance of pilot reading or typing error, it risks the use of the wrong memory device and uploading a similar, but wrong flight plan.

- Satellite Downlink — If your FMS provides for an electronic downlink of the flight plan you can eliminate most potential pilot induced errors, except one notable error from which all three methods suffer. (See the next paragraph.)

- FMS Limitations — No matter which method you use, it is imperative you check every leg of the master document's flight plan against that in the FMS. Some aircraft have their own peculiarities that require cross checking. Earlier GV's, for example, had a 99-leg limit on FMS flight plans and would simply drop any legs over the limit.

The G450 offers a reliable satellite downlink and we have our flight plan in its entirety on all three FMS.

Flight Plan Winds

Some FMS will not automatically include downlinked winds and you will have to take steps to ensure the winds are included in the FMS flight plan. A few cautions:

- A downlinked wind may be tied to the flight plan itself and could be hours out of date. You should either update each leg with current winds or downlink current winds if available.

- Entering an average wind might work for some areas of the world but not others. Between Hawaii and California you normally have steady winds, but not always. Between the U.S. and Europe the winds often change dramatically half way across, but not always.

- You should get to know how your FMS adapts to changes in the flight plan with previously downlinked, averaged, or manually entered winds. Some FMS will zero the winds for some types of changes.

FMS Flight Plan Versus Filed Flight Plan

You should check the flight plan that was actually filed versus what is in your FMS, just in case. Even a down linked flight plan could have differences that are important. At some locations the local airport is required to enter the flight plan manually and may give you a copy of what they filed. Use that against your FMS.

Our example trip was filed through ARINCDirect and the last page of the master document includes the filed flight plan. We check that against our primary FMS and are satisfied they are the same.

```
TAS          Altitude
(FPL-N7700-IG
-GLF4/M-SBDE2E3FGHIJ3J5M1RWXYZ/SD1
-KBED1700
-N0451F410 DCT LBSTA DCT ENE J581 YJT/N0457F390 DCT CYMON DCT
DENDU/M080F390 DCT 51N050W 52N040W/M080F410 52N030W 52N020W DCT
DINIM DCT ELSOX DCT GAPLI/N0449F410 UL739 LIZAD UN160
PIGOP UN491 RESMI UM975 LUSAR DCT
-LSGG0622
-PBN/A1B1C1D1O1S2 NAV/RNVD1E2A1
EET/CZQM0031 CZQX0105 CYMON0133 DENDU0147 50W0156 40W0239
30W0322 20W0406 DINIM0429 ELSOX0434 GAPLI0501 LFRR0518 LFFF0538
LFMM0618
SEL/NONE CODE/A147D6
ALTN KBED FROM PNR 5150N
-E/0707 R/VE S/M A/WHT RED)          Oceanic Routing
```

Filed Flight Plan Verification

[AC 91-70A, ¶3-5.b.]

- Verify the waypoints by comparing the master document and the LRNS;

- Circle the waypoint, waypoint number, or symbol to signify that another crewmember independently crosschecks the entry of the coordinates in the navigation computer;

- Tick or diagonally slash the circled waypoint, waypoint number, or symbol to signify the crosschecking of track and distance information within a specified tolerance;

Be careful about waypoint shorthand used by the FMS. The shorthand maynot be as intuitive as you think. It is easy to create your own gross navigational error. See the Appendices, Chapter 9, ARINC-424 Shorthand.

[ICAO NAT Doc 007, ¶8.2.6]

- For aircraft equipped with FMS databases, FMS generated or inserted waypoints should be carefully compared to master document waypoints and crosschecked by both pilots.

- An appropriate symbology should be adopted to indicate the status of each waypoint listed on the master document.

CPT FREQ LAT	FLT TRO	T TDV LONG	WIND COMP	S	TAS GRS	AWY	MH MCRS	DST DSTR	ETE ATE	ETR ATR	FU AFU	FR AFR	FF/E
CYMON	390 36	-55 M02	287123 P084	3	457 542	DCT	080 088	0160 2438	018	0449	896	22874	1518
N49430		W054599											
DENDU	390 36	-52 P04	288105 P075	7	463 538	DCT	083 090	0123 2315	014	0435	698	22176	1531
N50302		W052041											
5150N	390 36	-50 P06	288090 P067	4	465 531	DCT	095 097	0084 2231	009	0426	485	21690	1531
N51000		W050000											
5240N	390 52	-50 P07	276063 P060	2	466 527	DCT	106 104	0379 1851	043	0343	2204	19487	1516
N52000		W040000											
5230N	410 52	-51 P06	252054 P051	1	465 516	DCT	103 100	0371 1481	043	0300	2076	17411	1445
N52000		W030000											
5220N	410 31	-53 P05	241060 P051		464 515	DCT	124 117	0371 1110	043	0217	2026	15385	1407
N52000		W020000											
DINIM	410 36	-55 P03	236069 P040	1	462 502	DCT	102 097	0197 0913	024	0153	1081	14305	1377
N51000		W015000											
ELSOX	410 36	-56 P01	236075 P060	3	460 520	DCT	116 109	0038 0876	004	0149	198	14106	1359
N51000		W014000											

No matter the method used to enter the flight plan, best practices dictate that the other pilot verify the waypoints in the FMS are correct. The waypoint symbology is specified in several documents but personal preferences and company policies may be preferred. See the Appendices, Chapter 39, Waypoint Symbology.

Plotting

[FAA Order 8900.1 Volume 4, Chapter 1, Paragraph 4-80.A.1.] Plotting procedures are required for all turbojet operations where the route segment between the operational service volume of ICAO standard ground-based navigational aids exceeds 725 nm.

Plotting procedures are fairly straightforward but require a level of precision and perhaps some practice. See Part II, Chapter 5.

The plotting chart is typically measured from the midpoint between waypoints. The magnetic course on the master document may or may not be a midpoint measurement. A difference of more than +/- 2° or +/- 2 nm might be acceptable but should be a cause for a recheck and verification.

For our example route we've plotted a few points before the oceanic entry point as a reminder that things will get busy, and every point along the oceanic route up to the exit, which is at DINIM.

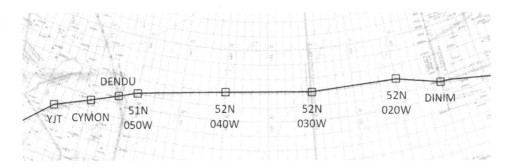

Plot Relevant Tracks

If your route or any potential diversionary routes cross any relevant track systems, the tracks should be plotted as well. Tracks should be considered relevant if the route of flight is within or over the track system and an aircraft drift down or diversion will conflict any of the tracks. This is especially true over the very crowded North Atlantic (NAT) Organized Track System (OTS).

[ICAO NAT Doc 001, Paragraph 1.12.7] The agreed OTS is then promulgated as a NAT Track Message via the Aeronautical Fixed Telecommunications Network (AFTN), to all interested agencies. A typical time of publication for the Westbound OTS is 0000 UTC and for the Eastbound OTS is 1200 UTC. This message gives full details of organized track coordinates as well as flight levels expected to be in use on each track. All aircraft operating in or above MNPS Airspace are required to carry a copy of the current OTS Message. Its correct interpretation by operators

```
ORGANIZED TRACK SYSTEM//
---------------------------------
NAT TRACKS FLS 310/390 INCLUSIVE
DEC 29/1130Z TO DEC 29/1900Z
A MALOT 54/20 55/30 55/40 55/50 OYSTR
EAST LVLS NIL
WEST LVLS 310 320 330 340 350 360 370 380 390
EUR RTS WEST NIL
NAR -
B LIMRI 53/20 54/30 54/40 54/50 CARPE
EAST LVLS NIL
WEST LVLS 310 320 330 340 350 360 370 380 390
EUR RTS WEST NIL
NAR -
C DINIM 52/20 53/30 53/40 53/50 HECKK
EAST LVLS NIL
WEST LVLS 310 320 330 340 350 360 370 380 390
EUR RTS WEST NIL
NAR -
D SOMAX 48/20 48/20 48/40 48/50 RONPO
EAST LVLS NIL
WEST LVLS 310 320 330 340 350 360 370 380 390
EUR RTS WEST NIL
NAR -
E BEDRA 47/20 47/30 47/40 47/50 URTAK
EAST LVLS NIL
WEST LVLS 310 320 330 340 350 360 370 380 390
EUR RTS WEST NIL
NAR -
F 47/40 44/50 41/60 JOBOC
EAST LVLS NIL
WEST LVLS 320 340 360 380
EUR RTS WEST
NAR -
REMARKS.
1. TMI IS 363 AND OPERATORS ARE REMINDED TO INCLUDE THE
TMI NUMBER AS PART OF THE OCEANIC CLEARANCE READ BACK. 2
CPDLC MANDATED OTS ARE AS FOLLOWS
   TRACK A 350 360 370 380 390
   TRACK B 350 360 370 380 390
   TRACK C 350 360 370 380 390
   TRACK D 350 360 370 380 390
```

and pilots is essential to both economy of operation and in minimizing the possibility of a misunderstanding which could lead to the use of incorrect track coordinates.

We've plotted all the tracks north of our route of flight, since we will have to cross them if we need to divert to Iceland. We've also plotted one track to our south, as a reminder about how far we can maneuver if turning right of track.

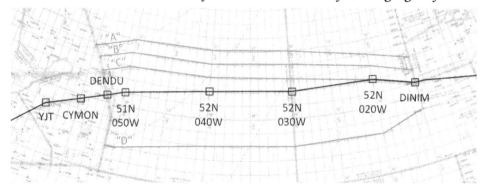

Compute and Plot Equal Time Points (ETPs)

Besides telling you they are needed, there is very little regulatory guidance on Equal Time Points (ETPs). Having an ETP plotted gives you a decision making tool if you find yourself between suitable airports with an engine failure requiring an altitude drift down, a medical emergency requiring a divert without requiring an altitude change, or a loss of cabin pressurization requiring an immediate descent.

You can calculate your ETP's with pencil and paper, have your flight plan provider automatically compute them, or your aircraft FMS may have an appropriate function. I recommend using the flight plan provider's, at least as a start, since they would be using the same winds as used in the flight plan. See the Appendices, Chapter 18, Equal Time Points.

Our flight plan provider includes ETP's on request, as shown in the figure.

```
                            CRITICAL FUEL SUMMARIES
1E INOP
LAT/LONG        N52 05.0/W037 17.3         CYQX              EINN
TIME TO ETP DIVRSN PT        02.51
DIST TO ETP DIVRSN PT        01510
FUEL TO ETP DIVRSN PT/RMNG   010177 /18923
FL/BURN/TIME TO ETP AP       300/05553/02.36   310/05557/02.37
TAS/ETA/DIST TO ETP AP       340/2227/000686   340/2228/001036
MAG CRS/AVG WIND COMP TO ETP AP    271/M076       105/P052
ISA TEMP DEV TO ETP AP              M000           M003
TOTAL FUEL TO ETP AP /RMNG     15730/13366     15734/13366

DEPRESS - FL PROFILE: OXYGEN ALTITUDE FOR 120 MIN THEN FL150
LAT/LONG        N52 05.8/W036 28.0         CYQX              EINN
TIME TO ETP DIVRSN PT        02.55
DIST TO ETP DIVRSN PT        01541
FUEL TO ETP DIVRSN PT/RMNG   010347 /18753
FL/BURN/TIME TO ETP AP       150/11951/03.00   150/11974/02.57
TAS/ETA/DIST TO ETP AP       278/2254/000717   281/2252/001007
MAG CRS/AVG WIND COMP TO ETP AP    271/M046       105/P051
ISA TEMP DEV TO ETP AP              M016           M010
TOTAL FUEL TO ETP AP /RMNG     22298/06779     22321/06779

MEDICAL
LAT/LONG        N52 05.3/W037 00.9         CYQX              EINN
TIME TO ETP DIVRSN PT        02.52
DIST TO ETP DIVRSN PT        01521
FUEL TO ETP DIVRSN PT/RMNG   010234 /18866
FL/BURN/TIME TO ETP AP       200/11482/02.49   200/11505/02.48
TAS/ETA/DIST TO ETP AP       302/2241/000697   304/2240/001027
MAG CRS/AVG WIND COMP TO ETP AP    271/M060       105/P057
ISA TEMP DEV TO ETP AP              M012           M010
TOTAL FUEL TO ETP AP /RMNG     21716/07361     21739/07361
```

The ETP's are plotted with a line off to one side with arrows pointing to the ETP airports. As a technique, if the engine-out, medical, and pressurization loss ETP's are within 100 nm of each other, only the middle ETP need be plotted.

In our example, the 1E INOP, DEPRESS, and MEDICAL ETPs are 1510, 1541, and 1521 nautical miles from CYQX, so only the 1521 is plotted. The point is at 52° 05.8'N 37° 00.9'W. Since we know the point will be on our course line, we just need to put our tick mark along the course at 37° 00.9'W. The line is drawn away from the course for clarity and arrows are drawn in the direction of CYQX and EINN.

If we have any reason to divert prior to this ETP, we will choose to reverse course to CYQX. Beyond that point, we press forward to EINN.

Compute and Plot PSRs, if required

The Point of Safe Return (PSR) provides the pilot with the farthest point to which the aircraft can go and be able to return safely to the departure point with

```
                 CRITICAL FUEL SUMMARIES

PNR
LAT/LONG      N51 26.5/W046 36.0          KBED
TIME TO ETP DIVRSN PT           02.11
DIST TO ETP DIVRSN PT           01161
FUEL TO ETP DIVRSN PT/RMNG      008170 /20930
FL/BURN/TIME TO ETP AP          200/20928/04.46
TAS/ETA/DIST TO ETP AP          308/2357/001141
MAG CRS/AVG WIND COMP TO ETP AP    262/M072
ISA TEMP DEV TO ETP AP                  M003
TOTAL FUEL TO ETP AP /RMNG         29098/00001
```

adequate holding, approach, landing, and alternate fuel. It is normally used when flying to remote island destinations with no diversion possibilities en route but can be useful even when alternates are available. See the Appendices, Chapter 30.

ARINCDirect will provide a "PNR" upon request, as shown. The "Point of No Return" is the same thing as the "Point of Safe Return," with a more dramatic name.

If any of our passengers decide they need to go back to our departure airport (KBED), the last moment you can do this without having to make a fuel stop is shown with the red bracket on the chart. Keep in mind that if you return at this point, you will need to fly direct to the airport, the PSR does not use normal routings that anyone less than an emergency aircraft will be offered.

Add CPDLC Addresses, if desired

You can add the applicable CPDLC FIR boundaries, AFN and ATSU addresses, if you are so equipped and would like the information available on the chart. For more about this see: Part IV, Chapter 5.

For our example we'll highlight the FIR boundary between Gander and Shanwick, and enter the addresses found in the ICAO Gold Manual, Appendix E.

Figure: ICAO Gold Appendix E, from ICAO Gold Manual, Appendix E.

Our plotting chart is now ready for the flight.

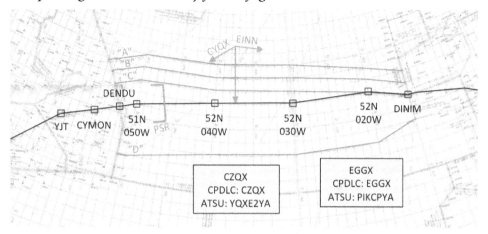

Ramp

UTC Time Check

[AC 91-70A, Appendix 2, ¶2.b.(1)] It is a requirement to have a master clock onboard synchronized to universal coordinated time (UTC) or GPS. Use this time source, which is typically the flight management system (FMS), for all ETAs and ATAs. The use of multiple time sources on the aircraft has lead to inconsistencies in reporting times to ATC and resulted in a loss of longitudinal separation.

Fuel Check

Record fuel onboard on the master document; this quantity will become the basis for subsequent fuel checks.

Domestic Clearance

You will typically have a domestic clearance that will include your destination but not the oceanic portion of the trip. Your clearance at this stage does not normally give you clearance into oceanic airspace.

Our domestic clearance is: "Gulfstream seven seven zero zero is cleared to Geneva via radar vector Lobstah then as filed. After takeoff maintain runway heading and climb to two thousand feet, expect flight level four three zero ten minutes after takeoff. Contact departure control on one two four point four, squawk four three two one." We are cleared to our destination but we do not have clearance into oceanic airspace.

SELCAL Configuration

Some aircraft encode their SELCAL codes in software and may lose the code on occasion. In the G450, for example, the code can be entered from any cockpit audio control panel but only when on the ground. It is a good idea to make sure the code is entered and correct when you can.

Altimeters

[AC 91-70A, ¶3-12.c.(2)] Operators should review their documentation to ensure that it provides all the information required to reconstruct the flight. These records also satisfy the ICAO standard of keeping a journal. Specific requirements could include, but do not only apply to, the following:

- Record of the initial ramp position (latitude/longitude) in the LRNS, original planned flight track, and levels.

- Record of the LRNS gross error check, RVSM altimeter comparisons, and heading reference crosschecks before entering oceanic airspace.

[AC 91-70A, Appendix 2, ¶2.b.(4)] Before taxi, crews should set their altimeters to the airport QNH. Both primary altimeters must agree within ± 75 feet of field elevation. The two primary altimeters must also agree within the limits noted in the aircraft operating manual.

Groundspeed Check

[AC 91-70A, ¶3-6.i.] After leaving the ramp, check INS groundspeeds. Perform a check of the malfunction codes while the aircraft stops but after it has taxied at least part of the way to the takeoff position. Any significant groundspeed indication while stationary may indicate a faulty unit.

An inertial ground speed while stationary is an indication there is significant drift in the unit. Some aircraft offer a "quick align" to reset the inertial's ground speed to zero. In older Gulfstreams, for example, switching from NAV to ALIGN to NAV in less than six seconds causing such a quick align. Other aircraft with Hybrid IRS, such as the G450, automatically perform a quick realign any time the aircraft is motionless for more than 7.5 minutes.

RVSM/NAV Performance Log

You should have a log to record your altimeter and navigation system performance so that you remember to check all that needs to be checked, and so that you have a written record of it. A blank log is available in the Appendices, Chapter 29.

CPDLC Checklist

If you are CPDLC-equipped and departing into an area with CPDLC coverage, you have several steps to accomplish while still sitting on the ramp. It may be helpful to add a printed copy of your CPDLC checklist to the RVSM/NAV Performance Log and Master Document. See Part IV, Chapter 6.

Local Procedures Review

The Jeppesen Airway Manual approach charts for the airport may have several pages of local procedures that should be reviewed prior to request for clearance or engine start. These proce-

Oceanic Checklist and RVSM/NAV Performance Log

Preflight

☑ Label one copy of the computer flight plan "Master Document"
☑ Plot route over Class II airspace and any relevant tracks
☑ Add ETPs (loss of pressurization, all-engine cruise, loss of engine) if required
☑ Position Check: Ramp (GPS) N/S ____42°27.6____ E/W ____71°17.4____

IRS #1	IRS #2	IRS #3	GPS #1	GPS#2
Diff 0.0	Diff 0.0	Diff 0.0	Diff 0.0	Diff 0.0

☑ Altimeter Check: QNH 2992 Pilot's 120 Stby 130 Copilot's 120
☑ Time Check: Source (circle) WWV/GPS/ATC +/- 10 sec ____
☑ Compare Master Document course/distance with plotting or en route chart, circle waypoint
☑ Compare Master Document course/distance with FMS, draw diagonal over waypoint
☑ Record fuel onboard on the Master Document

Coast Out

☐ Check both HFs, check SELCAL prior to entering oceanic airspace
☐ Nav Accuracy Check:

RAW: Fix _____ Radial _____ Distance _____
FMS: Fix _____ Radial _____ Distance _____

☐ Altimeter Check: QNH ____ Pilot's ____ Stby ____ Copilot's ____
☐ Record oceanic clearances on the Master Document

At Each Waypoint

☐ Record ATA, fuel remaining, winds/temperature (if required), next ETA, HF frequencies, three altimeters on Master Document
☐ Make the position report, draw a second diagonal over waypoint on Master Document
☐ Check distance, time, heading, and fuel remaining to the next waypoint against the Master Document
☐ Plot aircraft position approximately 10 minutes after waypoint passage

Coast In

☐ Nav Accuracy Check:

RAW: Fix _____ Radial _____ Distance _____
FMS: Fix _____ Radial _____ Distance _____

Post-flight

☐ Position Check: Ramp (GPS) N/S _____ E/W _____

IRS #1	IRS #2	IRS #3	GPS #1	GPS#2
Diff _____	Diff _____	Diff _____	Diff _____	Diff _____

☐ Altimeter Check: QNH ____ Pilot's ____ Stby ____ Copilot's ____

dures can include specific instructions that are critical to successfully operating at the airport, such as:

- Engine start procedures

- Clearance delivery procedures

- Start-up, push-back and taxi procedures

- Noise abatement procedures

- Speed restrictions on departure and arrival

- Runway entry and exit procedures

If you are at an unfamiliar airport it always pays to listen to the ground control or tower frequencies for a while to get the "lay of the land" and a heads up as to your immediate future. A few things to listen for:

- Is ground control giving ATC clearances before taxi? (That is not the normal procedure for most of the world.) If they are giving ATC clearance that is what you ask for, "Request ATC clearance."

- Which departure procedures are in use? At locations where advance ATC clearance is not given, you will be listening to your ATC clearance while you are taxiing, just minutes away from takeoff. You will often have a difficult time understanding what the departure procedure is and it will be to your benefit to have an idea early on. Some airports group departures based on the runway in use, for example.

- Taxi routings can include instructions you've never heard before. You may hear other aircraft instructed to "Holding Point Whiskey" but not see that immediately on any charts. Hearing this given to another airplane gives you some time to look it up.

Oceanic Clearance Prior to Departure

You normally request your oceanic clearance while airborne but there are exceptions for some airports that are close to oceanic airspace. For example:

[Jeppesen Airway Manual / State Rules and Procedures - Ireland] NAT flights departing Irish aerodromes excluding Dublin, Weston and Casement (Baldonnel) airports, planned to enter NAT airspace between GOMUP and BEDRA (inclusive) should request Oceanic Clearance from Shanwick Oceanic via ORCA Datalink prior to departure. Shannon ACC will on request obtain Oceanic Clearance from Shanwick Oceanic and pass the clearance to the flight prior to departure.

If you are departing from an airport that is near the oceanic airspace you will be transitting, you should check the applicable Jeppesen Airway Manual page for a requirement to obtain oceanic clearance prior to departure.

Prior to Oceanic Boundary/Oceanic Clearance

Departure Timing

- Time to Taxi. If assigned a wheels up time or a time crossing your first oceanic point, you may need to carefully plan when you plan leaving the chocks. You can estimate your taxi time using the airfield diagram:

- Scale: The longitude scale should include the degree minutes in the format degree - minutes. 46-14, for example, means 46°14'. Each minute of longitude equals one nautical mile.

- Distance to Taxi: Using that scale, you can estimate the distance from your parking stand to the runway holding point.

- Time to Taxi: If you taxi at twenty knots, you will cover each nautical mile in 3 minutes. Remember to add a few seconds for each turn as you will probably slow a bit.

Time to climb - FMS Capable

A modern FMS should give you an accurate ETA to your first oceanic way-point if you input the estimated takeoff time.

If in EINN, for example, expecting the ERAB2B departure to ERABI, DOGAL, and then oceanic routing, you can enter expected takeoff times and see the ETA for each point update. If your oceanic clearance stipulates a 0837Z time over-head DOGAL, you can subtract the FMS time at DOGAL from the planned departure time to come up with an ETE, then use that to adjust the departure time. For our G450, we see it takes 37 minutes, so we enter /0800Z at LSK 1L on the first page of the flight plan. The FMS computes we will reach DOGAL at 0837Z. Now we know we must takeoff at 0800Z to make that happen.

Time to climb - FMS Not Capable

Some older FMS will not correctly compute ETAs during or following a climb to altitude. In the older G-IIIs, for example, the FMS assumed 250 knots ground speed until level off, which was way too slow. We found adding 5 minutes to the ETA for any point between FL 300 and FL 350 plus an additional 1 minute per every additional 5,000 feet worked well. Of course that was for the G-III, you will have to experiment to find a rule for your FMS.

Transition Altitude.

[ICAO Document 4444, Ch 1]

- Transition altitude: The altitude at or below which the vertical position of an aircraft is controlled by reference to altitudes.

- Transition Layer: The airspace between the transition altitude and the transition level.

- Transition Level: The lowest flight level available for use above the transition altitude.

Crews should brief the transition altitude based on information from approach plates, ATIS, or the applicable State pages. After climbing through the transition altitude, the altimeters should be reset to 29.92 inches or 1013.2 hPa. See the Appendices, Chapter 6.

Climb Level-off Procedure.

[ICAO NAT Doc 007, ¶9.1.13] To prevent unwanted TCAS/ACAS warnings or alerts, when first approaching any cleared flight level in NAT RVSM airspace, pilots should ensure that the vertical closure speed is not excessive. It is considered that, with about 1500 ft to go to a cleared flight level, vertical speed should be reduced to a maximum of 1500 ft per minute and ideally, to between 1000 ft per minute and 500 ft per minute. Additionally, it is important to ensure that the aeroplane neither undershoots nor overshoots the cleared level by more than 150 ft, manually overriding if necessary.

This seems to be necessary more in Europe than in the United States. Perhaps the skies are more crowded or there is an abundance of older TCAS software. Whatever the reason, reducing climb rates near level off appears to be necessary.

En Route Timing (Prior to Oceanic Airspace).

If en route to the oceanic entry waypoint with a timing restriction, you can make minor adjustments with speed, larger adjustments with routing changes. If late more than a few minutes you may need to get a re-clearance.

Adjusting speed — If flying at typical en route speeds, it will take about 100 nm to impact your ETA by 1 minute if adjusting by 30 knots.

360° Turn — A half-standard rate turn takes 4 minutes.

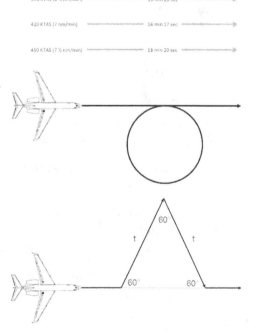

Timing Triangle — A turn 60° off course, followed t-seconds by a turn 60° back towards course, followed t-seconds later by a turn back onto course costs a total of t-seconds.

Note: These adjustments are only for making adjustment aimed at making your oceanic entry point good. Once you are in oceanic airspace, these techniques are expressly forbidden. See Part VIII, Chapter 26, Mach Number Technique.

HF Radio.

[AC 91-70A, Appendix 2, ¶2.b.(8)] Conduct an HF check on the primary and secondary HF radios in areas where dual HF radios are required. If possible, do the HF checks on the ground or before entering oceanic airspace. You should also accomplish a Selective Call (SELCAL) check.

[ICAO NAT Doc 007, ¶6.1.8] When using HF communications and even when using ADS-C and/or CPDLC, pilots should maintain a listening watch on the assigned frequency, unless SELCAL is fitted, in which case they should ensure the following sequence of actions:

- provide the SELCAL code in the flight plan; (any subsequent change of aircraft for a flight will require passing the new SELCAL information to the OAC);

- check the operation of the SELCAL equipment, at or prior to entry into oceanic airspace, with the appropriate aeradio station. (This SELCAL check must be completed prior to commencing SELCAL watch); and

- maintain thereafter a SELCAL watch.

Proper HF frequency selection can be a challenge in some regions and is not always facilitated by VHF center controllers when leaving domestic airspace. Some HF radios can be damaged if set to the same frequency as another radio's transmitter, it is good practice to avoid setting the same frequency in more than one HF radio.

CPDLC or ADS.

[ICAO Gold, ¶ 5.2.2] When CPDLC and/or ADS-C services are available for the flight, the flight crew should initiate an AFN logon in accordance with the conditions provided in [the table]:

Condition(s)	When	Logon address of ATSU
Prior to takeoff, where permitted or required	No earlier than 45 minutes prior to ETD	Current ATSU for the FIR that the departure airport is located within
15 minutes or more prior to FIR boundary estimate	Above 10,000 feet	Current ATSU for the FIR in which the aircraft is operating
Less than 15 minutes prior to FIR boundary estimate	Above 10,000 feet	Next ATSU that provides CPDLC and/or ADS-C services for the FIR on that flight

Oceanic Clearance

```
OCEANIC CLX

1939 120313 LSGG
CLRNCE 599
N7700 CLRD TO LSGG VIA
DENDU
RANDOM ROUTE
51N050W 52N040W 52N030W
52N020W DINIM
FM DENDU/1850 MNTN F390
M080
END OF MESSAGE
```

[AC 91-70A, Appendix 2, ¶2.f.(4)] Obtain Oceanic Clearance. Both pilots must obtain oceanic clearance from the appropriate clearance delivery (OCD). (Clearance via voice should be at least 40 minutes prior to oceanic entry and via data link should be 30 to 90 minutes prior to oceanic entry). An oceanic clearance typically includes a route, FL and assigned Mach. Crews should include their requested FL in their initial clearance request. Some oceanic centers require pilots to advise them at the time of their oceanic clearance When Able Higher (WAH). Crews should be confident that they are able to maintain requested FLs based on aircraft performance capabilities.

[AC 91-70A, Appendix 2, ¶2.f.(4)] Re-Clearance. A re-clearance (that is different from the oceanic route requested with the filed flight plan) is the number one scenario which leads to a GNE. Crews must be particularly cautious when receiving a re-clearance. Both pilots should receive and confirm the new routing and conduct independent crosschecks after updating the LRNS, Master CFP, and plotting chart. It is critical that crews check the magnetic course and distance between the new waypoints as noted in PRE-FLIGHT under the paragraph "LRNS Programming."

A few notes about oceanic clearances:

- CPDLC (Everywhere except NYC) — If you are CPDLC- or ACARS-equipped in any region other than the NYC FIR you can downlink your oceanic through a datalink service provider. See: International Operations / CPDLC - Oceanic Clearance (DSP).

- CPDLC (NYC FIR) — If you are CPDLC in the NYC FIR, you can downlink your oceanic clearance directly through CPDLC. See: International Operations / CPDLC - Oceanic Clearance (NYC).

- Voice Procedures (Gander) — Panel 1 of the Jeppesen Atlantic Orientation Chart includes Gander OCA procedures and frequencies needed to obtain an eastbound oceanic clearance.

- Voice Procedures (Shanwick) — Panel 11 of the Jeppesen Atlantic Orientation Chart includes Shanwick OCA procedures and frequencies needed to obtain oceanic westbound clearance.

We receive our clearance via data link and notice that we have been cleared at FL390, which is a bit unusual for us. A quick glance at the flight plan reveals that we are too heavy to cross any higher but there is a plan to climb to FL410 passing 030W. Of course the flight plan accounts for this but what if, for some reason, we don't get clearance to climb? A quick look at the fuel burns tells us we are okay even if the entire crossing is made at the lower altitude, but just the same we made a note on the plotting chart to remind ourselves to climb.

Master Document

```
FLIGHTPLAN N7700    KBED TO LSGG GLF4  M80 /F  IFR   29DEC13   -- AB
COMPUTED 2024Z FOR ETD 1700Z    PROGS 281200Z                 WGT IN LBS

           FUEL   TIME   DIST ARRIVE TAKEOFF  LAND   AV PLD  OPNLWT
DEST LSGG  019340 06:22  3261 2322Z  073508  054168 000500  043908
RESV       001931 00:45
ALTN       000000 00:00  0000  0000Z
HOLD       000000 00:00
REQD       029100 10:10                        ES ZFW   MX ZFW
TAXI       000400                                44408   49000
XTRA       007829 03:03                        ES LNDG  MX LNDG
TOTL       29500  10:10                          54168  058500

KBED DCT LBSTA ENE J581 YJT CYMON DENDU 5150N 5240N 5230N 5220N
DINIM ELSOX GAPLI UL739 LIZAD UN160 PIGOP UN491 RESMI UM975 LUSAR
DCT LSGG

WIND P062   MXSH 10/LUSAR   AVG WIND 268/071
TAS 451     FL 410 YJT 390 5240N 410

CLIMB SCHED:300/M80    CRUISE SCHED:M80    DESCENT SCHED:M80/300
```

LSGG RV LBSTA TAF RH 2000'
CLEARANCE *X430/10MIN D124.4 / 4321*
Oceanic: DENDU 51N050W, 52N040W, 52N030W, 52N020W, DINIM, X DENDU @ M.80 FL390 1850Z

```
CPT   FLT T    WIND   S TAS AWY    MH   DST  ETE ETR  FU   FR   FF/E
FREQ  TRO TDV  COMP     GRS        MCRS DSTR ATE ATR  AFU  AFR
LAT   LONG                         ATD 1705Z    Fuel: 29,200

LBSTA CLB              DCT    005  0036 006 0616 1103 27997
                             016  3225
N42480 W070368

ENE   CLB              J581   048  0037 005 0611 518  27479
117.1                        058  3188
N43255 W070368

TOC   410              J581   047  0099 011 0600 1065 26414
                             060  3089
N44398 W069059

ODIKE 410 -64 260133 2 451 J581  049  0000 000 0600 2    26413 1517
      39 M08   P095   546         060  3088
N44440 W069056

BGR   410 -64 264130 3 451 J581  069  0014 002 0558 78   26334 1512
114.8 39 M08   P089   540         077  3074
N44505 W068524
```

SELCAL Check

[AC 91-70A, Appendix 2, ¶2.f.(2)] If the crew was unable to accomplish the HF and SELCAL checks on the ground, they must accomplish these checks before oceanic entry.

The SELCAL check is more than a test of your radio equipment, it is a test of the complete connection from your airplane to the radio station. You need to check it every time you change frequencies or FIR. If you are unable to get a good SELCAL check, you must maintain a listening watch on the frequency, even if you are CPDLC equipped.

Coast-Out Navigation Accuracy Check

[AC 91-70A, Appendix 2, ¶2.f.(1)] Gross Error Accuracy Check. Before oceanic entry, check the accuracy of the LRNS against a ground-based NAVAID. Record the results of the accuracy check with the time and position. A large difference between the ground-based NAVAID and the LRNS may require immediate corrective action. Operators should establish a gross error check tolerance based on the type of LRNS. It is not advisable for crews to attempt to correct an error by doing an air alignment or by manually updating the LRNS since this has often contributed to a gross navigation error (GNE).

Before you stray out of ground-based NAVAID range — sooner actually, before you leave the service volume of an appropriate NAVAID — you need to compare what it is telling you versus what your FMS is telling you. The procedure can be checking a VOR Radial/DME plot versus your FMS latitude/longitude on your plotting chart, or using an FMS "Cross Points" function versus the VOR Radial/DME. See the Appendices, Chapter 27.

Prior to Oceanic Boundary Altimeter Check

[AC 91-70A, Appendix 2, ¶2.f.(6)] Altimeter Checks. Crews are required to check the two primary altimeters which must be within 200 feet of each other. Conduct this check while at level flight. You should also note the standby altimeter. Record the altimeter readings with the time.

If your altimeters fail this check you may or may not be able to continue the flight, depending which part of the world you are about to transit. See Part VI, Chapter 4, Loss of RVSM Capability in Oceanic Airspace.

Oceanic Checklist and RVSM/NAV Performance Log

Preflight

- ☑ Label one copy of the computer flight plan "Master Document"
- ☑ Plot route over Class II airspace and any relevant tracks
- ☑ Add ETPs (loss of pressurization, all-engine cruise, loss of engine) if required
- ☑ Position Check: Ramp (GPS) N/S ___42°27.6___ E/W ___71°17.4___

IRS #1	IRS #2	IRS #3	GPS #1	GPS#2
Diff 0.0	Diff 0.0	Diff 0.0	Diff 0.0	Diff 0.0

- ☑ Altimeter Check: QNH 2992 Pilot's 120 Stby 130 Copilot's 120
- ☑ Time Check: Source (circle) WWV/GPS/ATC +/- 10 sec ✓
- ☑ Compare Master Document course/distance with plotting or en route chart, circle waypoint
- ☑ Compare Master Document course/distance with FMS, draw diagonal over waypoint
- ☑ Record fuel onboard on the Master Document

Coast Out

- ☑ Check both HFs, check SELCAL prior to entering oceanic airspace
- ☑ Nav Accuracy Check:

  RAW: Fix YQX Radial 270 Distance 113

  FMS: Fix YQX Radial 270 Distance 112

- ☑ Altimeter Check: QNH 2992 Pilot's 1000 Stby 0900 Copilot's 41020
- ☑ Record oceanic clearances on the Master Document

At Each Waypoint

- ☐ Record ATA, fuel remaining, winds/temperature (if required), next ETA, HF frequencies, three altimeters on Master Document
- ☐ Make the position report, draw a second diagonal over waypoint on Master Document
- ☐ Check distance, time, heading, and fuel remaining to the next waypoint against the Master Document
- ☐ Plot aircraft position approximately 10 minutes after waypoint passage

Coast In

- ☐ Nav Accuracy Check:

  RAW: Fix _____ Radial _____ Distance _____

  FMS: Fix _____ Radial _____ Distance _____

Post-flight

- ☐ Position Check: Ramp (GPS) N/S _____ E/W _____

IRS #1	IRS #2	IRS #3	GPS #1	GPS#2
Diff ___	Diff ___	Diff ___	Diff ___	Diff ___

- ☐ Altimeter Check: QNH ___ Pilot's ___ Stby ___ Copilot's ___

Chapter 3

Oceanic En Route

*F*lying in oceanic airspace requires pilots take on some of the burden that domestically belongs to air traffic control with radar contact. There are a few extra steps prior to and during the oceanic crossing. While procedures worldwide have become much more standardized, there are differences in various regions. The basic procedures are covered here, with regional differences noted. Of course these procedures are changing every day and you should check prior to every trip.

This section continues an example G450 trip from Bedford, Massachusetts (KBED) to Geneva, Switzerland (LSGG), to Mumbai, India (VABB), to Tokyo, Japan (RJAA), to Honolulu, Hawaii (PHNL), to San Francisco, California (KSFO), back to Bedford. For the purpose of covering an oceanic departure, this section will focus on the KBED to LSGG leg. To view the steps required prior to oceanic airspace entry, see the previous chapter.

Entering Oceanic Airspace

There are two sets of rules when it comes to making these ETAs.

• Prior to entering oceanic airspace, it is usually worth your while to adjust speed or use other techniques to make the ETA plus or minus 2 minutes. See Part VII, Chapter 2, En Route Timing, for techniques.

• After entering oceanic airspace you are expressly forbidden from adjusting speed in an attempt to make an ETA good. See the next section for the rationale behind this restriction.

Mach Number Technique

The primary method of maintaining proper longitudinal separation between aircraft throughout almost all of the world's oceanic airspace is for each aircraft to maintain a constant Mach Number. See the Appendices, Chapter 25, Mach Number Technique.

Do not chase the Mach indicator to make your ETA's good. Fly your cleared Mach Number and monitor your ETA progress. If you are off by three minutes or more, inform ATC. If you adjust your speed and the aircraft ahead or behind you do not, there could be a loss of longitudinal separation.

We were assigned Mach 0.80 for our example flight's oceanic clearance and our G450 cockpit indica-

CPT FREQ LAT	FLT T TRO TDV LONG	WIND COMP	S TAS AWY GRS	MH MCRS	DST DSTR	ETE ATE	ETR ATR	FU AFU	FR AFR	FF/E
					ATD 1705 Fuel 29,200 (-300)					
CYMON N49430	390 -55 36 M02 W054599	287123 P084	3 457 DCT 542	080 088	0160 2438	018	0449	896	22874	1518
DENDU N50302	390 -52 36 P04 W052041	288105 P075	7 463 DCT 538	083 090	0123 2315	014 *ETA 1705* *Direct*	0435	698	22176	1531
(•)50N	390 -50 36 P06 W050000	288090 P067	4 465 DCT 531	095 097	0084 2231	009 *ETA 1713*	0426	485	21690	1531
(•)40N	390 -50 52 P07 W040000	276063 P060	2 466 DCT 527	106 104	0379 1851	043	0343	2204	19487	1516
(•)30N	410 -51 52 P06 W030000	252054 P051	1 465 DCT 516	103 100	0371 1481	043	0300	2076	17411	1445
(•)20N	410 -53 31 P05 W020000	241060 P051	464 DCT 515	124 117	0371 1110	043	0217	2026	15385	1407
DCNIM N51000	410 -55 36 P03 W015000	236069 P040	1 462 DCT 502	102 097	0197 0913	024	0153	1081	14305	1377
ELSOX N51000	410 -56 36 P01 W014000	236075 P060	3 460 DCT 520	116 109	0038 0876	004	0149	198	14106	1359

tion gives us a True Mach. So we set 0.80 and allow the auto throttles to manage the speed control. We keep an eye on each ETA and if they vary by three minutes or more, we inform ATC. Since we are in the North Atlantic, we'll wait 30 minutes after DENDU before switching the transponder to Code 2000.

VHF Switch from ATC to Guard / Interplane

[AC 91-70A, Appendix 2, ¶2.g.(3)] After going beyond the range of the assigned VHF frequency, crews should set their radios to interplane (123.45) and guard frequency (121.5).

[ICAO Annex 10 Vol V, ¶4.1.3.2.1] An air-to-air VHF communications channel on the frequency of 123.45 MHz shall be designated to enable aircraft engaged in flights over remote and oceanic areas out of range of VHF ground stations to exchange necessary operational information and to facilitate the resolution of operational problems.

Hand off procedures are not standard, but HF frequencies are normally given by ATC on VHF or CPDLC, and may also be published on en route charts.

- *When checking in on HF, you normally call the station by name, add your call sign and the frequency being called.*

- *If the domestic controller advised you to contact the radio station with a position report, you add the word "position" to your initial call. For example: "Gander Radio, November Seven Seven Zero Zero, Position on eight eight six four."*

- *Tune and listen to the frequency for a few moments to make sure you don't block someone's transmission and to get a feel for how good the frequencies are. If the frequencies are clear, you can combine your SELCAL request with the initial call. For example, let's say you are CPDLC equipped, your call could be: "Gander Radio, November seven seven zero zero, CPDLC, Shanwick Next, flight level four one zero, request SELCAL check Alpha Bravo Charlie Delta." For more about CPDLC procedures, see: International Operations / CPDLC - Coast Out.*

- *Once ATC with VHF is terminated, you should switch to 123.45 and 121.5, as discussed next.*

Gander gives us direct to 51N 050W before we reach DENDU and asks for our "five zero west" estimate. We turn the aircraft direct 51N 050W and see the FMS estimates that point at 1713Z. We pass that on to Gander and record that on the master document, since we will now have to make that time plus or minus 2 minutes or have to revise it.

Since we are CPDLC equipped, Gander Radio tells us "November seven seven zero zero, Gander Radio, voice reports not required in Gander OCA, at thirty west contact Shanwick on three zero one six primary or five five niner eight secondary." We tune 121.5 and 123.45 on our VHF radios, turn the cockpit speakers on to listen to those frequencies and rely on the SELCAL for any HF contact.

Transponder Code

[AC 91-70A, Appendix 2, ¶2.g.] Thirty minutes after oceanic entry, crews should squawk 2000, if applicable. There may be regional differences such as squawking 2100 in Bermuda's airspace or maintaining last assigned squawk in the West Atlantic Route System (WATRS). Crews transiting Reykjavik's airspace must maintain last assigned squawk.

Other exceptions:

- Caribbean / South America. [AC 91-70A, ¶ 8-16.b.] Use code 2000 when beyond radar coverage if there is no specification for another code.

- Iceland. [AC 91-70A, ¶ 13-9.b.] Pilots will operate SSR transponders continuously on Mode A, Code 2000, except that departing aircraft will retain the last assigned code for 30 minutes after entry into NAT oceanic airspace unless otherwise instructed by ATC.

- North Pacific Oceanic. [AC 91-70A, ¶ 5-5.b.] When reaching oceanic airspace, squawk 2000 and monitor VHF 121.5 and the pacific air-to-air frequency 123.45.

- Polar Routes. [AC 91-70A, ¶ 14-3.b.] On polar routes beyond areas of radar coverage, squawk 2000.

Thirty minutes after DENDU we switch the transponder to Code 2000.

Traffic Information Broadcasts by Aircraft (TIBA)

In areas where Traffic Information Broadcasts by Aircraft (TIBA) or the IATA In-Flight Broadcast Procedure is mandated by the country specific AIP, Jeppesen Airway ATC pages, or en route charts, cockpit radios should be set up and procedures for these broadcasts. See the Appendices, Chapter 34, Traffic Information Broadcast by Aircraft (TIBA).

For our example flight, there are no TIBA requirements in the North Atlantic, so we do not bother with this.

Strategic Lateral Offset (SLOP)

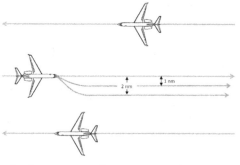

Aircraft with an automatic FMS offset capability should routinely fly 1 nm or 2 nm right of course centerline while in oceanic airspace in most of the world. The selection of on course, 1 nm, or 2 nm right of course can be made based on wake turbulence considerations. Where authorized, there is no ATC clearance required and it is not necessary to advise ATC. Voice position reports are based on the waypoints of the current ATC clearance and not offset positions. Aircraft without an automatic FMS offset capability should fly the centerline only.

SLOP is not universal, you cannot use it everywhere, but where it is authorized you should use it. See the Appendices, Chapter 35, Strategic Lateral Offset Procedure (SLOP).

SLOP is recommended in the North Atlantic and it is the one oceanic area where we are certain it is allowed for aircraft with ADS-C, so we initiate a 2 nm SLOP to the right. (Statistics show 40% of aircraft choose 1 nm, 20% choose 2 nm, and the remaining 40% remain on the centerline; we figure 2 nm right improves our odds of having the space to ourselves.)

Waypoint Passage

Approaching Each Waypoint

[AC 91-70A, Appendix 2, ¶2h.] Within a few minutes of crossing an oceanic waypoint, crews should crosscheck the coordinates of that waypoint and the next waypoint. This check should be done by comparing the coordinates against the Master CFP based on the currently effective ATC clearance.

[ICAO NAT Doc 007, ¶8.4.14.(c)] at the waypoint, check the distance to the next waypoint, confirm that the aircraft turns in the correct direction and takes up a new heading and track appropriate to the leg to the next waypoint.

You will be fairly busy during waypoint passage and with most FMSs the distance between waypoints starts to decrease once the waypoint is crossed. A good technique to get around all this is to place the pilot's heading bug on the next expected mag-

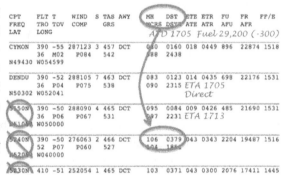

CPT	FLT T	WIND	S	TAS	AWY	MH	DST	ETE	ETR	FU	FR	FF/E
FREQ	TRO TOV	COMP		GRS		MCRS	DSTR	ATE	ATR	AFU	AFR	
LAT	LONG					ATD	1705		*Fuel 29,200 (-300)*			
CYMON	390 -55	287123	3	457	DCT	040	0160	018	0449	896	22874	1518
	36 M02	P084		542		088	2438					
N49430	W054599											
DENDU	390 -52	288105	7	463	DCT	083	0123	014	0435	698	22176	1531
	36 P04	P075		538		090	2315	*ETA 1705*				
N50302	W052041								*Direct*			
5150N	390 -50	288090	4	465	DCT	095	0084	009	0426	485	21690	1531
N51050	W050000	P06		531		097	2231	*ETA 1713*				
5240N	390 -50	276063	2	466	DCT	106	0379	043	0343	2204	19487	1516
N52000	W040000	52 P07		527		104	1854					
5230N	410 -51	252054	1	465	DCT	103	0371	043	0300	2076	17411	1445

netic heading listed on the flight plan a minute or so prior to the waypoint and at that point make sure the distance to the next waypoint checks. At waypoint passage, if a turn is needed, the aircraft should turn to the heading bug.

We are heading direct to 51N 050W and our next waypoint will be 52N 040W. Our example flight plan shows the heading to 52N 040W should be 106° and the distance will be 379 nm. We set the heading bug to 106 and verify the distance shown on the FMS is correct.

Master Document Update

[AC 91-70A, Appendix 2, ¶2.g.(5)] Crews are to observe the primary and stand-by altimeters each hour. We recommend that you record these hourly checks with the readings and times. This documentation can aid crews in determining the most accurate altimeter if an altimetry problem develops.

The first thing we do passing the waypoint is make note of the fuel, since that number is constantly changing. The annotation "21,300 (-400)" tells us how much we had at that point and that the amount is 400 lbs short of the flight plan estimate. Since we started at "(-300)" on takeoff, we know the trend is against us and make note of the fact we need to keep an eye on this.

CPT / FREQ / LAT	FLT T / TRO TDV / LONG	WIND / COMP	S	TAS / GRS	AWY	MH / MCRS	DST / DSTR	ETE / ATE	ETR / ATR	FU / AFU	FR / AFR	FF/E
							ATD 1705 Fuel 29,200 (-300)					
CYMON N49430 W054599	390 -55 36 M02	287123 P084	3	457 542	DCT	080 088	0160 2438	018	0449	896	22874	1518
DENDU N50302 W052041	390 -52 36 P04	288105 P075	7	463 538	DCT	083 090	0123 2315 ETA 1705	014 *Direct*	0435	698	22176	1531
5?50N A5100 W050000	390 -50 36 P06	288090 P067	4	465 531	DCT	095 097	0084 2231 ETA 1713	009	0426	485	21690	1531
					3016/5598 - 39000/38700/39020 - ATA 1713					21,300 (-400)		
5?40N A520? W040000	390 -50 52 P07	276063 P060	2	466 527	DCT	106 104	0379 1851 ETA 1756	043	0343	2204	19487	1516
5?30N A520? W030000	410 -51 52 P06	252054 P051	1	465 516	DCT	103 100	0371 1481	043	0300	2076	17411	1445
5?20N A520? W020000	410 -53 31 P05	241060 P051		464 515	DCT	124 117	0371 1110	043	0217	2026	15385	1407
D?NIM A5100 W015000	410 -55 36 P03	236069 P040	1	462 502	DCT	102 097	0197 0913	024	0153	1081	14305	1377

We also make note of the ATA, the frequencies, all three altimeters, and the next ETA.

Position Report

[AC 91-70A, Appendix 2, ¶2.i.(3)] After passing over the oceanic waypoint, crews that give a position report to ATC must use the standard format. Flights designated as meteorology information (MET) reporting flights or flights on random routes should be including in the position report additional items such as winds and temperatures. Crews should also note and record their field status at each oceanic waypoint. This is especially important if the cleared route and FL differ significantly from the filed flight plan.

Position reports can be made via voice or CPDLC. See Part IV, Chapter 3, Voice Position Reports; and Part IV, Chapter 5, CPDLC.

Since we are CPDLC-equipped, our HF radio conversation goes like this:

Us: "Gander Radio, November seven seven zero zero, on three zero one six."

Them: "November seven seven zero zero, Gander Radio, go ahead."

Us: "November seven seven zero zero, CPDLC, Shanwick next, flight level three niner zero, request SELCAL check alpha bravo charlie delta."

Them: "November seven seven zero zero, Gander Radio, voice reports not required in Gander OCA, at thirty west contact Shanwick on five five niner eight primary, three zero one six secondary, SELCAL check alpha bravo charlie delta."

At this point we get the SELCAL, acknowledge that, and get ready for our next chores.

After Waypoint Passage

Heading Check

If you preset the heading bug during the Approaching Each Waypoint step, you need only verify that the aircraft turned to the correct heading. Otherwise you should now crosscheck the aircraft's heading against the master document.

We make a second diagonal on the 050W waypoint, signifying the waypoint duties have been completed. At this point you should set a timer to make the post-position plot, about ten minutes after waypoint passage. Flying east-to-west or west-to-east at a mid-latitude, two degrees on longitude will make this chore easier. More on that next. . .

Oceanic Checklist and RVSM/NAV Performance Log

Preflight

☑ Label one copy of the computer flight plan "Master Document"
☑ Plot route over Class II airspace and any relevant tracks
☑ Add ETPs (loss of pressurization, all-engine cruise, loss of engine) if required
☑ Position Check: Ramp (GPS) N/S ___42°27.6___ E/W ___71°17.4___

IRS #1	IRS #2	IRS #3	GPS #1	GPS#2
Diff 0.0	Diff 0.0	Diff 0.0	Diff 0.0	Diff 0.0

☑ Altimeter Check: QNH 2992 Pilot's 120 Stby 130 Copilot's 120
☑ Time Check: Source (circle) WWV/GPS/ATC +/- 10 sec ✓
☑ Compare Master Document course/distance with plotting or en route chart, circle waypoint
☑ Compare Master Document course/distance with FMS, draw diagonal over waypoint
☑ Record fuel onboard on the Master Document

Coast Out

☑ Check both HFs, check SELCAL prior to entering oceanic airspace
☑ Nav Accuracy Check:

RAW: Fix YQX Radial 270 Distance 113
FMS: Fix YQX Radial 270 Distance 112

☑ Altimeter Check: QNH 2992 Pilot's 41000 Stby 0900 Copilot's 41020
☑ Record oceanic clearances on the Master Document

At Each Waypoint

☑ Record ATA, fuel remaining, winds/temperature (if required), next ETA, HF frequencies, three altimeters on Master Document
☑ Make the position report, draw a second diagonal over waypoint on Master Document
☑ Check distance, time, heading, and fuel remaining to the next waypoint against the Master Document
☐ Plot aircraft position approximately 10 minutes after waypoint passage

Coast In

☐ Nav Accuracy Check:

RAW: Fix _____ Radial _____ Distance _____
FMS: Fix _____ Radial _____ Distance _____

Post-flight

☐ Position Check: Ramp (GPS) N/S _____ E/W _____

IRS #1	IRS #2	IRS #3	GPS #1	GPS#2
Diff _____	Diff _____	Diff _____	Diff _____	Diff _____

☐ Altimeter Check: QNH _____ Pilot's _____ Stby _____ Copilot's _____

Post-Position Plot

[AC 91-70A, Appendix 2, ¶2.j.] Approximately 10 minutes after passing an oceanic waypoint, crews should plot the latitude, longitude and time on the plotting chart. It is advisable to plot the non-steering LRNS. A 10-minute plot can alert the crew to any lateral deviation from their ATC clearance prior to it becoming a GNE. A good crosscheck for the position of the 10-minute plot is that it is approximately 2° of longitude past the oceanic waypoint.

The "non-steering LRNS" may not apply to many aircraft, since triple FMS with hybrid IRUs tend to blend everything together. The point, however, is to plot the aircraft's position after about ten minutes to ensure the next waypoint wasn't entered in error. If, for example, the flight plan download (or manual entry) entered the next waypoint as 51N 040W, one degree south of the clearance, it would look perfectly normal on the cockpit displays but plotting the position would alert the crew that something is amiss. See the Part II, Chapter 5, Plotting, and the Appendices, Chapter 30, Post Position Plot.

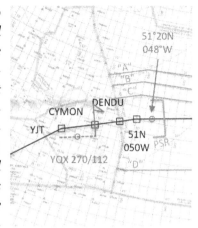

Next Waypoint Preparation

[AC 91-70A, Appendix 2, ¶2.i.(2)] Crews must be vigilant in passing an accurate ETA to ATC for the next waypoint. A change of 3 minutes or more requires that ATC receives notification in a timely manner. There is substantial emphasis on reducing longitudinal separation and this timely update must be a priority for the crews.

Midpoint Weather

[AC 91-70A, Appendix 2, ¶2.k.] Midway Between Waypoints. It is good practice to crosscheck winds midway between oceanic waypoints by comparing the Master CFP, LRNS and upper millibar wind chart. As noted before, this information will be in a position report if the flight is either a MET reporting flight or is a flight on a random route. This crosscheck will also aid crews in case there is a need for a contingency such as DR.

From here on each waypoint uses the same procedure, but we'll have to remember to:

- *Note when we pass our ETP that our primary divert location changes from Gander to Shannon.*

- *Look for new ADS-C contracts with Shanwick approaching 030W, followed by a "NEXT CTR" notification with CPDLC, in the case of a Honeywell-equipped Gulfstream.*

- *Contact Shanwick at 030W and request our climb to FL410.*

Chapter 4

Oceanic Arrival

Transforming your craft from an oceanic vessel back to domestic operations is just a matter of making the right contacts, finishing some paperwork, removing SLOP (if any), and getting the cockpit ready for airways, radar contact, and full time air traffic control. This section continues an example G450 trip from Bedford, Massachusetts (KBED) to Geneva, Switzerland (LSGG), to Mumbai, India (VABB), to Tokyo, Japan (RJAA), to Honolulu, Hawaii (PHNL), to San Francisco, California (KSFO), back to Bedford. For the purpose of covering an oceanic arrival, this section will focus on the KBED to LSGG leg. To view the steps required prior to oceanic airspace entry and the en route portion, see the previous chapters in this part.

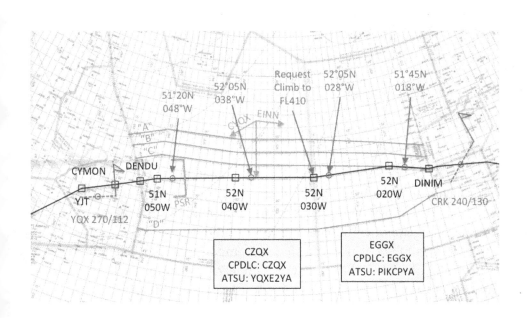

Coast-in Navigation Accuracy Check

[AC 91-70A, Appendix 2, ¶2.l.(1)] Compare Ground-Based NAVAID to LRNS. When departing oceanic airspace and acquiring ground-based NAVAIDs, crews should note the accuracy of the LRNS by comparing it to those NAVAIDs. Note any discrepancy in the maintenance log.

The coast-in navigation accuracy check is conducted in the same manner as for coast-out, except that the earliest possible navigation aid is sought for the first opportunity to check navigation performance, keeping in mind the service volume of the navaid is limited. See the Appendices, Chapter 26, Navigation Accuracy Check.

Strategic Lateral Offset

[AC 91-70A, Appendix 2, ¶2.l.(2)] Remove Strategic Lateral Offset. Crews using a lateral offset of 1 nm or 2 nm right of CL at oceanic entry need a procedure to remove this lateral offset at coast in prior to exiting oceanic airspace. It is advisable to include this as a checklist item. See the Appendices, Chapter 33, Strategic Lateral Offset.

Domestic Routing

[AC 91-70A, Appendix 2, ¶2.l.(3)] Confirm Routing after Oceanic Exit. Before entering the domestic route structure, crews must confirm their routing to include aircraft speed.

Transition Level

[AC 91-70A, Appendix 2, ¶2.m.] Descent and Transition Level. During the approach briefing, crews should note the transition level on the approach plate or verified by automated terminal information service (ATIS). Crews must be diligent when descending through the transition level to reset the altimeters to QNH. This is particularly important when encountering instrument flight rules (IFR), night or high terrain situations. Clarify any confusion between a QNH set with inches of Mercury or hPa.

[ICAO Document 4444, Ch 1]

- Transition altitude: The altitude at or below which the vertical position of an aircraft is controlled by reference to altitudes.

- Transition Layer: The airspace between the transition altitude and the transition level.

- Transition Level: The lowest flight level available for use above the transition altitude.

See the Appendices, Chapter 6, Altimetery (Transition Level).

Other Coast-in Notes

Position Reporting will be continued until Air Traffic Control instructs: "discontinue position reports," or that "radar contact" is regained.

Mach Number Technique will be continued until returning to domestic airspace or Air Traffic Control approves a change of speed.

Plotting can be discontinued once the aircraft has returned to Class I airspace.

Much of your paperwork will need to retained, see: Record Keeping, below.

At the very least you will need to record altimeter readings after landing and if you do not have a hybrid IRU that records inertial performance, you should record those as well. It would be a good idea to put your RVSM/Nav Performance log near the top of your paperwork so you don't forget it.

Post-Flight

[AC 91-70A, Appendix 2, ¶2.n.(1)] Navigation Accuracy Check. When arriving at the destination gate, crews should note any drift or circular error in the LRNS. A GPS primary means system normally should not exceed 0.27 nm for the flight. Some inertial systems may drift as much as 2 nm per hour. Because the present generation of LRNSs is highly accurate, operators should establish a drift tolerance which, if exceeded, would require a write-up in the maintenance log. Required Navigation Performance (RNP) requirements demand close monitoring of drift.

Oceanic Checklist and RVSM/NAV Performance Log

Preflight

☑ Label one copy of the computer flight plan "Master Document"
☑ Plot route over Class II airspace and any relevant tracks
☑ Add ETPs (loss of pressurization, all-engine cruise, loss of engine) if required
☑ Position Check: Ramp (GPS) N/S ___42°27.6___ E/W ___71°17.4___

IRS #1	IRS #2	IRS #3	GPS #1	GPS#2
Diff 0.0	Diff 0.0	Diff 0.0	Diff 0.0	Diff 0.0

☑ Altimeter Check: QNH 2992 Pilot's 120 Stby 130 Copilot's 120
☑ Time Check: Source (circle) WWV/GPS/ATC +/- 10 sec ___✓___
☑ Compare Master Document course/distance with plotting or en route chart, circle waypoint
☑ Compare Master Document course/distance with FMS, draw diagonal over waypoint
☑ Record fuel onboard on the Master Document

Coast Out

☑ Check both HFs, check SELCAL prior to entering oceanic airspace
☑ Nav Accuracy Check:

RAW: Fix YQX   Radial 270   Distance 113
FMS: Fix YQX   Radial 270   Distance 112

☑ Altimeter Check: QNH 2992 Pilot's 41000 Stby 40900 Copilot's 41020
☑ Record oceanic clearances on the Master Document

At Each Waypoint

☑ Record ATA, fuel remaining, winds/temperature (if required), next ETA, HF frequencies, three altimeters on Master Document
☑ Make the position report, draw a second diagonal over waypoint on Master Document
☑ Check distance, time, heading, and fuel remaining to the next waypoint against the Master Document
☑ Plot aircraft position approximately 10 minutes after waypoint passage

Coast In

☑ Nav Accuracy Check:

RAW: Fix CRK   Radial 240   Distance 130
FMS: Fix CRK   Radial 240   Distance 129

Post-flight

☑ Position Check: Ramp (GPS) N/S ___46°13.0___ E/W ___06°06.4___

IRS #1	IRS #2	IRS #3	GPS #1	GPS#2
Diff 0.4	Diff 0.2	Diff 1.2	Diff 0.0	Diff 0.0

☑ Altimeter Check: QNH 1010 Pilot's 1410 Stby 1440 Copilot's 1430

[AC 91-70A, Appendix 2, ¶2.n.(2)] RVSM Write-Ups. Note problems noted in the altimetry system, altitude alert, or altitude hold in the maintenance log. Closely monitor the RVSM airspace for any height deviations. Do not flight plan an aircraft not meeting the strict RVSM standards into RVSM airspace without corrective action.

Record Keeping.

[AC 91-70A, ¶3-6.t.] At the end of each flight, determine the accuracy of the navigational system to facilitate correction of performance. You may perform a check to determine the radial error at the ramp position as soon as the aircraft parks. Radial errors for INSs in excess of 2 nm per hour are generally considered excessive (part 121, appendix G). Keep records on each individual navigation system performance.

[AC 91-70A, ¶3-12.c.]

1. Record Documentation. Decisions regarding monitoring of an aircraft's navigation performance are largely the prerogative of individual operators. In deciding what records to keep, airlines should consider the stringent requirements associated with special use airspaces such as MNPS. Investigating all errors of 20 nm or greater in MNPS airspace is a requirement for airlines. Whether radar or the flight crew observes these deviations, it is imperative to determine and eliminate the cause of the deviation. Therefore, operators should keep complete flight records so that they can make an analysis. The retention of these documents must include the original and any amended clearances.

2. Documentation Requirements. Operators should review their documentation to ensure that it provides all the information required to reconstruct the flight. These records also satisfy the ICAO standard of keeping a journal. Specific requirements could include, but do not only apply to, the following:

   a. Record of the initial ramp position (latitude/longitude) in the LRNS, original planned flight track, and levels.

   b. Record of the LRNS gross error check, RVSM altimeter comparisons, and heading reference crosschecks before entering oceanic airspace.

   c. Plotting charts to include post waypoint 10-minute plots.

   d. All ATC clearances and revisions.

   e. All position reports made to ATC (e.g., voice, data link).

   f. The master document used in the actual navigation of the flight, including a record of waypoint sequencing allocated to specific points, ETA, and actual times of arrival (ATA).

g.   Comments on any navigation problems relating to the flight, including any discrepancies relating to ATC clearances or information passed to the aircraft following ground radar observations, including weather deviations or wake turbulence areas.

It may be useful to carry an envelope for each planned oceanic leg, labeled with the following information:

- *Date*
- *Departure/destination*
- *PIC/SIC/Relief Pilot*

The following items, as applicable, should be retained at the aircraft base:

- *Master Document*
- *RVSM/Nav Performance Log*
- *Navigation Worksheet*
- *Plotting chart*
- *Weather reports*
- *Track Messages*
- *Over-flight/landing permits*
- *INOTAMS/NOTAMS*
- *Post-Flight report form*

There is no regulatory guidance on how long these records should be retained, other than "within reasonable limits." (AC 91-70A, ¶3-12.b.) We use six months.

Chapter 1

Agriculture Import

*T*he USDA no longer offers a booklet on what you can bring into the United
States. Instead, they have website, http://www.aphis.usda.gov/wps/portal/
aphis/home, with guidance on what can and cannot be imported. You don't
often get asked by your passengers what is okay and what isn't, but you as the
pilot are still the one in jeopardy. You should have an idea of what is okay and
where to look if you aren't sure.*

*The USDA website does not easily link and they often change those links in
an effort to make things harder than they should. I will try to point you in the
right direction but they seem to change things every six months or so.*

Generally Allowed Food Items

[www.aphis.usda.gov] — Click "Resources" / "Travelers International" and
under "Related Links" select "Generally Allow Food and Agricultural Items
by Category"

The following food items are generally allowed entry:

- Condiments such as oil, vinegar, mustard, catsup, pickles, syrup, honey
  without honey combs, jelly, and jam.

- Foodstuffs such as bakery items, candy, and chocolate.

- Hard cured cheeses without meat, such as Parmesan or cheddar.

- Canned goods and goods in vacuum-packed jars (except those containing meat or poultry products) for personal use.

- Fish or fish products for personal use.

- Powdered drinks sealed in original containers with ingredients listed in
  English.

- Dry mixes containing dairy and egg ingredients (such as baking mixes,
  cocoa mixes, drink mixes, instant cake mixes, instant pudding mixes,

liquid drink mixes containing reconstituted dry milk or dry milk products, potato flakes, and infant formula) that are commercially labeled, presented in final finished packaging, and require no further manipulation of the product are generally allowed.

Remember, you must declare all food and agricultural products, including those listed above, to a CBP agriculture specialist or officer when you arrive in the United States.

Fruits and Vegetables

The United States Department of Agriculture (USDA) Animal and Plant Health Inspection Service (APHIS) maintains a website where you plug in the country or the food item and get a ruling on import. The web site is: epermits.aphis.usda.gov.

If you enter "Papaya," for example, you will find out you can never bring one to Hawaii. You are also restricted from bringing any papaya from Chile, Ecuador, or Malaysia to any port of the United States.

The web site works well but the list is rather large. If you are en route and don't have an Internet connection, the USDA publishes phone numbers for inquiries: 1-301-851-2046 or 1-877-770-5990.

Animal Products and Animal By-Products

[http://www.aphis.usda.gov/wps/portal/aphis/home] — Click "Resources" / "Travelers International" and then "Animal Products and By Products"

- Meat, milk, egg, poultry, and products such as dried soup mix or bouillon, are either prohibited or restricted from entering the United States, depending on the types of animal diseases that occur in the country of origin. Fresh (chilled or frozen), dried, cured, and fully cooked meat is generally prohibited from most countries. Canned meat is allowed entry, except beef, veal, lamb, mutton, venison, elk, bison, etc., from countries affected by bovine spongiform encephalopathy.

- Products containing raw egg ingredients are not allowed from most regions.

- Pork and pork products are not allowed from Mexico, except for cooked pork in small amounts for a meal.

- Effective January 14, 2010, cooked pork skins (also known as pork rinds) entering as commercial cargo or in passenger baggage from some countries must be accompanied by additional documents. For more details, contact USDA's National Center for Import and Export at (301) 734-3277, or email AskNCIE.Products@aphis.usda.gov

Violations

[USDA - APHIS] Individuals who fail to declare non-commercial agricultural items may be subject to penalties ranging from $1,100 to $60,000 per violation. These penalties are based on authorities granted to USDA through the Plant Protection Act and the Animal Health Protection Act.

If you discover a banned item on the aircraft it is best to declare it on inspection. I've done that and had the item confiscated, which was better than the times the item was discovered and the passenger was forced to write a very large check.

Airport Rescue and Fire Fighting (ARFF) Codes

There is no 14 CFR 91 or 14 CFR 135 requirement for any fire coverage at all at the airports these operators use, but some companies have instituted such requirements. Even if you don't have such a requirement, knowing your aircraft's Airport Rescue and Fire Fighting (ARFF) code may help you decide between two airports of otherwise equal attractiveness. A G450, for example has a US code of A and an ICAO code of 5. A G550 raises these to a US code of B and an ICAO code of 6.

United States ARFF

[14 CFR 139.315] For the purpose of Index determination, air carrier aircraft lengths are grouped as follows:

1. Index A includes aircraft less than 90 feet in length.

2. Index B includes aircraft at least 90 feet but less than 126 feet in length.

3. Index C includes aircraft at least 126 feet but less than 159 feet in length.

4. Index D includes aircraft at least 159 feet but less than 200 feet in length.

5. Index E includes aircraft at least 200 feet in length.

ICAO

[ICAO Annex 14, Table 9-1]

Aerodrome category	Aeroplane overall length	Maximum fuselage width
1	0 m up to but not including 9 m	2 m
2	9 m up to but not including 12 m	2 m
3	12 m up to but not including 18 m	3 m
4	18 m up to but not including 24 m	4 m
5	24 m up to but not including 28 m	4 m
6	28 m up to but not including 39 m	5 m
7	39 m up to but not including 49 m	5 m
8	49 m up to but not including 61 m	7 m
9	61 m up to but not including 76 m	7 m
10	76 m up to but not including 90 m	8 m

Chapter 3

Altimeter Settings

*T*he altimeter is a standard piece of equipment throughout the world but it isn't used in the same way. In the chapters to follow there are concerns about metric setting, QFE/QNH, temperature corrections, and transition layers. But first you will need some basics.

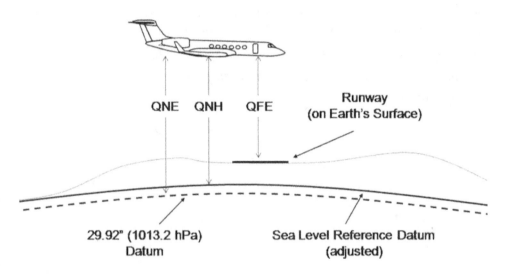

QFE

[ICAO Document 8168, Vol 1, Ch 2] Atmospheric pressure at aerodrome elevation (or at runway threshold)

"Field Elevation" - Based on setting a locally provided altimeter setting which is determined by adjusting an altimeter on the ground until it reads zero. QFE allows us to read height above the runway.

QNH

[ICAO Document 8168, Vol 1, Ch 2] Altimeter sub-scale setting to obtain elevation when on the ground

"Height" - Based on setting a locally provided altimeter setting which is determined by adjusting an altimeter on the ground until it reads the station's correct elevation above the sea level reference datum. QNH allows us to read field elevation on landing.

QNE

[ICAO Document 8168, Vol 1, Ch 2] A pressure type altimeter calibrated in accordance with the Standard Atmosphere . . . when set to a QNE altimeter setting, will indicate height above the QNE reference datum.

"En Route" - Based on setting 29.92" or 1013.2 hPa, gives height above a theoretical datum which is not adjusted for atmospheric conditions. QNE provides the basis for flight levels.

Chapter 4

Altimetry (Metric)

*F*lying an instrument approach to minimums when you are uncertain the
altimeter is reading fact or fiction would seem to be a preposterous situation, but that is exactly what you will be thinking the first time you let down
into a metric environment. It wouldn't be too difficult except for the language
problem between you and the person on the other end of the radio. You can
make things easier on yourself if you really understand what the approach
chart is saying to you.

*The Jeppesen Airway Manuals do not explain charting differences and in some
cases the differences are not consistent. You are left to compare one chart with
another and look for someone with recent experience to determine what procedures are really being used at a particular airport. You can learn a few things
by comparing three types of charts, and from that draw three conclusions:*

- *Millimeters vs. Hectopascals. If the approach briefing information says "Alt
  Set: MM (hPa on req)" then you set millimeters, if it says "Alt Set: hPa" you
  are setting Hectopascals.*

- *QFE vs QNH. If you are expected to fly QFE, the heights inside the parentheses will be bolded, i.e., DA(H) 820' (200'). You should also see "QNH on
  req (QFE)" in the briefing information.*

- *Metric vs. Feet. If you see feet to meters conversion tables, you will probably
  be vectored in meters.*

*The number of airports using QFE or metric has declined dramatically over the
last two decades but you need to be cautious when flying anywhere that used
to be a associated with the former USSR. It pays to talk to a pilot with recent
experience.*

ICAO Procedures

[ICAO Document 4444, §4.10]

4.10.1.1 For flights in the vicinity of aerodromes and within terminal control areas the vertical position of aircraft shall, except as provided for in 4.10.1.2, be expressed in terms of altitudes at or below the transition altitude and in terms of flight levels at or above the transition level. While passing through the transition layer, vertical position shall be expressed in terms of flight levels when climbing and in terms of altitudes when descending.

4.10.1.2 When an aircraft which has been given clearance to land is completing its approach using atmospheric pressure at aerodrome elevation (QFE), the vertical position of the aircraft shall be expressed in terms of height above aerodrome elevation during that portion of its flight for which QFE may be used, except that it shall be expressed in terms of height above runway threshold elevation:

a.   for instrument runways, if the threshold is 2 metres (7 feet) or more below the aerodrome elevation, and

b.   for precision approach runways.

4.10.1.3 For flights en route the vertical position of aircraft shall be expressed in terms of:

c.   flight levels at or above the lowest usable flight level;

d.   altitudes below the lowest usable flight level;

except where, on the basis of regional air navigation agreements, a transition altitude has been established for a specified area, in which case the provisions of 4.10.1.1 shall apply.

These ICAO procedures are almost universally used. There are exceptions by country (e.g., North Korea) and within countries (e.g., China). You must check the applicable AIP or Jeppesen Airway Manual, Air Traffic Control, State Rules and Procedures to be sure.

Chart Identification is left up to you, but as a general rule if the chart says "Alt Set: hPa" and there are no metric conversion tables, you are probably dealing with an ICAO standard chart requiring you to fly altitudes in feet and the altimeter set to QNH. (Note that the QNH altitudes are in bold.)

Figure: Example ICAO Standard Approach Chart, from Jeppesen Airway Manual, Singapore Changi ILS DME Rwy 02L, WSSS, page 11-1, 25 Nov 11

Metric Procedures

- *If the approach will be flown using QNH procedures, you should plan on setting primary and secondary altimeters to QNH once descending through the transition layer.*

- *Vector heights will be given in meters. The approach plate will contain a conversion box for these altitudes. Read back the height in meters but fly the height in feet.*

- *Approach procedure heights are shown in feet. On most QNH approach plates, DA or MDA altitudes are bolded: DA(H) 308' (200').*

Chart Identification is left up to you, but as a general rule if the chart says "Alt Set: hPa" you will set your altimeter to Hectopascals, if the heights outside the parentheses are bolded you will be flying QNH, and if the chart has feet to meter conversion tables, you can expect to be vectored in meters.

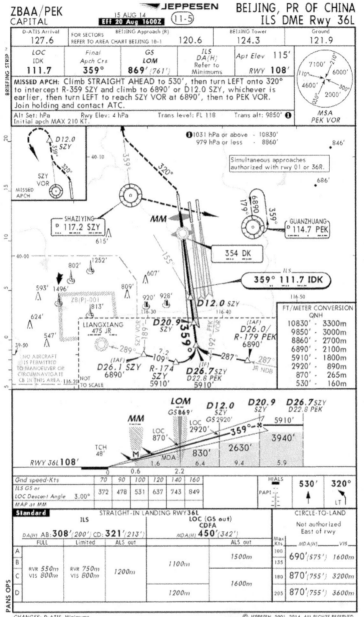

Figure: Example Metric/QNH Approach Chart, from Jeppesen Airway Manual, Beijing ILS DME Rwy 18R, ZBAA, page 11-5, 15 Aug 14

QFE Procedures

- *On most QFE approach plates, the altimeter setting block will say (QFE) in bold print and the DA or MDA heights are shown in bold: DA(H) 820' (200'). There are exceptions and the only way to be sure is to check the appropriate Jeppesen Airway Manual ATC pages. If the approach will be flown using QFE procedures, you should plan on setting primary and secondary altimeters to QFE once descending through the transition layer.*

- *Vector heights will be given in meters. The approach plate will contain a conversion box for these altitudes. Read back the height in meters but fly the height in feet.*

- *Approach procedure heights are shown in feet. DA(H) or MDA(H) is given with the altitude based on QNH outside the parenthesis and the height based on QFE inside the parenthesis. It is critically important to remember whenever you have set QFE as your altimeter setting, you are flying to the "H" - the height inside the parenthesis. Reminder: When you set a QFE altimeter setting, your altimeter will read zero after you have landed.*

Chart Identification is left up to you, but as a general rule if the chart says "Alt Set: MM" you will set your altimeter to millimeters, if the heights inside the parentheses are bolded you are probably dealing with a QFE chart, and the presence of feet-to-meters tables means you will be vectored with altitudes in meters.

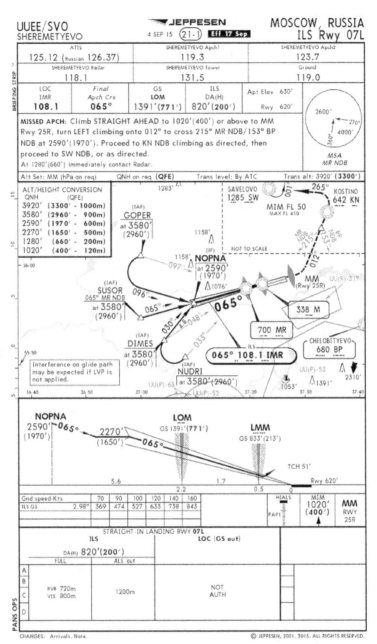

Figure: Example Metric/QFE Approach Chart, from Jeppesen Airway Manual, Moscow Sheremetyevo ILS or PAR Rwy 07L, UUEE, page 21-1, 4 Sep 15.

Hybrid Procedures

Some countries have additional procedures at airports where no transition levels/layers are provided or where the elevation makes setting QFE impossible. Some countries have several procedures within their own borders, China for example.

[Jeppesen Airway Manual, Air Traffic Control, State Rules and Procedures, China, Rules and Procedures, 11 Oct 2013] At aerodromes of high elevation: When the aircraft altimeter subscale cannot be set to the atmospheric pressure at the aerodrome elevation, it will then be set to 1013.2hPa before takeoff, with the indicated altitude interpreted as zero altitude. When the aircraft altimeter subscale cannot be set to the atmospheric pressure at the aerodrome elevation, landing is to be made with the assumed zero altitude notified by the air traffic controller before landing.

At these airports you to use an altimeter setting with an altitude pad provided by the tower, since you would not be able make your altimeter read zero on the ground at these high elevations. Tower gives you an altimeter setting and tells you that runway elevation will indicate, for example, 2000 meters on touchdown. It appears most of these high elevation airports, like this one, have converted to QNH. But the high altitude note still appears in the ATC pages.

Chapter 5

Altimetry (Temperature Correction)

*Y*our altimeter is a marvelous piece of machinery that is highly accurate throughout almost the entire flight envelope of your aircraft. Almost, but not all. When it gets very cold, the error can be enough to lower your actual altitude well below any minimums. You, ATC, or your aircraft will have to make adjustments.

As a pilot, what you need to know is that when it gets cold, your altimeter puts the airplane lower than it should. In most cases the error is insignificant. The colder than 0°C it is, and the higher you are than the airport's elevation, the more significant the error. You can use a set of tables or if your aircraft is allowed to automatically compensate, you can do that. But if you make the corrections, you need to let ATC know. They might be giving you corrected altitudes or your correction could put you in the way of aircraft that are not correcting.

The procedures vary by country and you will have to study individual state procedures to be sure.

Altimeter Temperature Correction

[ICAO Doc 8168 - Aircraft Operations - Vol I, Part III, §1, Ch. 4] Note.— This chapter deals with altimeter corrections for pressure, temperature and, where appropriate, wind and terrain effects. The pilot is responsible for these corrections, except when under radar vectoring. In that case, the radar controller issues clearances such that the prescribed obstacle clearance will exist at all times, taking the cold temperature correction into account.

4.1.1 Pilot's responsibility. The pilot-in-command is responsible for the safety of the operation and the safety of the aeroplane and of all persons on board during flight time (Annex 6, 4.5.1). This includes responsibility for obstacle clearance, except when an IFR flight is being vectored by radar.

4.1.3 State's responsibility. Annex 15, Appendix 1 (Contents of Aeronautical Information Publication), indicates that States should publish in Section GEN 3.3.5, "The criteria used to determine minimum flight altitudes". If nothing is published, it should be assumed that no corrections have been applied by the State. Note.— The determination of lowest usable flight levels by air traffic control units within controlled airspace does not relieve the pilot-in-command of the responsibility for ensuring that adequate terrain clearance exists, except when an IFR flight is being vectored by radar.

4.1.4 Air traffic control (ATC). If an aircraft is cleared by ATC to an altitude which the pilot-in-command finds unacceptable due to low temperature, then the pilot-in-command should request a higher altitude. If such a request is not received, ATC will consider that the clearance has been accepted and will be complied with. See Annex 2 and the PANS-ATM (Doc 4444), Chapter 6.

4.3.1 Requirement for temperature correction. The calculated minimum safe altitudes/heights must be adjusted when the ambient temperature on the surface is much lower than that predicted by the standard atmosphere. In such conditions, an approximate correction is 4 percent height increase for every 10°C below standard temperature as measured at the altimeter setting source. This is safe for all altimeter setting source altitudes for temperatures above –15°C.

4.3.2 Tabulated corrections. For colder temperatures, a more accurate correction should be obtained from Tables III-1-4-1 a) and III-1-4-1 b). These tables are calculated for a sea level aerodrome. They are therefore conservative when applied at higher aerodromes. To calculate the corrections for specific aerodromes or altimeter setting sources above sea level, or for values not tabulated, see 4.3.3, "Corrections for specific conditions".

Note 1.— The corrections have been rounded up to the next 5 m or 10 ft increment.

Note 2.— Temperature values from the reporting station (normally the aerodrome) nearest to the position of the aircraft should be used.

These are the same tables reproduced by Jeppesen. No matter where you get them, if you do a lot of cold weather flying you should either have the tables handy or have an aircraft that can do the math for you.

Table III-1-4-1 a).   Values to be added by the pilot to minimum promulgated heights/altitudes (m)

Aerodrome temperature (°C)	Height above the elevation of the altimeter setting source (metres)													
	60	90	120	150	180	210	240	270	300	450	600	900	1 200	1 500
0	5	5	10	10	10	15	15	15	20	25	35	50	70	85
−10	10	10	15	15	25	20	25	30	30	45	60	90	120	150
−20	10	15	20	25	25	30	35	40	45	65	85	130	170	215
−30	15	20	25	30	35	40	45	55	60	85	115	170	230	285
−40	15	25	30	40	45	50	60	65	75	110	145	220	290	365
−50	20	30	40	45	55	65	75	80	90	135	180	270	360	450

Table III-1-4-1 b).   Values to be added by the pilot to minimum promulgated heights/altitudes (ft)

Aerodrome temperature (°C)	Height above the elevation of the altimeter setting source (feet)													
	200	300	400	500	600	700	800	900	1 000	1 500	2 000	3 000	4 000	5 000
0	20	20	30	30	40	40	50	50	60	90	120	170	230	280
−10	20	30	40	50	60	70	80	90	100	150	200	290	390	490
−20	30	50	60	70	90	100	120	130	140	210	280	420	570	710
−30	40	60	80	100	120	140	150	170	190	280	380	570	760	950
−40	50	80	100	120	150	170	190	220	240	360	480	720	970	1 210
−50	60	90	120	150	180	210	240	270	300	450	590	890	1 190	1 500

U.S. Procedures

U.S. Procedures changed effective January 8, 2015, as discussed in Notices to Airmen (NTAP), U.S. Cold Temperature Restricted Airports, Part 4, Section 1 and soon to be added to the Aeronautical Information Manual. This publication includes a list of U.S. airports where altimeter corrections for cold temperatures are mandatory. See also InFO 15002, Implementation of cold temperature altitude corrections at "Cold Temperature Restricted Airports" found in Notice to Airmen Publication (NTAP).

[Notices to Airmen, U.S. Cold Temperature Restricted Airports, Part 4, Section 1]

Pilots must make an altitude correction to the published, "at", "at or above" and "at or below" altitudes on designated segment(s) [shown in the NTAP], on all published procedures and runways, when the reported airport temperature is at or below the published airport cold temperature restriction.

Pilots without temperature compensating aircraft are responsible to calculate and make a manual cold temperature altitude correction to the designated segment(s) of the approach using the AIM 7-2-3, ICAO Cold Temperature Error Table.

No extrapolation above the 5000 ft column required. Pilots should use the 5000 ft "height above airport in feet" column for calculating corrections of greater than 5000ft above reporting station. Pilots will add correction(s) from the table to the segment altitude(s) and fly at the new corrected altitude. PILOTS SHOULD NOT MAKE AN ALTIMETER CHANGE to accomplish an altitude correction.

Pilots with temperature compensating aircraft must ensure the system is on and operating for each segment requiring an altitude correction. Pilots must ensure they are flying at corrected altitude. If the system is not operating, the pilot is responsible to calculate and apply a manual cold weather altitude correction using the AIM 7-2-3 ICAO Cold Temperature Error Table. PILOTS SHOULD NOT MAKE AN ALTIMETER CHANGE to accomplish an altitude correction.

Pilots must report cold temperature corrected altitudes to Air Traffic Control (ATC) whenever applying a cold temperature correction on an intermediate segment and/or a published missed approach final altitude. This should be done on initial radio contact with the ATC issuing approach clearance. ATC requires this information in order to ensure appropriate vertical separation between known traffic. Pilots must not apply cold temperature compensation to ATC assigned altitudes or when flying on radar vectors in lieu of a published missed approach procedure. Pilots should query ATC when vectors to an intermediate segment are lower than the requested intermediate segment altitude corrected for temperature. Pilots are encouraged to self-announce corrected altitude when flying into uncontrolled airfields.

If you are using temperature compensation during the intermediate segment of an approach or when executing the missed approach, ATC needs to know in case there are other airplanes out there not using temperature compensation. When flying down to a DA/MDA, however, you are free to use cold temperature compensation with or without ATC authorization. (It keeps you higher and the worst outcome will be a missed approach.)

Example. Hayden/Yampa Valley. Hayden, CO, Reported Temperature -26_ C: Cold weather temperature restriction is -26°C / -15F for both the intermediate and missed approach segment. RNAV (GPS) RWY 28:

- Intermediate altitude (FAF) (BEEAR) = 10000 ft.

- Airport elevation = 6606 ft.

- Difference: 10000 ft. – 6606 ft. = 3394 ft.

- AIM 7-2-3 ICAO Cold Temperature Error Table: Interception of 3394 ft. and -26_

C 550ft. Add correction to altitudes inside of IF thru FAF. IF HIPNA; 13,000. Stepdown fix PICIN; 11500 + 550 = 12050 (12100). FAF BEEAR; 10000 + 550 = 10550 (10600).

- Fly new altitudes leaving HIPNA. Passing BEEAR no correction required on final.

- Missed approach altitude. Follow steps 1 thru 4 to calculate and apply correction. New holding altitude is 10600 ft.

The following is an example of appropriate pilot-to-ATC communication when applying cold-temperature altitude corrections.

- On initial check-in with ATC providing approach clearance: Hayden, CO (example).

- Intermediate segment: "Require 10600 ft. for cold temperature operations until BEEAR",

- Missed Approach segment: "Require final holding altitude, 10600 ft. on missed approach for cold temperature operations"

Pilots must use the corrected MDA or DA/DH as the minimum for an approach. Pilots must meet the requirements in 14 CFR Part 91.175 in order to operate below the corrected MDA or DA/DH. Pilots must see and avoid obstacles when descending below the MDA.

The temperature restriction at a "Cold Temperature Restricted Airport" is mutually exclusive from the charted temperature restriction published for "uncompensated baro-VNAV systems" on 14 CFR Part 97 RNAV (GPS) and RNAV (RNP) approach plates. The charted temperature restriction for uncompensated baro-VNAV systems is applicable to the final segment LNAV/ VNAV minima. The charted temperature restriction must be followed regardless of the cold temperature restricted airport temperature.

In other words, if the approach says the use of baro-VNAV is not authorized below a certain temperature, you can't use VNAV below that temperature and these compensation rules do not apply.

Example

Flying into Lebanon, New Hampshire on the ILS Rwy 18 the ATIS reports the surface temperature is -10°C and you have been vectored to intercept the ILS at 3500 feet. What should you do?

This altitude is 3,000 feet above the altimeter setting source so, using the correction table, you need to add 290 feet to your indicated altitude. You should request to fly the intercept at 3,800 feet indicated altitude, then check your glide slope crossing at 2,930 feet and the minimum stepdown at 1,700'.

Notice that this correction, in accordance with the U.S. Cold Temperature Restricted Airports list is not mandatory at Lebanon, New Hampshire until -20°C and even then only on the intermediate and final approach segments. You can apply it, but regardless of the temperature you need to inform ATC that you are doing so.

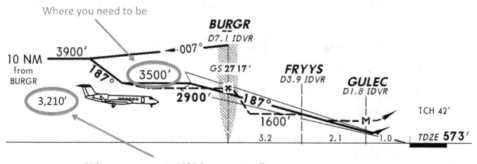

Chapter 6

Altimetry (Transition Altitude, Layer, Level)

Where you change your altimeter from QNH to QNE and back is not standard across the world. Fortunately, the way you grew up is pretty much the way most of the world does it and is the ICAO standard. What is different that could trip you up is the location of the transition layer. In the United States it is usually between 18,000 and 19,000 feet. Having an abnormally high altimeter setting could eliminate FL 180; but unless you normally cruise there, you may not notice the change at all. In most of the world the transition layer is significantly lower and you could find yourself significantly off altitude unless you understand when transition altitude or transition level needs to be heeded.

Not everyone in the world obeys these rules and you will find some areas where you need to listen carefully and question the controller when in doubt.

Definitions

Transition altitude

[ICAO Document 4444, Ch 1] The altitude at or below which the vertical position of an aircraft is controlled by reference to altitudes.

Transition Layer

[ICAO Document 4444, Ch 1] The airspace between the transition altitude and the transition level.

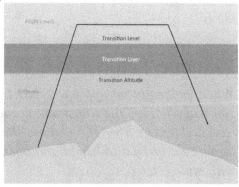

Transition Level

[ICAO Document 4444, Ch 1] The lowest flight level available for use above the transition altitude.

Climbs and Descents

[ICAO Document 4444, ¶4.10.2.1] The appropriate ATS unit shall establish the transition level to be used in the vicinity of the aerodrome(s) concerned and, when relevant, the terminal control area (TMA) concerned, for the appropriate period of time on the basis of QNH (altimeter sub-scale setting to obtain elevation when on the ground) reports and forecast mean sea level pressure, if required.

[ICAO Document 4444, ¶4.10.1.1] For flights in the vicinity of aerodromes and within terminal control areas the vertical position of aircraft shall, except as provided for in 4.10.1.2, be expressed in terms of altitudes at or below the transition altitude and in terms of flight levels at or above the transition level. While passing through the transition layer, vertical position shall be expressed in terms of flight levels when climbing and in terms of altitudes when descending.

[ICAO Document 4444, ¶4.10.1.2] When an aircraft which has been given clearance to land is completing its approach using atmospheric pressure at aerodrome elevation (QFE), the vertical position of the aircraft shall be expressed in terms of height above aerodrome elevation during that portion of its flight for which QFE may be used, except that it shall be expressed in terms of height above runway threshold elevation: for instrument runways, if the threshold is 2 metres (7 feet) or more below the aerodrome elevation, and for precision approach runways.

The key takeaway here is the transition altitude expresses the highest possible altitude, above that they don't exist. So when you are climbing, once you've passed the transition altitude, they no longer exist so you might as well go to 29.92/1013. When you are descending, the lowest possible flight level is at the Transition Level and once you have passed it, you might as well go back to QNH.

Example: Luton

When looking at an approach plate from outside the United States prepared you will often see the transition altitude specifically listed and the transition level declared as "By ATC" if at all. The transition altitude is in reference to the airport elevation and height and does not change. The transition level varies with atmospheric pressure.

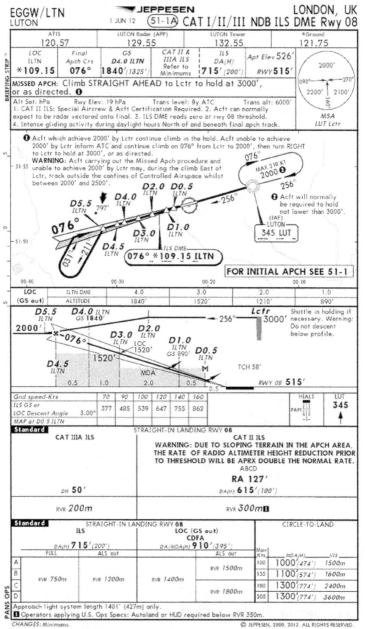

Figure: Luton Cat I/II/III NDB ILS DME Rwy 08, from Jeppesen Airway Manual, EGGW, Page 51-1A, 1 Jun 12

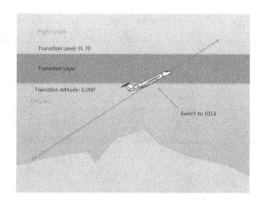

Climb

The transition level at Luton will typically be FL 70 unless altimeter setting is very low, in which case the transition level could be higher. In either case, you are concerned with the transition altitude, which does not change. If given a level off below 6,000 feet you will be given that altitude in feet. Make sure your altimeter is set to the local QNH.

Passing the transition altitude, 6,000', you set QNE. You should not be given any further altitudes and your next altitude will be a flight level.

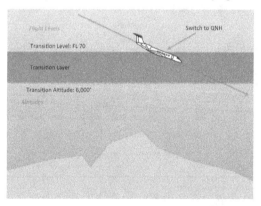

Descent

The transition level will be given on the ATIS or by ATC and depends on the airport's altimeter setting. It will typically be FL 70 unless the Luton altimeter setting is very high, in which case the transition level could be higher. In either case, you are concerned with the transition level, which determines the lowest usable flight level.

Passing the transition level, FL 70, you set QNH.

Chapter 7

Approach Ban

*Y*ou can think of the term "approach ban" as the U.S. 14 CFR 135 rule that *says you can't takeoff unless the weather at your destination is good enough to land. Simple. It is the ICAO Law of the Land, but there are exceptions.*

ICAO Standards and Recommended Practices

Commercial Aviation

[ICAO Annex 6, Part I, ¶4.2.8.1 Aerodrome operating minima] The State of the Operator shall require that the operator establish aerodrome operating minima for each aerodrome to be used in operations and shall approve the method of determination of such minima. Such minima shall not be lower than any that may be established for such aerodromes by the State in which the aerodrome is located, except when specifically approved by that State.

Note 1.— This Standard does not require the State in which the aerodrome is located to establish aerodrome operating minima.

Note 2.— The use of head-up displays (HUD) or enhanced vision systems (EVS) may allow operations with lower visibilities than normally associated with the aerodrome operating minima.

[ICAO Annex 6, Part I, ¶4.4.1 Aerodrome operating minima]

4.4.1.1 A flight shall not be continued towards the aerodrome of intended landing, unless the latest available information indicates that at the expected time of arrival, a landing can be effected at that aerodrome or at least one destination alternate aerodrome, in compliance with the operating minima established in accordance with 4.2.8.1.

4.4.1.2 An instrument approach shall not be continued beyond the outer marker fix in case of precision approach, or below 300 m (1,000 ft) above the aerodrome in case of non-precision approach, unless the reported visibility or controlling RVR is above the specified minimum.

4.4.1.3 If, after passing the outer marker fix in case of precision approach, or after descending below 300 m (1,000 ft) above the aerodrome in case of non-precision approach, the reported visibility or controlling RVR falls below the specified minimum, the approach may be continued to DA/H or MDA/H. In any case, an aeroplane shall not continue its approach-to-land at any aerodrome beyond a point at which the limits of the operating minima specified for that aerodrome would be infringed.

Note.— Controlling RVR means the reported values of one or more RVR reporting locations (touchdown, mid-point and stop-end) used to determine whether operating minima are or are not met. Where RVR is used, the controlling RVR is the touchdown RVR, unless otherwise specified by State criteria.

General Aviation

[ICAO Annex 6, Part II, ¶2.2.2.2 Aerodrome operating minima] The pilot-in-command shall not operate to or from an aerodrome using operating minima lower than those which may be established for that aerodrome by the State in which it is located, except with the specific approval of that State. Note.— It is the practice in some States to declare, for flight planning purposes, higher minima for an aerodrome when nominated as an alternate, than for the same aerodrome when planned as that of intended landing.

[ICAO Annex 6, Part II, ¶2.2.4.1] Aerodrome operating minima

2.2.4.1.1 A flight shall not be continued towards the aerodrome of intended landing, unless the latest available information indicates that at the expected time of arrival, a landing can be effected at that aerodrome or at least one destination alternate aerodrome, in compliance with the operating minima established in accordance with 2.2.2.2.

2.2.4.1.2 An instrument approach shall not be continued beyond the outer marker fix in case of precision approach, or below 300 m (1,000 ft) above the aerodrome in case of non-precision approach, unless the reported visibility or controlling RVR is above the specified minimum.

2.2.4.1.3 If, after passing the outer marker fix in case of precision approach, or after descending below 300 m (1,000 ft) above the aerodrome in case of non-precision approach, the reported visibility or controlling RVR falls below the specified minimum, the approach may be continued to DA/H or MDA/H. In any case, an aeroplane shall not continue its approach-to-land beyond a point at which the limits of the aerodrome operating minima would be infringed.

Note.— Controlling RVR means the reported values of one or more RVR reporting locations (touchdown, midpoint and stop-end) used to determine whether operating minima are or are not met. Where RVR is used, the controlling RVR is the touchdown RVR, unless otherwise specified by State criteria.

ICAO Annex 6 Part I is "International Commercial Air Transport - Aeroplanes" and Part II is "International General Aviation - Aeroplanes." The approach ban policy applies to both.

EASA Exception

The rules in Europe, at one point, were known as JAA OPS but that gave way to EU Ops under the EASA.

[EU Regulation No 965/2012, ¶CAT.OP.MPA.305]

a.   The commander or the pilot to whom conduct of the flight has been delegated may commence an instrument approach regardless of the reported RVR/VIS.

You can start the approach regardless of weather, but there is a limit to how low you can go . . .

b.   If the reported RVR/VIS is less than the applicable minimum the approach shall not be continued:

    1.   below 1,000 ft above the aerodrome; or

    2.   into the final approach segment in the case where the DA/H or MDA/H is more than 1,000 ft above the aerodrome.

c.   Where the RVR is not available, RVR values may be derived by converting the reported visibility.

d.   If, after passing 1,000 ft above the aerodrome, the reported RVR/VIS falls below the applicable minimum, the approach may be continued to DA/H or MDA/H.

If the visibility then goes below, you can continue to the DA/H or MDA/H.

e.   The approach may be continued below DA/H or MDA/H and the landing may be completed provided that the visual reference adequate for the type of approach operation and for the intended runway is established at the DA/H or MDA/H and is maintained.

And if you have the visual references you need to land at that point, you may.

U.S. Exception

[14 CFR 135, §135.219] No person may takeoff an aircraft under IFR or begin an IFR or over-the-top operation unless the latest weather reports or forecasts, or any combination of them, indicate that weather conditions at the estimated time of arrival at the next airport of intended landing will be at or above authorized IFR landing minimums.

[14 CFR 135, §135.225]

(a) Except to the extent permitted by paragraph (b) of this section, no pilot may begin an instrument approach procedure to an airport unless—

(1) That airport has a weather reporting facility operated by the U.S. National Weather Service, a source approved by U.S. National Weather Service, or a source approved by the Administrator; and

(2) The latest weather report issued by that weather reporting facility indicates that weather conditions are at or above the authorized IFR landing minimums for that airport.

(b) A pilot conducting an eligible on-demand operation may begin an instrument approach procedure to an airport that does not have a weather reporting facility operated by the U.S. National Weather Service, a source approved by the U.S. National Weather Service, or a source approved by the Administrator if—

(1) The alternate airport has a weather reporting facility operated by the U.S. National Weather Service, a source approved by the U.S. National Weather Service, or a source approved by the Administrator; and

(2) The latest weather report issued by the weather reporting facility includes a current local altimeter setting for the destination airport. If no local altimeter setting for the destination airport is available, the pilot may use the current altimeter setting provided by the facility designated on the approach chart for the destination airport.

(c) If a pilot has begun the final approach segment of an instrument approach to an airport under paragraph (b) of this section, and the pilot receives a later weather report indicating that conditions have worsened to below the minimum requirements, then the pilot may continue the approach only if the requirements of §91.175(l) of this chapter, or both of the following conditions, are met—

(1) The later weather report is received when the aircraft is in one of the following approach phases: (i) The aircraft is on an ILS final approach and has passed the final approach fix;

(ii) The aircraft is on an ASR or PAR final approach and has been turned over to the final approach controller; or

(iii) The aircraft is on a nonprecision final approach and the aircraft—

(A) Has passed the appropriate facility or final approach fix; or

(B) Where a final approach fix is not specified, has completed the procedure turn and is established inbound toward the airport on the final approach course within the distance prescribed in the procedure; and

(2) The pilot in command finds, on reaching the authorized MDA or DA/DH, that the actual weather conditions are at or above the minimums prescribed for the procedure being used.

(d) If a pilot has begun the final approach segment of an instrument approach to an airport under paragraph (c) of this section and a later weather report indicating below minimum conditions is received after the aircraft is—

(1) On an ILS final approach and has passed the final approach fix; or

(2) On an ASR or PAR final approach and has been turned over to the final approach controller; or

(3) On a final approach using a VOR, NDB, or comparable approach procedure; and the aircraft— (i) Has passed the appropriate facility or final approach fix; or

(ii) Where a final approach fix is not specified, has completed the procedure turn and is established inbound toward the airport on the final approach course within the distance prescribed in the procedure; the approach may be continued and a landing made if the pilot finds, upon reaching the authorized MDA or DH, that actual weather conditions are at least equal to the minimums prescribed for the procedure.

(e) The MDA or DA/DH and visibility landing minimums prescribed in part

97 of this chapter or in the operator's operations specifications are increased by 100 feet and 1/2 mile respectively, but not to exceed the ceiling and visibility minimums for that airport when used as an alternate airport, for each pilot in command of a turbine-powered airplane who has not served at least 100 hours as pilot in command in that type of airplane.

(f) Each pilot making an IFR take- off or approach and landing at a military or foreign airport shall comply with applicable instrument approach procedures and weather minimums prescribed by the authority having jurisdiction over that airport. In addition, no pilot may, at that airport—

(1) Takeoff under IFR when the visibility is less than 1 mile; or

(2) Make an instrument approach when the visibility is less than 1/2 mile.

(g) If takeoff minimums are specified in part 97 of this chapter for the takeoff airport, no pilot may takeoff an aircraft under IFR when the weather conditions reported by the facility described in paragraph (a) (1) of this section are less than the takeoff minimums specified for the takeoff airport in part 97 or in the certificate holder's operations specifications.

(h) Except as provided in paragraph (i) of this section, if takeoff minimums are not prescribed in part 97 of this chapter for the takeoff airport, no pilot may takeoff an aircraft under IFR when the weather conditions reported by the facility described in paragraph (a)(1) of this section are less than that prescribed in part 91 of this chapter or in the certificate holder's operations specifications.

(i) At airports where straight-in instrument approach procedures are authorized, a pilot may takeoff an aircraft under IFR when the weather conditions reported by the facility described in paragraph (a)(1) of this section are equal to or better than the lowest straight-in landing minimums, unless otherwise restricted, if—

(1) The wind direction and velocity at the time of takeoff are such that a straight-in instrument approach can be made to the runway served by the instrument approach;

(2) The associated ground facilities upon which the landing minimums are predicated and the related airborne equipment are in normal operation; and

(3) The certificate holder has been approved for such operations.

The bottom line in the U.S. is this: if you are a commercial operator you cannot takeoff if your destination is below minimums, once you get there you cannot start the approach unless the weather is good enough, and once you've started the approach if the weather goes down you have to abandon the approach. If you are not a commercial operator, this does not apply to you. You can takeoff even if your destination is below minimums. You can begin the approach. If you find yourself at minimums and have the necessary visual references, you can land.

Other Exceptions

Other countries remove approach ban restrictions for some or all operators, or impose further restrictions. You should refer to the country's Jeppesen Airways Manual Air Traffic Control pages. A few examples:

India

[Jeppesen Airway Manual / Air Traffic Control / State Rules and Procedures - India, 20 Dec 2013]

1) An instrument approach shall not be commenced if the reported RVR/Visibility is below the applicable minimum. If, after commencing an instrument approach, the reported RVR/Visibility falls below the applicable minimum, the approach shall not be continued:

a) below 1000ft above the aerodrome; or

b) into the final approach segment in the case where the DA/H or MDA/H is more than 1000ft above the aerodrome.

2) Where the RVR is not available, RVR values may be derived by converting the reported visibility.

3) If, after passing 1000ft above the aerodrome elevation, the reported RVR/visibility falls below the applicable minimum, the approach may be continued to DA/H or MDA/H.

4) The approach may be continued below DA/H or MDA/H and the landing may be completed provided that the required visual reference is established at the DA/H or MDA/H and is maintained.

Japan

[Jeppesen Airway Manual / Air Traffic Control / State Rules and Procedures - Japan, 20 Dec 2013]

* An aircraft shall not takeoff or start an approach to land at any airport if the observed RVR is less than the meteorological minimums for that airport.

* Prior to commencing an instrument approach, if the weather conditions at the airport are below the published or the pilot's landing minimums, the pilot should notify the ATC facility or Airport Advisory Service Units and request clearance to hold or to proceed to an alternate airport.

* After commencing an instrument approach and it is determined that the pilot can continue the approach beyond a prescribed point such as the FAF, OM, 1000 ft above aerodrome elevation or other points accepted by the authority and if the reported weather conditions have worsened to below the published or the pilot's landing minimums, the pilot may continue the approach to DA or MDA. An approach to land may be continued if the pilot, upon reaching the DA/H or MDA/H, finds the actual weather conditions are at or above the lowest weather condition for landing.

United Kingdom

[Jeppesen Airway Manual / Air Traffic Control / State Rules and Procedures - United Kingdom, 20 Dec 2013]

* An aircraft may commence an instrument approach regardless of the reported RVR/Visibility but the approach shall not be continued below 1000ft above the aerodrome if the relevant RVR/Visibility for that runway is at the time less than the specified minimum for landing.

Note: Where the Missed Approach Point is designated as 1 nm after RTR, talkdown will still cease at 2 nm (RTR), and it will be the pilots responsibility to determine when the Missed Approach Point has been reached.

* If, after passing 1000ft in accordance with above paragraph, the reported RVR/Visibility falls below the applicable minimum, the approach may be continued to DA/H or MDA/H.

* The approach may be continued below DA/H or MDA/H and the landing may be completed provided that the required visual reference is established at the DA/H or MDA/H and is maintained.

Chapter 8

Approach Categories

*Y*our *approach category deals with more than just the circling approach. It determines your maximum speeds, maneuvering airspace, and obstacle clearance on approach as well as missed approach. It is always based on your maximum certificated landing weight. The speed that is used might be different between ICAO and U.S. FAA, depending on aircraft.*

Approach Category Determination — United States

[14 CFR 97.3] Aircraft approach category means a grouping of aircraft based on a speed of V_{REF}, if specified, or if V_{REF} is not specified, $1.3V_{SO}$ at the maximum certificated weight. $V_{SO,}$ and the maximum certificated landing weight are those values as established for the aircraft by the certification authority of the country of registry.

These categories are as follows:

Category A: Speed less than 91 knots

Category B: Speed 91 knots or more but less than 121 knots

Category C: Speed 121 knots or more but less than 141 knots

Category D: Speed 141 knots or more but less than 166 knots

Category E: Speed 166 knots or more

There are some who would argue that maximum certificated weight only applies to $1.3V_{SO}$ based on the placement of a comma in the regulation. Specifically, the CL-604 has a V_{REF} based on $1.23V_{SO}$ and some in that community argue that 14 CFR 97.3 means their approach category is not based on maximum landing weight. Even if this were so — and it's not — you could not use that argument when flying outside the United States. (See "Approach Category Determination," below.)

STANDARD CIRCLING APPROACH MANEUVERING RADIUS

Circling approach protected areas developed prior to late 2012 used the radius distances shown in the following table, expressed in nautical miles (NM), dependent on aircraft approach category. The approaches using standard circling approach areas can be identified by the absence of the **C** symbol on the circling line of minima.

Circling MDA in feet MSL	Approach Category and Circling Radius (NM)				
	CAT A	CAT B	CAT C	CAT D	CAT E
All Altitudes	1.3	1.5	1.7	2.3	4.5

C EXPANDED CIRCLING APPROACH MANEUVERING AIRSPACE RADIUS

Circling approach protected areas developed after late 2012 use the radius distance shown in the following table, expressed in nautical miles (NM), dependent on aircraft approach category, and the altitude of the circling MDA, which accounts for true airspeed increase with altitude. The approaches using expanded circling approach areas can be identified by the presence of the **C** symbol on the circling line of minima.

Circling MDA in feet MSL	Approach Category and Circling Radius (NM)				
	CAT A	CAT B	CAT C	CAT D	CAT E
1000 or less	1.3	1.7	2.7	3.6	4.5
1001-3000	1.3	1.8	2.8	3.7	4.6
3001-5000	1.3	1.8	2.9	3.8	4.8
5001-7000	1.3	1.9	3.0	4.0	5.0
7001-9000	1.4	2.0	3.2	4.2	5.3
9001 and above	1.4	2.1	3.3	4.4	5.5

Figure: Standard Circling Appraoch Maneuvering Areas, from AIM figure 5-4-28.

[US AIM ¶5-4-20.b.a.] Circling approach protected areas developed prior to late 2012 used fixed radius distances, dependent on aircraft approach category, as shown in the table on page B2 of the U.S. TPP. The approaches using standard circling approach areas can be identified by the absence of the "negative C" symbol on the circling line of minima. Circling approach protected areas developed after late 2012 use the radius distance shown in the table on page B2 of the U.S. TPP, dependent on aircraft approach category, and the altitude of the circling MDA, which accounts for true airspeed increase with altitude. The approaches using expanded circling approach areas can be identified by the presence of the "negative C" symbol on the circling line of minima.

Approach Category Determination — International

[ICAO Doc 8168 PANS-OPS Vol 1, §4, ¶1.3]

1.3.1 Aircraft performance has a direct effect on the airspace and visibility required for the various manoeuvres associated with the conduct of instrument approach procedures. The most significant performance factor is aircraft speed.

1.3.2 Accordingly, categories of typical aircraft have been established. These categories provide a standardized basis for relating aircraft manoeuvrability to specific instrument approach procedures. For precision approach procedures, the dimensions of the aircraft are also a factor for the calculation of the obstacle clearance height (OCH). For Category DL aircraft, an additional obstacle clearance altitude/height (OCA/H) is provided, when necessary, to take into account the specific dimensions of these aircraft (see Part II, Section 1, Chapter 1, 1.3).

1.3.3 The criterion taken into consideration for the classification of aeroplanes by categories is the indicated airspeed at threshold (Vat), which is equal to the stall speed Vso multiplied by 1.3, or stall speed Vs1g multiplied by 1.23 in the landing configuration at the maximum certificated landing mass. If both Vso and Vs1g are available, the higher resulting Vat shall be applied.

1.3.4 The landing configuration that is to be taken into consideration shall be defined by the operator or by the aeroplane manufacturer.

1.3.5 Aircraft categories will be referred to throughout this document by their letter designations as follows:

Category A: less than 169 km/h (91 kt) indicated airspeed (IAS)

Category B: 169 km/h (91 kt) or more but less than 224 km/h (121 kt) IAS

Category C: 224 km/h (121 kt) or more but less than 261 km/h (141 kt) IAS

Category D: 261 km/h (141 kt) or more but less than 307 km/h (166 kt) IAS

Category E: 307 km/h (166 kt) or more but less than 391 km/h (211 kt) IAS

Category H: see 1.3.10, "Helicopters".

These speeds are the same as used in the United States but the criteria is slightly different. If you have a V_{SO} and a V_{S1G} for your aircraft, you must use the higher of V_{SO} times 1.3 or V_{S1G} times 1.23. Regardless of the speed used, it must be

based on the aircraft's maximum certificated landing mass.

[ICAO Doc 8168 Vol I PANS OPS ¶7.3.1] The visual manoeuvring area for a circling approach is determined by drawing arcs centred on each runway threshold and joining those arcs with tangent lines (see Figure I-4-7-1). The radius of the arcs is related to:

a) aircraft category;

b) speed: speed for each category;

c) wind speed: 46 km/h (25 kt) throughout the turn; and

d) bank angle: 20° average or 3° per second, whichever requires less bank.

Table I-4-7-1.   Example of determining radii for visual manoeuvring (circling) area
for aerodromes at 300 m MSL (SI units)

Category of aircraft/IAS (km/h)	A/185	B/250	C/335	D/380	E/445
TAS at 600 m MSL + 46 km/h wind factor (km/h)	241	310	404	448	516
Radius (r) of turn (km)	1.28	2.08	3.46	4.34	5.76
Straight segment (km)	0.56	0.74	0.93	1.11	1.30
Radius (R) from threshold (km)	3.12	4.90	7.85	9.79	12.82

Table I-4-7-2.   Example of determining radii for visual manoeuvring (circling) area
for aerodromes at 1 000 ft MSL (non-SI units)

Category of aircraft/IAS (kt)	A/100	B/135	C/180	D/205	E/240
TAS at 2 000 ft MSL + 25 kt wind factor (kt)	131	168	215	242	279
Radius (r) of turn (NM)	0.69	1.13	1.85	2.34	3.12
Straight segment (NM) (this is a constant value)	0.30	0.40	0.50	0.60	0.70
Radius (R) from threshold (NM)	1.68	2.66	4.20	5.28	6.94

Note.— Radius from threshold (R) = 2r + straight segment.

Figure: Determining Visual Maneuvering Radii, from ICAO Doc 8168, Vol I

Maximum Speeds During Approach

While the speeds used for determining approach categories are based on maximum certificated landing weight, the maximum speed actually used for approach can be different.

[US AIM §5-4-7] A pilot must use the minima corresponding to the category determined during certification or higher. Helicopters may use Category A minima. If it is necessary to operate at a speed in excess of the upper limit of the speed range for an aircraft's category, the minimums for the higher category must be used. For example, an airplane which fits into Category B, but is circling to land at a speed of 145 knots, must use the approach Category D minimums. As an additional example, a Category A airplane (or helicopter) which is operating at 130 knots on a straight-in approach must use the approach Category C minimums. See the following category limits:

1. Category A: Speed less than 91 knots.

2. Category B: Speed 91 knots or more but less than 121 knots.

3. Category C: Speed 121 knots or more but less than 141 knots.

4. Category D: Speed 141 knots or more but less than 166 knots.

5. Category E: Speed 166 knots or more.

In the U.S., the maximum speed for determining an approach category is also the maximum speed for maneuvering. If the pressure altitude, winds, temperature, or any other factor requires you to increase your maneuvering speed, your turn radius goes up and the obstacle clearance is no longer guaranteed. You must increase your approach category. Back to the case of the CL-604: under ideal conditions you could get that airplane's V_{REF} at maximum weight down to 140.5 knots but the airplane circles at 150 knots, throwing out all their arguments saying they are Category C.

Aircraft category	Vat	Range of speeds for initial approach (and reversal and racetrack procedures)	Range of final approach speeds	Maximum speeds for circling	Maximum speeds for intermediate missed approach	Maximum speeds for final missed approach
A	<91	90/150 (110)	70/110	100	100	110
B	91/120	120/180 (110)	85/130	135	130	150
C	121/140	160/240	115/160	180	160	240
D	141/165	185/250	130/185	205	185	265
E	166/210	185/250	155/230	240	230	275

Figure: ICAO Doc 8168 PANS-OPS Vol 1 §4, Table I-4-1-2.

While the speed ranges used to determine an aircraft's approach category are identical to 14 CFR 97.3, ICAO Doc 8168 PANS-OPS Vol 1 §4, ¶1.3.5, the maximum permitted speed for visual maneuvering is significantly higher. Additionally, speed ranges are specified for other segments of the approach. While it is true the speeds permitted are higher, the circling approach area is larger too.

Variable Approach Category

We used to say you, the pilot, can move your category up but never down. If, for example, the weight, pressure altitude, or other factor meant we would exceed the maximum permitted speed for our approach category, we could simply move up to the next higher category.

Some aircraft manufacturers published maintenance procedures that would, by virtue of a piece of paper in the airplane flight manual, reduce the maximum certificated landing gross weight. That could, in effect, lower the airplane's approach category. This only became a problem when pilots started arbitrarily lowering their approach categories for convenience. The FAA's position is that this is a maintenance action; it has to be done by a mechanic's signature and can only be undone by a mechanic's signature.

Chapter 9

ARINC-424 Shorthand

*I*t is an elegant idea but that isn't the point. Your FMS uses these oceanic codes to represent various points around the globe so you need to know how to decode the code. Once you understand how the points are built, you will be able to crosscheck what is on your screen with reality. Note there has been a change to the specification in the North Atlantic to allow for half-degree latitude spacing.

Oceanic Waypoints

The specification itself comes from Rockwell-Collins who will charge you $504 for a copy. Fortunately you can piece together what you know from a little experience:

These waypoints are named according to ARINC-424 navigation database specification:

1. Southern hemisphere uses the letters S or W

2. Northern hemisphere uses the letters N or E

3. Latitude always proceeds longitude

4. Only the last two digits of longitude are used

5. Placement of the letter designator (N, S, E, W) in the string of five characters indicates the value of the longitude one-hundredths digit

   a. The letter in the last position indicates longitude < 100

   b. The letter in the third position indicates longitude ≥ 100

   c. Jeppesen will add Half Degree Grid Waypoints in the Gander and Shanwick Oceanic Control Areas (OCAs): "Hxxyy," where xx = degrees and 30 minutes of NORTH latitude and yy = degrees of WEST longitude (e.g., H5250 = 52°30' NORTH 050°00' WEST).

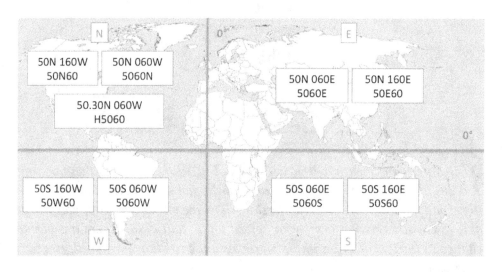

Examples:

N 52 00 / W 075 00   = 5275N

N 75 00 / W 170 00   = 75N70

S 50 00 / E 020 00   = 5020S

N 50 00 / E 020 00   = 5020E

S 52 00 / W 075 00   = 5275W

N 45 30 / W 050 00   = N4550

N 45 00 / W 050 00   = 4550N

CAUTION: Remember this shorthand is for the benefit of your FMS but every possible combination of this shorthand does not work in your FMS. You need to make sure each point translates correctly.

CAUTION: Air traffic control doesn't understand this shorthand. You must format your position reports, voice or CPDLC, with the correct latitude / longitude terminology.

Chapter 10

Cabotage

*C*abotage is simply the legal way of saying transporting people and things within a country. If that country is not your own, you may need permission to do that. The penalty for making a mistake here can be severe, so you need to be smart about the subject if you plan on making multiple stops in a country with people and things you didn't bring with you in the first place.

U.S. Policy

[AC 91-70A Oceanic Operations, ¶3-1.n.] Private pilots and commercial operators should understand cabotage, formally defined as "Air transport of passengers and goods within the same national territory." The definition adopted by ICAO at the Chicago Convention is as follows: "Each state shall have the right to refuse permission to the aircraft of other contracting states to take on its territory passengers, mail, and cargo destined for another point within its territory." Although cabotage rules are different in various countries and usually incorporate the term "for hire," some countries do not allow foreign aircraft within their boundaries to carry even non-revenue passengers. The restrictions range from no restrictions to not allowed. The fines for cabotage can be extremely high; therefore, pilots and flight departments should be absolutely sure of a country's cabotage rules before carrying passengers. The corporate aircraft restraints section for each country in the IFIM list the cabotage requirements and restrictions of individual countries. Refer to chapter II, article 7 of the Chicago Convention.

Generally speaking, you cannot fly to some foreign countries, pick up local citizens and transport them within that country. Not all countries have cabotage restrictions and many that do will allow exceptions if the citizens are employees of a company associated with the airplane. The rules vary by country and you need to ensure you follow them. AC 91-70A, ¶3- 1.n. offers an FAA web page that was very helpful in determining country-specific cabotage rules but that service is no longer offered. You are left to ask your flight planning service provider or looking for the country's AIP.

"The Chicago Convention"

So what is this convention we hear so much about? During World War II it became obvious that having a bunch of airplanes from different countries share the same airspace wouldn't work if they all used the operating rules and standards from their home countries. The powers that be met in Chicago and agreed upon a set of rules that became known as the Convention on International Civil Aviation Done at Chicago on the 7th Day of December 1944.

[ICAO Chicago Convention Article 7]. Each contracting State shall have the right to refuse permission to the aircraft or other contracting States to take on in its territory passengers, mail and cargo carried for remuneration or hire and destined for another point within its territory. Each contracting State undertakes not to enter into any arrangements which specifically grant any such privilege on an exclusive basis to any other State or airline of any other State, and not to obtain any such exclusive privilege from any other State.

While the web site recommended by AC 91-70A is quite good and worth viewing prior to every trip, it doesn't offer much help with cabotage. The next step is to the particular country's International Flight Information Manual (IFIM), but those aren't easy to come by. I've found the best course of action is to use an international handler, like Rockwell-Collins or Universal, with boots on the ground in country. Tell them what you plan to do and ask "is it legal?" and "will the local authorities object?"

You might be tempted to blow the entire topic off, thinking you are not operating for remuneration or hire. Think again, many countries have expanded the definition to include just about any business purpose.

Thankfully, many countries consider an employee of a multinational a part of a U.S. branch of the same company. I've done this as a pilot for Compaq Computer, for example: flown German nationals employed by Compaq in Germany within points in Germany. We asked the local authorities first who did not object. Ask first!

Chapter 11

Call Signs

The following applies to any "November" registered aircraft flying with the aircraft registration as their call sign. If you have an ICAO registered call sign that is not your aircraft registration, the following does not apply to you. Generally speaking you are better off pronouncing your entire call sign, starting with "November," when overseas. Remember the controller is probably used to dealing with local aircraft and hearing "November" gets his or her attention. Is this required? No, but advisable.

All that being said, by the book, you can indeed use aircraft type as a prefix, but you still need the "November" as part of the call sign. You need to use the entire call sign on initial call up. (The only time you can use an abbreviated call sign is after you have been addressed "in this manner.") The bottom line: you want to get their attention, you want to avoid confusion, you want to make it easy for Air Traffic Control to understand who you are and what you want.

Full Call Signs

[ICAO Annex 10, Vol II, ¶5.2.1.7.2.] Radiotelephony call signs for aircraft

5.2.1.7.2.1 Full call signs

5.2.1.7.2.1.1 An aircraft radiotelephony call sign shall be one of the following types:

Type a) — the characters corresponding to the registration marking of the aircraft; or

Type b) — the telephony designator of the aircraft operating agency, followed by the last four characters of the registration marking of the aircraft;

Type c) — the telephony designator of the aircraft operating agency, followed by the flight identification.

Note 1.— The name of the aircraft manufacturer or of the aircraft model may be used as a radiotelephony prefix to the Type a) call sign (see Table 5-1).

Table 5-1. Examples of full call signs and abbreviated call signs
(*see* 5.2.1.7.2.1 and 5.2.1.7.2.2)

		Type a)		Type b)	Type c)
Full call sign	N 57826	*CESSNA FABCD	*CITATION FABCD	VARIG PVMA	SCANDINAVIAN 937
Abbreviated call sign	N26	CESSNA CD	CITATION CD	VARIG MA	(no abbreviated form)
	or	or	or	or	
	N826	CESSNA BCD	CITATION BCD	VARIG VMA	

* Examples illustrate the application of Note 1 to 5.2.1.7.2.1.1.

Figure: Examples of full call signs and abbreviated call signs, from ICAO Annex 10, Vol II, Table 5-1.

Note 2.— The telephony designators referred to in Types b) and c) are contained in Doc 8585 — Designators for Aircraft Operating Agencies, Aeronautical Authorities and Services.

Note 3.— Any of the foregoing call signs may be inserted in field 7 of the ICAO flight plan as the aircraft identification. Instructions on the completion of the flight plan form are contained in PANS-ATM, Doc 4444.

Generally speaking, if you are operating under a registered call sign as a commercial operator in the United States, your call sign should be okay when operating internationally. If the 3-letter identifier isn't obvious and well known, however, you might expect a few problems. The "Jet Speed" call sign, for example, has a three letter identifier of "EJM" and that is what will be filed in your flight plan. Do not be surprised if air traffic control looks for you as "Echo Juliet Mike" instead.

If your flight plan is filed under your registration you will be better off using that full registration. "November Seven Seven Zero Zero," for example, will be more quickly recognized than "Gulfstream Seven Seven Zero Zero."

Abbreviated Call Signs

[ICAO Annex 10, Vol II, ¶5.2.1.7.2.]

5.2.1.7.2.2 Abbreviated call signs

5.2.1.7.2.2.1 The aircraft radiotelephony call signs shown in 5.2.1.7.2.1.1, with the exception of Type c), may be abbreviated in the circumstances prescribed in 5.2.1.7.3.3.1. Abbreviated call signs shall be in the following form:

Type a) — the first character of the registration and at least the last two characters of the call sign;

Type b) — the telephony designator of the aircraft operating agency, followed by at least the last two characters of the call sign;

Type c) - no abbreviated form.

5.2.1.7.3.2 Establishment of radiotelephony communications

5.2.1.7.3.2.1 Full radiotelephony call signs shall always be used when establishing communication. The calling procedure of an aircraft establishing communication shall be in accordance with Table 5-2.

Table 5-2. Radiotelephony calling procedure* (see 5.2.1.7.3.2.1)

	Type a)	Type b)	Type c)
Designation of the station called	NEW YORK RADIO	NEW YORK RADIO	NEW YORK RADIO
Designation of the station calling	GABCD**	SPEEDBIRD ABCD**	AEROFLOT 321**

* In certain cases where the call is initiated by the aeronautical station, the call may be effected by transmission of coded tone signals.

** With the exception of the telephony designators and the type of aircraft, each character in the call sign shall be spoken separately. When individual letters are spelled out, the radiotelephony spelling alphabet prescribed in 5.2.1.3 shall be used. Numbers are to be spoken in accordance with 5.2.1.4.

Figure: Radiotelephony calling procedure, from ICAO Annex 10, Vol II, Table 5-2.

5.2.1.7.3.3 Subsequent radiotelephony communications

5.2.1.7.3.3.1 Abbreviated radiotelephony call signs, as prescribed in 5.2.1.7.2.2, shall be used only after satisfactory communication has been established and provided that no confusion is likely to arise. An aircraft station shall use its abbreviated call sign only after it has been addressed in this manner by the aeronautical station.

5.2.1.7.3.3.2 After contact has been established, continuous two-way communication shall be permitted without further identification or call until termination of the contact.

5.2.1.7.3.3.3 In order to avoid any possible confusion, when issuing ATC clearances and reading back such clearances, controllers and pilots shall always add the call sign of the aircraft to which the clearance applies.

A good rule of thumb is "to respond in kind" when it comes to call signs. If the controller in question abbreviates your call sign, you might be better of using the exact same abbreviation to increase the chances the controller understand it is your readback he or she is hearing.

Table 5-3. Radiotelephony reply procedure (*see* 5.2.1.7.3.2.3)

	Type a)	*Type b)*	*Type c)*
Designation of the station called	GABCD*	SPEEDBIRD ABCD*	AEROFLOT 321*
Designation of the answering station	NEW YORK RADIO	NEW YORK RADIO	NEW YORK RADIO
Invitation to proceed with transmission	GO AHEAD	GO AHEAD	GO AHEAD

* With the exception of the telephony designators and the type of aircraft, each character in the call sign shall be spoken separately. When individual letters are spelled out, the radiotelephony spelling alphabet prescribed in 5.2.1.3 shall be used. Numbers are to be spoken in accordance with 5.2.1.4.

Figure: Radiotelephony reply procedure, from ICAO Annex 10, Vol II, Table 5-3.

Chapter 12

CANPASS

*I*f you have fewer than 15 persons on board and meet a few other requirements, you can enter and depart Canada by calling into a phone number
and you may end up not having to see any customs officials at all. There are
two methods:

- *Telephone Reporting Center (TRC) — You will need to call ahead of time
  and once you arrive, but it is all pretty easy. You do have restrictions on
  which airports you can use and when you can use them, however.*

- *CANPASS — The CANPASS Private Aircraft program of the Canada Border Services Agency is a voluntary program for private aircraft carrying
  no more than 15 people (including crew) that gives you greater flexibility,
  quicker entry and exit, and it is all very easy.*

*Using the TRC is certainly easy. They maintain a good database and you may
find it suits everything you need to do. If, on the other hand, you are a frequent
visitor, go to unusual airports, or keep odd hours, CANPASS might be for you.*

Telephone Reporting Center

[CANPASS]

When general aviation aircraft enter Canada, they report to the CBSA by
telephone. Travellers on private, company-owned, or charter aircraft carrying no more than 15 people (including the crew), must call the Telephone
Reporting Centre (TRC) to get authorization from the CBSA to enter or
return to Canada. General aviation aircraft must land at an approved airport
of entry (AOE) during the CBSA's hours of business.

If the aircraft is carrying more than 15 people, the pilot has to contact the
CBSA office at the proposed AOE in advance to arrange for customs clearance on arrival.

How does it work?

The pilot has to report the estimated time of arrival (ETA) by calling 1-888-226-7277 at least two hours, but no more than 48 hours, before flying into Canada. The pilot may also call the Hamilton, Ontario Office at 905-679-2073. The pilot has to provide the TRC with the following information:

- ETA;
- aircraft license or registration number;
- destination in Canada;
- the full name, date of birth, and citizenship of all persons on board;
- purpose of the trip and length of stay in Canada for non-residents;
- length of absence from Canada for Canadian residents;
- a declaration for each person aboard; and
- any updates concerning the original ETA, passengers, or destination.

All travellers aboard must declare any personal goods they are importing, including firearms and weapons, and report all currency and/or monetary instruments totaling CAN$10,000 or more. For more information, see Cross Border Currency Reporting. If duties or taxes are payable, the CBSA officer will ask for the traveller's mailing address and VISA or MasterCard number and expiry date.

General aviation aircraft have to land at an approved AOE during normal hours of business for the CBSA unless they have made other arrangements with the local CBSA office. In this case, cost recovery charges will apply.

Immediately on landing in Canada, the pilot must make a final phone call to the TRC at 1-888-226-7277 to report the plane's arrival. The pilot and all travellers aboard cannot leave the aircraft until authorized to do so.

Two important notes:

- *When speaking to the CANPASS inspector, all times are local.*
- *The PIC must make these calls; they cannot be delegated to another member of the crew or a dispatcher.*

Exceptional circumstances

If the aircraft has to land at a place not designated for customs reporting due to weather conditions or other circumstances, the pilot must call either

1-888-226-7277 or the nearest CBSA office or Royal Canadian Mounted Police office. Depending on the circumstances, the flight may be cleared over the phone, the pilot may be requested to await the arrival of a CBSA officer at that site, or the pilot may be requested to fly to the nearest AOE at the first opportunity.

CANPASS

Eligibility

[CANPASS]

To be eligible for CANPASS – Private Aircraft, you must meet these criteria:

- Be a citizen or permanent resident of Canada or the U.S. and have lived in Canada and/or the U.S. continuously for the last three years;
- You are admissible to Canada under applicable immigration laws;
- You have provided true and accurate information on the application;
- You have not been convicted of a criminal offence for which a pardon or rehabilitation has not been granted;
- You have not had a customs seizure within the past five years; and
- You are not in violation of any customs or immigration legislation.

How CANPASS – Private Aircraft works

Private aircraft that meet the requirements of the CANPASS – Private Aircraft program can land at any airport of entry any time the site is open, regardless of the hours of operation of the local CBSA office. The aircraft can also land at a designated CANPASS-only airport.

The pilot must report all passengers and their goods on behalf of the aircraft. Pilots are responsible for reporting themselves, their crew and passengers to a telephone reporting centre (TRC) by calling 1-888-CANPASS (1-888-226-7277) at least 2 hours before but no more than 48 hours prior to the aircraft's estimated time of arrival in Canada.

The TRC allows individuals who enter Canada by private aircraft, corporate aircraft or private boat to report their arrival and make their declarations to the CBSA by telephone.

Where to call

The 1-888-CANPASS (1-888-226-7277) toll-free line is only available in Canada and the United States. If a flight originates outside Canada or the United States, the 1-888 number is not available and the pilot must call the TRC directly (long-distance charges may apply).

TRC for All of Canada: Hamilton, ON; telephone: 905-679-2073; fax: 905-679-6877

Pilot responsibilities

The pilot must ensure that all passengers have the appropriate travel documents for entering Canada. He or she must also call the TRC at least 2 hours before but no more than 48 hours prior to the aircraft's estimated time of arrival in Canada.

During that first telephone call to the TRC, the pilot must provide the following information to the CBSA:

- the estimated time of arrival (ETA);
- the aircraft tail number/registration number;
- the full name, date of birth and citizenship of all persons on board;
- passport and visa information of passengers (including the crew);
- the destination, purpose of the trip and length of stay in Canada for non-residents;
- the landing point (must be a designated airport of entry or CAN-PASS-only airport);
- the length of absence for each passenger who is a returning resident of Canada;
- a declaration of all goods being imported, including firearms and weapons;
- a declaration of all currency and/or monetary instruments totaling CAN$10,000 or more; and
- for returning residents of Canada, a report of all repairs or modifications made to goods (including the aircraft) while outside Canada.

Note: If the ETA changes by more than 30 minutes or if there are any changes to the point of arrival, the list of passengers or their declarations, the pilot must advise the TRC prior to arrival in Canada.

The pilot must remain at the point of arrival until the ETA reported to the TRC has elapsed. No second call to the TRC is required. If there is no officer waiting to meet the aircraft when it arrives at the reported ETA or actual time of arrival, whichever is later, the aircraft may proceed to the final destination and passengers may disembark.

In addition to the above, the person in charge of the conveyance is responsible for the following:

- ensuring that all persons being transported into Canada on board the aircraft are in possession of all travel documents required by the legislation, i.e. passports, visas, or other; and

- the removal of inadmissible passengers and any associated administrative and medical expenses and fees.

Note: Any contraventions of the legislation may result in detention, seizure or forfeiture of the conveyance and/or lead to criminal prosecution, monetary penalties and/or imprisonment.

Travelling with non-members

All persons aboard the aircraft must be CANPASS members. If there is a traveller aboard who is not a member, the pilot has to follow the procedures for Telephone Reporting - General Aviation Aircraft.

A person's CANPASS membership does not extend to members of his or her immediate family or to friends travelling with him or her. Each person on the aircraft has to be enrolled in the CANPASS – Private Aircraft program.

Declaring goods

All travellers aboard must declare any personal goods they are importing, including firearms and weapons, and report currency and/or monetary instruments totaling CAN$10,000 or more. For more information, see Cross Border Currency Reporting. If duties or taxes are payable, the border services officer at the TRC will ask for the traveller's mailing address and Visa or MasterCard number and expiry date.

Privacy

Once an applicant has completed and signed the CANPASS application form, the CBSA is authorized to collect personal information such as name, date of birth, address, citizenship, proof of citizenship and residency information.

The information will be used for background security checks and is not shared with a third party. All information is stored in a secure central database, which in turn is protected by various methods, including fire walls. Access to client information by employees is also controlled and monitored.

Security measures

Participation in the CANPASS – Private Aircraft program is restricted to pre-approved travellers. Applicants undergo a detailed security clearance check before being enrolled. Every time CANPASS – Private Aircraft members enter Canada, their membership information is verified against customs and immigration databases to ensure their compliance with the program's regulations. Each member's eligibility is re-assessed annually.

CANPASS is voluntary but will save you a lot of hassle. It costs $40 and membership is valid for five years. Details at: CANPASS Website.

Chapter 13

Conditional Clearances

You are waiting at the end of the runway when tower says "Behind the landing Airbus, line up and wait." In the United States you question the tower's sanity but under ICAO you are expected to acknowledge, repeating the clearance exactly, and as soon as you see the landing aircraft pass in front of you, you line up and wait. It is ICAO, to be sure, but I've only seen this done in Europe.

Phraseologies

[ICAO Doc 4444, ¶12.2.4] Conditional phrases, such as "behind landing aircraft" or "after departing aircraft", shall not be used for movements affecting the active runway(s), except when the aircraft or vehicles concerned are seen by the appropriate controller and pilot. In all cases a conditional clearance shall be given in the following order and consist of:

i. identification;

ii. the condition;

iii. the clearance; and

iv. brief reiteration of the condition,

for example:

"SAS 941, BEHIND DC9 ON SHORT FINAL, LINE UP BEHIND".

Note.— This implies the need for the aircraft receiving the conditional clearance to identify the aircraft or vehicle causing the conditional clearance.

It may exist someplace else, but this is the only place I've seen it in writing. In actual practice, however, I've seen it several places in Europe, usually in the form "Behind the landing _____, line up and wait."

Chapter 14

Continuous Descent Final Approach (CDFA)

Years ago, following a "dive and drive" mishap, a major airline had to remind its pilots that a non-precision approach must be flown with great precision. The U.S. Air Force must have lost a few airplanes to "dive and drive" because our criteria required crews be busted for flying even an inch below the MDA.

Levelling off at the MDA can be problematic if there are distractions or turbulence. Keeping the airplane at the MDA until the runway is sighted is another issue. But the worst problem may be resisting the urge to descend when you spot the runway too far out. So why not bypass all this?

Flying a Continuous Descent Final Approach (CDFA) eliminates the MDA level off, puts the airplane in a position to land when the runway is sighted, and forces you to go around if the runway is not sighted before a normal visual descent point. It is easier to fly than a dive and drive approach and you don't need any special equipment. It makes sense to use a CDFA on most non-precision approaches. About the only exceptions would be a circling approach or an approach where last minute maneuvering is required.

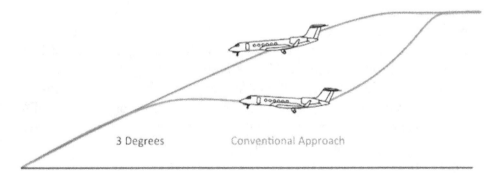

Continuous Descent Final Approach (CDFA)

3 Degrees   Conventional Approach

What is it?

A continuous descent final approach is what you do for every straight-in ILS and what you attempt to do for every visual straight-in approach: you hit the glide path and start down on an angle that ends up in the touchdown zone of the runway. You can do this even when in instrument conditions flying a non-precision approach.

[AC 120-108 §4.c] CDFA is a technique for flying the final approach segment of an NPA as a continuous descent. The technique is consistent with stabilized approach procedures and has no level-off. A CDFA starts from an altitude/height at or above the FAF and proceeds to an altitude/height approximately 50 feet (15 meters) above the landing runway threshold or to a point where the flare maneuver should begin for the type of aircraft being flown.

[ICAO Doc 8168, Vol I, Part I, Amdt 3, Definitions] CDFA: a technique, consistent with stabilized approach procedures, for flying the final approach segment of a non-precision instrument approach procedure as a continuous descent, without level-off, from an altitude/height at or above the final approach fix altitude/height to a point approximately 15 m (50 ft) above the landing runway threshold or the point where the flare manoeuvre should begin for the type of aircraft flown.

Is it Required?

In some countries: yes. In other countries: it is recommended but not mandatory.

ICAO Preferred Technique

[ICAO Doc 8168, Vol I, Part I, Amdt 3, ¶ 1.7.1] Studies have shown that the risk of controlled flight into terrain (CFIT) is high on non-precision approaches. While the procedures themselves are not inherently unsafe, the use of the traditional step down descent technique for flying non-precision approaches is prone to error, and is therefore discouraged. Operators typically employ one of three techniques for vertical path control on non-precision approaches. Of these, the continuous descent final approach (CDFA) technique is preferred. Operators should use the CDFA technique whenever possible as it adds to the safety of the approach operation by reducing pilot workload and by lessening the possibility of error in flying the approach.

EU Required

[EU Regulation No 859/2008, Appendix 1, ¶(d)2.] All non-precision approaches shall be flown using the continuous descent final approaches (CDFA) technique unless otherwise approved by the Authority for a particular approach to a particular runway.

FAA Recommended

[AC 120-108 §5] The FAA recommends CDFA for all of the following NPAs published with a vertical descent angle (VDA) or glideslope (GS):

- Very high frequency (VHF) Omnidirectional Range (VOR),
- VHF omni-directional range station/distance measuring equipment,
- Non-directional radio beacon (NDB),
- NDB/distance measuring equipment (DME),
- Localizer (LOC), Localizer Back-Course (LOC-BC),
- LOC/DME,
- Localizer-type directional aid (LDA),
- LDA/DME,
- Simplified Directional Facility (SDF),
- SDF/DME,
- Area Navigation (RNAV), and
- Global Positioning System (GPS).

Required by Some Countries

[ICAO Doc 8168, Vol I, Part I, Amdt 3, ¶ 1.7.2.1] Many Contracting States require the use of the CDFA technique and apply increased visibility or RVR requirements when the technique is not used.

Many countries require CDFA techniques be used but application of the technique is not consistent. Some countries list a CDFA approach with "CDFA" in the minimums section while others use "DA" or "DA/MDA". Even the countries that list "CDFA" are not consistent about the meaning. In India, for example, you are required to add the height loss additive to the CDFA altitude. But in France, you normally do not. The only way to ensure you are following the rules of the host nation is to look it up in the country's Aeronautical Information Publication or the Jeppesen Airways Manual ATC pages.

Do you need special equipment?

[AC 120-108 §6.a] CDFA requires no specific aircraft equipment other than that specified by the title of the NPA procedure. Pilots can safely fly suitable NPAs with CDFA using basic piloting techniques, aircraft flight management systems (FMS), and RNAV systems.

Aircraft with FMS, barometric vertical navigation (baro-VNAV), wide area augmentation system (WAAS), or that are similarly equipped typically provide the published VDA or GS when the IAP is selected from the database.

Aircraft equipped with Flight Path Angle (FPA) allow the pilot to enter an electronic descent angle based on the published GS or VDA. Pilots flying aircraft without either type of equipment must compute a required rate of descent.

How is a CDFA Depicted?

On an FAA chart, a vertical descent angle is indicated by the ">" bracket next to the angle and on top of the TCH.

On a Jeppesen chart, an RNAV(GPS) will be depicted with glide feathers in the profile view.

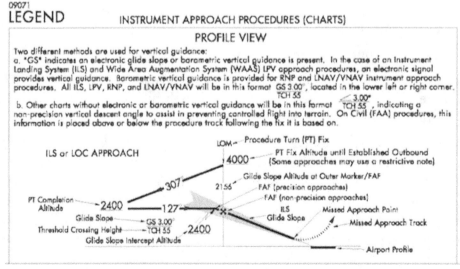

Figure: Instrument Approach Procedures Legend, from FAA

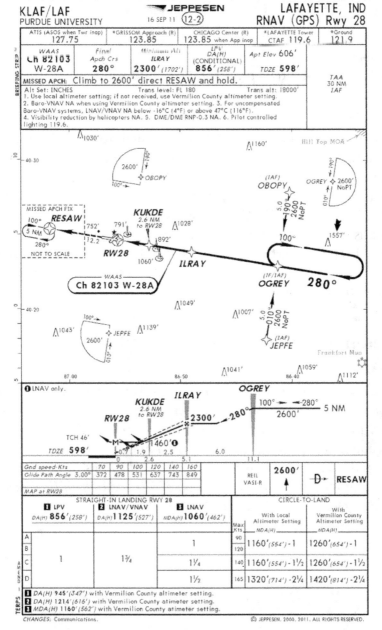

Figure: Example of glide feather, KLAF, page 12-2, 16 Sep 11.

Vertical Path Angle — Limitations

AC 120-108 does not impose a maximum vertical path angle, per se, but if you have OpSpec, MSpec, or LOA C073 you are already familiar with a VNAV DA(H) in lieu of MDA(H) provision that limits you to 3.77° (Category A, B, and C) or 3.5° (Category D and E). You really should adopt those limits for CDFA as well.

[AC 120-108 §6.d] The VDA or GS is calculated from the FAF/precise final approach fix (PFAF) altitude to the threshold crossing height (TCH). The optimum NPA descent angle (VDA or GS) is 3.0 degrees. Descent angles are found in the following range when the optimum VDA is not possible: 2.75°–3.77° (IAPs w/CAT C minimums), 2.75°–3.50° (IAPs w/CAT D/E minimums). On approaches with stepdown fixes, the goal is to publish a VDA that keeps the Vertical Path (VPATH) above the stepdown fix altitude. However, in some cases, the VDA is calculated from the stepdown fix altitude to the TCH.

Procedures: Determining a Derived Decision Altitude (DDA)

The MDA, under most cases, is still an altitude you cannot go below. The CDFA technique adds an "increment" (an altitude pad) to account for the aircraft's tendency to go below the altitude at which the missed approach is initiated, usually due to autopilot reaction time. In many aircraft a "maximum autopilot altitude loss" is published and can be used as this increment. The new altitude, that resulting from the addition of this pad to the MDA, is known as the Derived Decision Altitude (DDA).

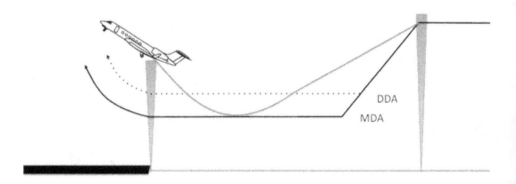

[ICAO Doc 8168, Vol I, Part I, Amdt 3, ¶ 1.7.2.5] An increment for the MDA/H may be prescribed by the operator to determine the altitude/height at which the vertical portion of the missed approach shall be initiated in order to prevent descent below the MDA/H. In such cases, there is no need to increase the RVR or visibility requirements for the approach. The RR and/or visibility published for the original MDA/H should be used.

[AC 120-108 §6.F] Pilots must not descend below the MDA when executing a missed approach from a CDFA. Operators should instruct their pilots to initiate the go-around at an altitude above the MDA (sometimes referred to as a DDA) to ensure the aircraft does not descend below the published MDA. Operators conducting approaches authorized by operations specification (OpSpec) C073, IFR Approach Procedures Using Vertical Navigation (VNAV), may use MDA as a DA.

C073 is now available also as a Letter of Authorization. These approaches, those with the "Only Authorized Operators" ball note, take into consideration the aircraft's momentary dip below the MDA.

Procedures: Leaving the Final Approach Fix

[ICAO Doc 8168, Vol I, Part I, Amdt 3, ¶ 1.7.2.2] This technique requires a continuous descent, flown either with VNAV guidance calculated by onboard equipment or based on manual calculation of the required rate of descent, without level-offs. The rate of descent is selected and adjusted to achieve a continuous descent to a point approximately 15m (50 ft) above the landing runway threshold or the point where the flare manoeuvre should begin for the type aircraft flown. The descent shall be calculated and flown to pass at or above the minimum altitude at any step down fix.

The objective of CDFA is to leave the final approach fix fully configured, on speed, and ready to land. You should not have to destabilize the aircraft by making airspeed or trim adjustments when spotting the runway.

Methodology: High Tech

*Some aircraft allow a CDFA be flown with ILS-like indications so that proce-
dures can be identical. Others may require adjustments, such as lowering the
altitude select to field elevation. The closer CDFA procedures can be to an ILS,
the better. Pilots simply follow the needles down to minimums, being mindful
of the decision altitude. (In either case, pilots should consult their aircraft manuals and practice these procedures in a simulator until comfortable.)*

Methodology: Low Tech

[AC 120-108 §6.c]

1.   Find the published VDA.

2.   Find the descent gradient that equates to [the] VDA.

3.   Find the descent rate based on groundspeed.

*If you don't have an FMS that does all this for you, or if you are flying an ap-
proach that prevents your FMS from doing all this for you, this table gives you
an idea of what vertical descent rate you are going to need. If you don't have
the table, you can approximate a 3° angle of descent by dividing your groundspeed by 2 and multiplying that by ten. A 120-knot ground speed, for example,
yields 600 fpm.*

*You can check your progress during the approach by placing tick marks at each
mile from the final approach fix to the missed approach point with the appropriate altitude. A 3° glide path should lose 318' every nautical mile. If, for
example, the final approach fix altitude is 2,000 feet, you should be at 1,682'
after one mile, 1,364' after two miles, 1,046' after three miles, and so on. You
can figure these out during your approach briefing, marking each target on the
approach plate.*

Procedures: When to go Missed Approach

*The CDFA places the aircraft right on glide path in a position to land in the
touchdown zone of the runway. If the runway is sighted after this point, the
aircraft will be too far down the runway to make that happen and a missed
approach will be needed. This eliminates the judgement calls when sighting the
runway early or late.*

RATE OF DESCENT TABLE

A rate of descent table is provided for use in planning and executing precision descents under known or approximate ground speed conditions. It will be especially useful for approaches when the localizer only is used for course guidance. A best speed, power, altitude combination can be programmed which will result in a stable glide rate and altitude favorable for executing a landing if minimums exist upon breakout. Care should always be exercised so that minimum descent altitude and missed approach point are not exceeded.

ANGLE OF DESCENT (degrees and tenths)	FEET /NM	GROUND SPEED (knots)										
		30	45	60	75	90	105	120	135	150	165	180
2.0	210	105	160	210	265	320	370	425	475	530	585	635
2.5	265	130	200	265	330	395	465	530	595	665	730	795
2.7	287	143	215	287	358	430	501	573	645	716	788	860
2.8	297	149	223	297	371	446	520	594	669	743	817	891
2.9	308	154	231	308	385	462	539	616	693	769	846	923
3.0	318	159	239	318	398	478	557	637	716	796	876	955
3.1	329	165	247	329	411	494	576	658	740	823	905	987
3.2	340	170	255	340	425	510	594	679	764	849	934	1019
3.3	350	175	263	350	438	526	613	701	788	876	963	1051
3.4	361	180	271	361	451	541	632	722	812	902	993	1083
3.5	370	185	280	370	465	555	650	740	835	925	1020	1110
4.0	425	210	315	425	530	635	740	845	955	1060	1165	1270

(Left margin label spanning rows 2.7 through 3.4: VERTICAL PATH ANGLE)

Figure: Rate of Descent Table, from FAA-H-8083-15B, figure 1-19.

[ICAO Doc 8168, Vol I, Part I, Amdt 3, ¶ 1.7.2.3] If the visual references required to land have not been acquired when the aircraft is approaching the MDA/H, the vertical (climbing) portion of the missed approach is initiated at an altitude above the MDA/H sufficient to prevent the aircraft from descending through the MDA/H. At not time is the aircraft flown in level flight at or near the MDA/H. Any turns on the missed approach shall not begin until the aircraft reaches the Misssed Approach Point. Likewise, if the aircraft reaches the Missed Approach Point before descending to near the MDA/H, the missed approach shall be initiated at the Missed Approach Point.

[ICAO Doc 8168, Vol I, Part I, Amdt 3, ¶ 1.7.2.6] It should be emphasized that upon reaching the MDA/H only two options exist for the crew: continue the descent below MDA/H to land with the required visual references in sight; or, execute a missed approach. There is no level flight segment after reaching the MDA/H.

Example: Published DA

The Swiss do not specifically mention CDFA on their approach plates or in the State Rules and Procedures pages, but a DA is listed on the non-precision approaches and the ICAO recommended technique should be employed. The Swiss do, however, specifically allow GPS overlays for specific approaches, including this one:

This approach can be flown almost like an RNAV (GPS) approach in the U.S. with the exception that in aircraft's "altitude pad" should be added to the published DA. (In some cases, the State will specify a minimum altitude increment to determine the DDA.) Both PFDs can be set to LRN data with the SFD showing VOR or one PFD to VOR data. Unlike flying a U.S. RNAV (GPS) approach, the Swiss ATC pages specifically require the ground based navaids be operational and used as the primary means of navigation. I would have the ground based navaids in view on a display with a CDI, either the copilot's or the standby system. This way you can fly the approach using the APPR button, once again treating it like an ILS.

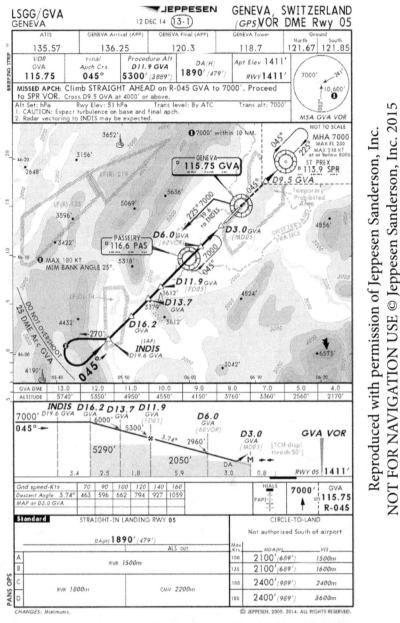

Figure: Geneva VOR DME Rwy 05, from Jeppesen Airways Manual, LSGG, pg. 13-1.

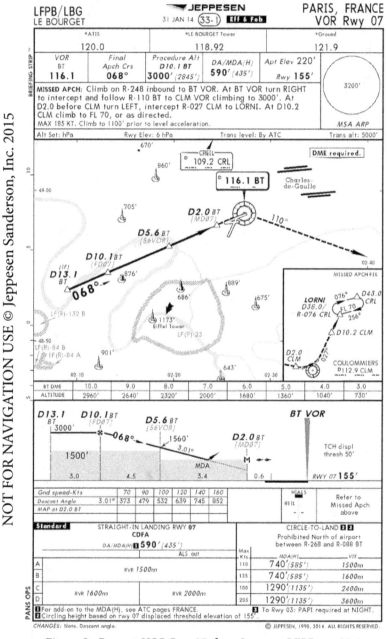

Figure: Le Bourget VOR Rwy 07, from Jeppesen LFPB, pg. 33-1.

Example: CFDA Published

The Jeppesen State Rules and Procedures pages for France: "The operational minima published on French non-precision approach charts have been determined based on the assumption that these approaches are flown using CDFA flight technique unless otherwise stated by the Authority for a particular approach to a particular runway."

This approach has already added the altitude pad so you can fly it down to the posted DA (590'). There is no provision in the French ATC pages stating you may fly this approach using RNAV.

By the book, you would have to fly this using the VOR as your navigation source, estimate your descent rate to fly the given altitudes on the chart, and 590 feet. Is that the best way to fly this approach? Probably not.

As technique, if you have the technology, the following will probably be safer:

- *Fly the approach using APPR, the FMS as your navigation source.*

- *Have the raw data available, with CDI, some place in the cockpit. You could use the copilot's display or the standby flight director.*

- *Set the missed approach altitude in the altitude preselector.*

- *Fly the approach LNAV/VNAV, using the published CDFA as your decision point to continue or go around.*

If you don't have the technology, you can determine your ground speed and compute an initial descent rate and a target altitude loss per nautical mile using the chart given above, Descent Table. Let's say you are moving along at 120 knots ground speed:

- *At 120 knots ground speed your feet/nm is 318 and your rate of descent will be 637 feet/minute.*

- *Check first that you can clear the step down fix restriction using this descent rate. This fix is 4.5 nm from the final approach fix, which means a 3° glide path will lose (4.5) (318) = 1,431' and you will cross the step down at 3,000 - 1,431 = 1,569' which places you above the restriction.*

- *You can start your descent from the final approach fix using a 637 feet/minute descent rate.*

- *You can check your progress by subtracting 318 feet per nautical mile from the final approach fix altitude. Specifically:*

At 9.1 DME you should be at 3,000 - 318 = 2,682'

At 8.1 DME you should be at 3,000 - 636 = 2,364'

At 7.1 DME you should be at 3,000 - 954 = 2,046'

At 6.1 DME you should be at 3,000 - 1,272 = 1,728'

At 5.1 DME you should be at 3,000 - 1,590 = 1,410'

At 4.1 DME you should be at 3,000 - 1,908 = 1,092'

At 3.1 DME you should be at 3,000 - 2,226 = 774'

At 2.1 DME you should be well on your way to landing or executing the missed approach.

Chapter 15

Course Reversals

In the United States it is common practice to use holding pattern procedures when flying a procedure turn, what is more properly called a course reversal under ICAO. The U.S. procedures will not always work in other parts of the world. You can use those same procedures in the United States now, just keep in mind you have to limit your entry speeds to 200 knots and you may not be able to fly as fast during some of the maneuvering.

You may have flown internationally for years not knowing the difference between a U.S. procedure turn and an ICAO course reversal. You probably got away with it too, since we hardly ever fly full procedures. And even when you do, chances are you can get away with using U.S. FAA procedures. But not always. An Air Force crew was violated for entering the 45°/180° course reversal shown here just has they had been taught, using U.S. FAA procedures. They were cleared direct to the NDB and for the approach. They hit the NDB and turned right. And they were violated. What would you have done?

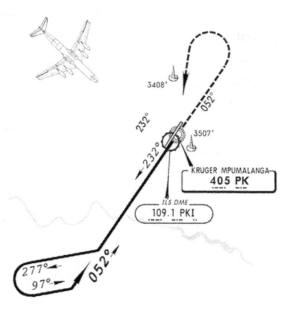

45°/180° Procedure Turn

[ICAO Document 8168, Vol 1 §4, ¶3.2.2.3 a] 45°/180° procedure turn starts at a facility or fix and consists of:

1. a straight leg with track guidance. This straight leg may be timed or may be limited by a radial or DME distance;

2. a 45° turn;

3. a straight leg without track guidance. This straight leg is timed. It is:

   a. 1 minute from the start of the turn for Category A and B aircraft; and

   b. 1 minute 15 seconds from the start of the turn for Category C, D and E aircraft; and

4. a 180° turn in the opposite direction to intercept the inbound track.

The 45°/180° procedure turn is an alternative to the 80°/260° procedure turn [b) below] unless specifically excluded.

Unlike the U.S. FAA Standard Procedure Turn, also known as the 45°/180° Procedure Turn, the straight leg without track guidance is timed under ICAO procedures. The timing is mandatory unless a DME limit is given.

In the Agana, Guam (PGUM) example, the procedure begins heading 242° and executing the left turn so as to remain with 10 nm of the VOR. Unlike U.S. procedures, the 45° leg is timed.

Figure: 45°/180° procedure turn, from ICAO Document 8168, Vol 1 Figure I-4-3-1.A.

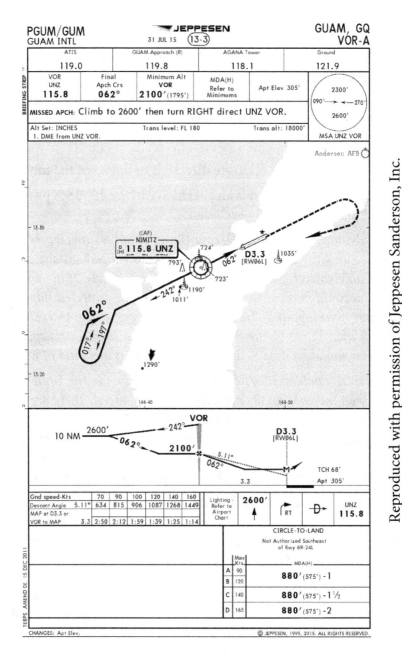

Figure: Agana VOR-A, from Jeppesen Airway Manual, page PGUM 13-3, 31 Jul 2015.

80°/260° Procedure Turn

[ICAO Document 8168, Vol 1 §4, ¶3.2.2.3 b] 80°/260° procedure turn starts at a facility or fix and consists of:

1. a straight leg with track guidance. This straight leg may be timed or may be limited by a radial or DME distance;

2. an 80° turn;

3. a 260° turn in the opposite direction to intercept the inbound track.

The 80°/260° procedure turn is an alternative to the 45°/180° procedure turn [a) above] unless specifically excluded.

The only advantage of the 80°/260 over the 45°/180° is time: it gets you pointed back to the runway more quickly. But there is a big disadvantage: adjusting for wind, the only correction available to you is bank angle. If the wind is strong enough, you could find yourself blown onto the non-protected side before completing your turn inbound. The ICAO says you can use a 45°/180° procedure turn as an alternative to the 80°/260° procedure turn unless specifically excluded. You would be wise to do just that if there is any kind of wind.

I've never seen a published 80°/260° Procedure Turn in the United States and those I've seen internationally are a disappearing breed. There are a few left in Papua New Guinea and I've seen one in Egypt. But most places that have had them long ago changed to racetrack, base turn, or standard procedure turns. The 80°/260° gives the pilot very little room to adjust for winds. If given a choice, any other course reversal should be preferred to the 80°/260°.

In the example shown you should avail yourself of the full 3 minutes outbound allowed to give yourself enough time to intercept the course inbound. If the winds are from the south the 80°/260° should work well. If the winds are from the north, the 45°/180° may be a better choice.

Figure: 80°/260° procedure turn, from ICAO Document 8168, Vol 1 Figure I-4-3-1.B.

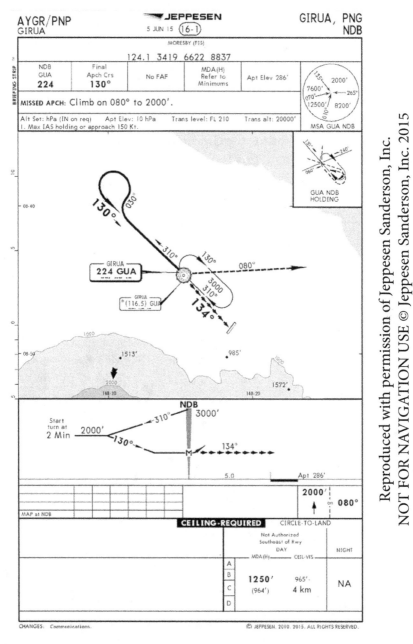

Figure: Girua NDB, from Jeppesen Airway Manual, page AYGR 16-1, 5 Jun 2015.

Base Turn

[ICAO Document 8168, Vol 1 §4, ¶3.2.2.3 c] Base turn consists of:

1.   a specified outbound track and timing or DME distance from a facility; followed by

2.   a turn to intercept the inbound track

The outbound track and/or the timing may be different for the various categories of aircraft. Where this is done, separate procedures are published.

I asked to fly the entire procedure, just to say I did, but they wouldn't have any of that and we ended up with vectors to final. Notice the alternative procedure, in this case, allows you to enter from the holding pattern.

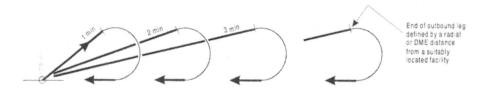

Figure: Base turn, from ICAO Document 8168, Vol 1 Figure I-4-3-1.C.

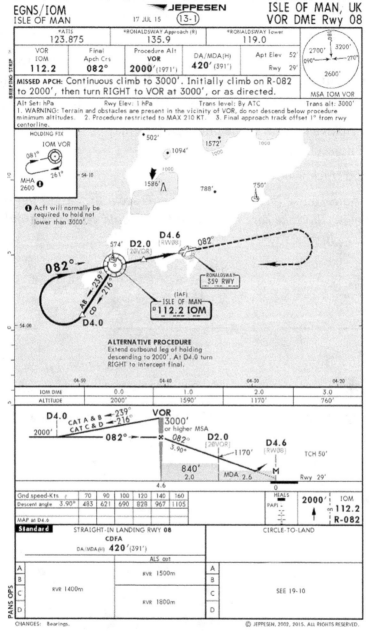

*Figure: Isle of Man VOR/DME Rwy 08, from Jeppesen Airway Manual,
Page EGNS 13-1, 17 Jul 2015.*

Racetrack

[ICAO Document 8168, Vol 1 §4, ¶3.2.3] A racetrack procedure consists of:

1.   a turn from the inbound track through 180° from overhead the facility or fix on to the outbound track, for 1, 2 or 3 minutes; followed by

2.   a 180° turn in the same direction to return to the inbound track.

As an alternative to timing, the outbound leg may be limited by a DME distance or intersecting radial/bearing.

The ground track is flown as depicted.

Of the various course reversals, this one may seem the easiest to execute and it probably is. But take care with the entry, it could get you in trouble. More about that right now . . .

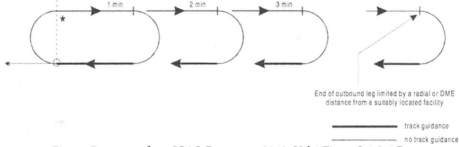

End of outbound leg limited by a radial or DME
distance from a suitably located facility

———————— track guidance
– – – – – – – – no track guidance

Figure: Base turn, from ICAO Document 8168, Vol 1 Figure I-4-3-1.D.

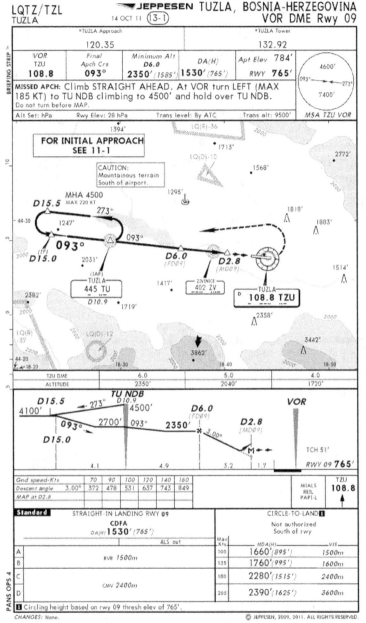

Figure: Tuzla VOR/DME Rwy 09, from Jeppesen Airway Manual,
Page LQTZ 13-1, 14 Oct 2011.

Entry Procedures

Course Reversal entry procedures are not the same as in the United States; the difference can get you into trouble. You need to understand the 30° entry sector, the base turn exception to the 30° entry sector, and racetrack entry procedures.

45°/180°, 80°/260°, and Base Turn Entry Procedures

[ICAO Document 8168, Vol 1 §4, ¶3.3.1] Unless the procedure specifies particular entry restrictions, reversal procedures shall be entered from a track within ±30° of the outbound track of the reversal procedure. However, for base turns, where the ±30° direct entry sector does not include the reciprocal of the inbound track, the entry sector is expanded to include it.

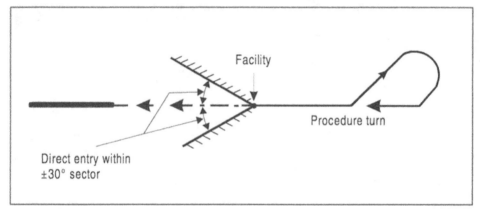

Figure: Direct entry to procedure turn, from ICAO Document 8168, Vol 1, figure I-4-3-2.

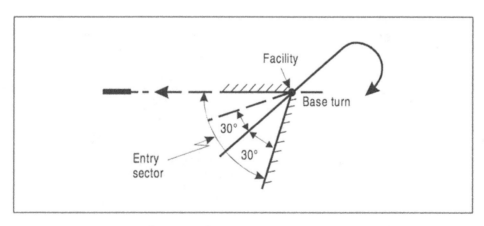

Figure: Direct entry to base turn, from ICAO Document 8168, Vol 1, figure I-4-3-3.

You've got to be within these entry sectors to be permitted to begin the 45°/180°, 80°/260°, or base turn procedure. What if you aren't?

Most of these procedures have a holding pattern nearby and ICAO Document 8168, Vol 1, figure I-4-3-4, states "arrivals from this sector must enter the holding prior to the reversal procedure." What if there isn't a holding pattern depicted? I would request "maneuvering airspace" opposite the course reversal so that I could maneuver the aircraft into the entry sector.

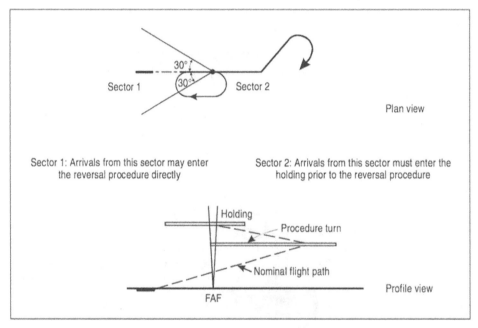

Figure: Omnidirectional arrival holding associated with reversal procedure, from ICAO Document 8168, Vol 1, figure I-4-3-4.

Racetrack Entry Procedures

[ICAO Document 8168, Vol 1 §4, ¶3.2.3.2] Normally a racetrack procedure is used when aircraft arrive overhead the fix from various directions. In these cases, aircraft are expected to enter the procedure in a manner similar to that prescribed for a holding procedure entry with the following considerations:

a.   offset entry from Sector 2 shall limit the time on the 30° offset track to 1 min 30 s, after which the pilot is expected to turn to a heading parallel to the outbound track for the remainder of the outbound time. If the outbound time is only 1 min, the time on the 30° offset track shall be 1 min also;

b.   parallel entry shall not return directly to the facility without first intercepting the inbound track when proceeding to the final segment of the approach procedure; and

c.   all manoeuvring shall be done in so far as possible on the manoeuvring side of the inbound track.

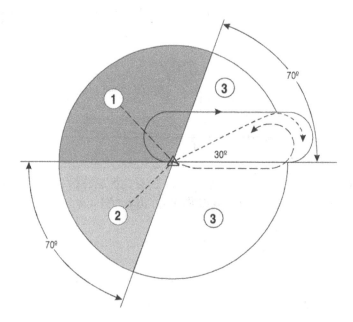

Figure: Entry Sectors, from ICAO Document 8168, Vol 1 Figure I-6-1-2.

Chapter 16

Customs

*T*here are three very good rules when it comes to dealing with the customs officials of another country:

- *Not all the rules are written and even if they are they are subject to change; it pays to know somebody with first-hand experience with the country.*

- *Sometimes things don't go well and having an advocate on the ground who speaks the language and actually lives there will work in your favor. If you don't have somebody like that, find a trip planning handler who does.*

- *Be prepared for delays, don't get upset in public, and make sure your passengers know to do the same. You are playing in someone else's sandbox and they can toss you into the penalty box for no reason at all. Don't give them the excuse to do just that.*

In fact, these rules also apply to dealing with the customs officials of your own country too. In the case of the United States, it is often difficult to find the information you need because the rules are always changing and links to their needed spots on their websites seldom stay put for more than a year. The best you can do is to do your best, answer their questions honestly, and don't get upset.

Before Departing the United States

Passports and Visas

You will need a passport to enter another country and then to return to United States. The rules are different for each country and can also change depending on the other countries on your itinerary. The rules of Visas can also be different for passengers and crewmembers. You may be surprised to hear that many countries even have rules on how many blank pages must be available in your passport or how many months remain before expiration. The best way to be certain is to visit: http://travel.state.gov/content/travel/english.html and use the "Learn about your destination" section.

Visa Waiver Program, "Green Cards"

A person who enters the United States under the Visa Waiver Program may not be aware that they cannot depart the country unless the entity providing the transportation is approved under the program. Even as a 14 CFR 91 operator you can be an approved Visa Waiver Program carrier, but even if you aren't and one of your passengers is travelling using the Visa Waiver Program, you need to be smart about it. See the Appendices, Chapter 34, Visa Waiver Program.

Minors Traveling Without Their Parents

Some countries require minors traveling without their parents have notarized travel permission from their legal guardians.

Canada

Getting into and out of Canada is fairly easy and it can be even easier if you, everyone on your crew, and all your passengers are enrolled in CANPASS or with the Telephone Reporting Center (TRC). See the Appendices, Chapter 12, CANPASS.

Electronic Advanced Passenger Information System (eAPIS)

You've got no choice in the matter anymore, you have to participate in the Electronic Advanced Passenger Information System (eAPIS). An international flight planning service can make this easy for you, but you can do it yourself. The system the Department of Homeland Security (DHS) gives you through Customs & Border Protection (CBP) is fair, at best, but it does work. It won't remember your passengers or crew, but it remembers you. Several flight planning services that you are probably already using can automate things and make the entire process a bit less painful. See the Appendices, Chapter 17, eAPIS.

Entry into the United States

The process of getting back into the country has gotten easier, thanks to the proliferation of electrons in the system. Things will go more smoothly if you have eAPIS complete, have your paperwork in order, and be patient with the guy wearing the badge and gun.

Electronic Advanced Passenger Information System (eAPIS)

You can't depart for the United States unless you have your eAPIS in order.

See the Appendices, Chapter 17, eAPIS.

Inspection of Certificates

[14 CFR 61] §61.3 (l) Inspection of certificate. Each person who holds an airman certificate, medical certificate, authorization, or license required by this part must present it and their photo identification as described in paragraph (a)(2) of this section for inspection upon a request from:

1.   The Administrator;

2.   An authorized representative of the National Transportation Safety Board;

3.   Any Federal, State, or local law enforcement officer; or

4.   An authorized representative of the Transportation Security Administration.

The customs and border inspector will ask for your pilot's license, medical, and a photo ID which is normally your passport.

Non-immigrant Visitors (CBP Form I-94, Arrival/Departure Record)

Foreign visitors to the U.S. arriving via air or sea no longer need to complete paper Customs and Border Protection Form I-94 Arrival/Departure Record or Form I-94W Nonimmigrant Visa Waiver Arrival/Departure Record. Those who need to prove their legal-visitor status—to employers, schools/universities or government agencies—can access their CBP arrival/departure record information online. More about this: http://www.cbp.gov/travel/international-visitors/i-94-instructions.

Customs Declaration Form 6059B

[http://www.cbp.gov/travel/clearing-cbp/traveler-entry-form]

Each individual arriving into the United States must complete the CBP Declaration Form 6059B. If you are traveling with other immediate family members who reside in one household, complete one form per family.

A family is considered people who are related by blood, marriage, domestic relationship or adoption. People in a domestic relationship include foster children, stepchildren, half-siblings, legal wards, other dependents or individuals with an in loco parentis or guardianship relationship. It also includes two adults who are in a committed relationship including, but not limited to, long-time companions and couples in civil unions or domestic partnerships, wherein the partners are financially interdependent and are not married to, or a partner of, anyone else. A "domestic relationship" does not extend to roommates or other cohabitants who do not meet this definition.

Crew Member's Declaration 5129

This form is required at only a few points of entry, KPBI to name one. To date, there is no central location of information detailing when the form is needed.

Forms available at: http://forms.cbp.gov/pdf/CBP_Form_5129.pdf.

General Declaration (CBP Form 7507)

They say the Gen Dec is no longer required in the United States, it has been replaced by eAPIS. More about that: International Operations / eAPIS.

The trouble is much of the rest of the world still requires them and the form is still in print, available here:http://forms.cbp.gov/pdf/CBP_Form_7507.pdf.

Chapter 17

Electronic Advanced Passenger Information System (eAPIS)

*Y**ou've got no choice in the matter anymore, you have to participate in the Electronic Advanced Passenger Information System (eAPIS). An international flight planning service can make this easy for you, but you can do it yourself. The system the Department of Homeland Security (DHS) gives you through Customs & Border Protection (CBP) is fair, at best, but it does work. It won't remember your passengers or crew, but it remembers you. Several flight planning services that you are probably already using can automate things and make the entire process a bit less painful.*

The regulatory guidance covering eAPIS is quoted from the references shown below. As with many things in aviation, the regulations are confusing and can mislead you. It can be more useful to follow those who have already cracked the code; I've tried to summarize those lessons in the sections shown that follow in italics.

The Legal Authority

[NPRM 19 CFR 122, ¶I.A.]

Pursuant to 19 U.S.C. 1433, 1644 and 1644a, the Secretary of Homeland Security has broad authority respecting all aircraft, including private aircraft, arriving in and departing from the United States. [The] pilot of any aircraft arriving in the United States or the U.S. Virgin Islands from any foreign location is required to comply with such advance notification, arrival reporting, and landing requirements as regulations may require. CBP can deny aircraft landing rights within the United States based on, among other considerations, security and/or risk assessments. Alternatively, CBP may specifically designate and limit the airports where aircraft may land. [An] aircraft pilot is required to present or transmit to CBP through an electronic data interchange system such information, data, documents, papers or manifests as the regulations may require. [Aircraft] after arriving in the United States or U.S. Virgin Islands may depart from the airport of arrival, but only in accordance with regulations prescribed by the Secretary.

[19 CFR 122, §122.0] Applicability. The regulations in this part relate to the entry and clearance of aircraft and the transportation of persons and cargo by aircraft, and are applicable to all air commerce.

Definitions

[19 CFR 122, §122.1]

A "commercial aircraft" is any aircraft transporting passengers and/or cargo for some payment or other consideration, including money or services rendered.

A "private aircraft" is any aircraft engaged in a personal or business flight to or from the U.S. which is not: carrying passengers and/or cargo for commercial purposes; leaving the U.S. carrying neither passengers nor cargo in order to lade passengers and/or cargo in a foreign area for commercial purposes; or returning to the U.S. carrying neither passengers nor cargo in ballast after leaving with passengers and/or cargo for commercial purposes;

Arrival Process

Private Aircraft (Regulatory)

[19 CFR 122, §122.22(b)(1)] The private aircraft pilot is responsible for ensuring the notice of arrival and manifest information regarding each individual onboard the aircraft are transmitted to CBP. The pilot is responsible for the submission, accuracy, correctness, timeliness, and completeness of the submitted information, but may authorize another party to submit the information on their behalf. Except as provided in paragraph (b)(7) of this section, all data must be transmitted to CBP by means of an electronic data interchange system approved by CBP and must set forth the information specified in this section.

[19 CFR 122, §122.22(b)(2)] The private aircraft pilot is responsible for ensuring that the information [. . .] of this section is transmitted to CBP:

For flights originally destined for the United States, any time prior to depar-

388

ture of the aircraft, but no later than 60 minutes prior to departure of the aircraft from the foreign port or place; or

For flights not originally destined to the United States, but diverted to a U.S. port due to an emergency, no later than 30 minutes prior to arrival; in cases of non-compliance, CBP will take into consideration that the carrier was not equipped to make the transmission and the circumstances of the emergency situation.

[19 CFR 122, §122.22(b)(6)] Prior to departure from the foreign port or place, the pilot of a private aircraft must receive a message from DHS approving landing within the United States, and follow any instructions contained therein prior to departure. Once DHS has approved departure, and the pilot has executed all instructions issued by DHS, the aircraft is free to depart with the intent of landing at the designated U.S. port of entry.

[19 CFR 122, §122.22(b)(7)] The private aircraft pilot is obligated to make necessary changes to the arrival manifest after transmission of the manifest to CBP. If changes to an already transmitted manifest are necessary, an updated and amended manifest must be resubmitted to CBP. Only amendments regarding flight cancellation, expected time of arrival (ETA) or changes in arrival location, to an already transmitted manifest may be submitted telephonically, by radio, or through existing processes and procedures. On a limited case-by-case basis, CBP may permit a pilot to submit or update notice of arrival and arrival/departure manifest information telephonically when unforeseen circumstances preclude submission of the information via eAPIS. Under such circumstances, CBP will manually enter the notice of arrival and arrival/departure manifest information provided by the pilot and the pilot is required to wait for CBP screening and approval to depart. Changes in ETA and arrival location must be coordinated with CBP at the new arrival location to ensure that resources are available to inspect the arriving aircraft. If a subsequent manifest is submitted less than 60 minutes prior to departure to the United States, the private aircraft pilot must receive approval from CBP for the amended manifest containing added passenger information and/or changes to information that were submitted regarding the aircraft and all individuals onboard the aircraft, before the aircraft is allowed to depart the foreign location, or the aircraft may be, as appropriate, diverted from arriving in the United States, or denied permission to land in the United States. If a subsequent, amended manifest is submitted by the pilot, any approval to depart the foreign port or location previously granted by CBP as a result of the original manifest's submission is invalid.

The process is easier than it seems and is explained in English, below.

Commercial Aircraft (Regulatory)

[19 CFR 122, §122.49a(b)(1)(i)] Basic requirement. Except as provided in paragraph (c) of this section, an appropriate official of each commercial aircraft (carrier) arriving in the United States from any place outside the United States must transmit to the Advance Passenger Information System (APIS; referred to in this section as the Customs and Border Protection (CBP) system), the electronic data interchange system approved by CBP for such transmissions, an electronic passenger arrival manifest covering all passengers checked in for the flight. A passenger manifest must be transmitted separately from a crew member manifest required under §122.49b if transmission is in U.S. EDIFACT format. The passenger manifest must be transmitted to the CBP system at the place and time specified in paragraph (b)(2) of this section, in the manner set forth under paragraph (b)(1)(ii) of this section.

[19 CFR 122, §122.49a(b)(2)] Place and time for submission. The appropriate official [. . .] must transmit the arrival manifest or manifest data [. . .] to the CBP system (CBP Data Center, CBP Headquarters), in accordance with the following:

i. For manifests transmitted under paragraph (b)(1)(ii)(A) or (B) of this section, no later than 30 minutes prior to the securing of the aircraft;

ii. For manifest information transmitted under paragraph (b)(1)(ii)(C) of this section, no later than the securing of the aircraft;

iii. For flights not originally destined to the United States but diverted to a U.S. port due to an emergency, no later than 30 minutes prior to arrival; in cases of non-compliance, CBP will take into consideration whether the carrier was equipped to make the transmission and the circumstances of the emergency situation; and

iv. For an aircraft operating as an air ambulance in service of a medical emergency, no later than 30 minutes prior to arrival; in cases of non-compliance, CBP will take into consideration whether the carrier was equipped to make the transmission and the circumstances of the emergency situation.

The various mysterious paragraphs and bracketed ellipses all refer to minutiae about batch reporting and the like. *The bottom line is you have to submit a crew and passenger manifest and CBP has a few extra steps to follow before approving your arrival. Once again this is broken down into English, as follows.*

Arrival Process (In English)

Ensure that an APIS manifest is submitted to CBP. The pilot is responsible for the submission of an accurate manifest and for validating APIS data for travelers arriving in to the United States. APIS manifests can be submitted as early as you like, but no later than 60 minutes prior to the flight's departure.

Receive an electronic clearance response from DHS. You should get a confirmation e-mail receipt from APISConfirmNoReply@dhs.gov within a few seconds saying your manifest was successfully processed and cleared, or CBP was unable to systematically clear your manifest.

If your manifest was not processed successfully, you will be given instructions on how to contact a DHS representative to assist with the flight's clearance. It could be a simple entry error or you could have somebody flagged on the "No Fly" list.

Report immediately to CBP for inspection upon arrival in to the United States.

You should keep a copy of the eAPIS e-mail during the flight.

Changes: you must submit another manifest in eAPIS if: additional travelers are added; you can resubmit the previous manifest if the pilot has not changed; the date of travel has changed; the aircraft changes.

Changes: you do not make change in eAPIS if: the travel time on the same day changes; just notify the CBP airport of arrival, the port changes; just notify the original and new CBP, passengers or crew do not fly; you don't need to do anything if the pilot is the same.

Departure Process

Private Aircraft (Regulatory)

[19 CFR 122, §122.22(c)(1)] The private aircraft pilot is responsible for ensuring that information regarding private aircraft departing the United States, and manifest data for all individuals onboard the aircraft is timely transmitted to CBP. The pilot is responsible for the accuracy, correctness, timeliness, and completeness of the submitted information, but may authorize another party to submit the information on their behalf. Data must be transmitted to CBP by means of an electronic data interchange system approved by CBP, and must set forth the information specified [. . .] All data pertaining to the aircraft, and all individuals onboard the aircraft must be transmitted at the same time. On a limited case-by-case basis, CBP may permit a pilot to submit or update notice of arrival and arrival/departure manifest information telephonically to CBP when unforeseen circumstances preclude submission of the information via eAPIS. Under such circumstances, CBP will manually enter the notice of arrival and arrival/departure manifest information provided by the pilot and the pilot is required to wait for CBP screening and approval to depart.

[19 CFR 122, §122.22(c)(2)] The private aircraft pilot must transmit the electronic data required [in this] section to CBP any time prior to departing the United States, but no later than 60 minutes prior to departing the United States.

[19 CFR 122, §122.22(c)(5)] Prior to departure for a foreign port or place, the pilot of a private aircraft must receive a message from DHS approving departure from the United States and follow any instructions contained therein. Once DHS has approved departure, and the pilot has executed all instructions issued by DHS, the aircraft is free to depart.

[19 CFR 122, §122.22(c)(6)] If any of the data elements change after the manifest is transmitted, the private aircraft pilot must update the manifest and resubmit the amended manifest to CBP. Only amendments regarding flight cancellation, expected time of departure or changes in departure location, to an already transmitted manifest may be submitted telephonically, by radio, or through existing processes and procedures. If an amended manifest is submitted less than 60 minutes prior to departure, the private aircraft pilot must receive approval from CBP for the amended manifest containing added passenger information and/or changes to information that were submitted regarding the aircraft before the aircraft is allowed to depart the U.S. location, or the aircraft may be denied clearance to depart from the United States. If a subsequent amended manifest is submitted by the pilot, any clearance previously granted by CBP as a result of the original manifest's submission is invalid.

The process is easier than it seems and is explained in English, below.

Commercial Aircraft (Regulatory)

[19 CFR 122, §122.75a(b)(1)(i)] Basic requirement. Except as provided in paragraph (c) of this section, an appropriate official of each commercial aircraft (carrier) departing from the United States en route to any port or place outside the United States must transmit to the Advance Passenger Information System (APIS; referred to in this section as the Customs and Border Protection (CBP) system), the electronic data interchange system approved by CBP for such transmissions, an electronic passenger departure manifest covering all passengers checked in for the flight. A passenger manifest must be transmitted separately from a crew member manifest required under §122.75b if transmission is in U.S. EDIFACT format. The passenger manifest must be transmitted to the CBP system at the place and time specified in paragraph (b)(2) of this section, in the manner set forth under paragraph (b)(1)(ii) of this section.

[19 CFR 122, §122.75a(b)(2)] The appropriate official specified in paragraph (b)(1)(i) of this section (carrier) must transmit the departure manifest or manifest data as required under paragraphs (b)(1)(i) and (ii) of this section to the CBP system (CBP Data Center, CBP Headquarters), in accordance with the following:

i. For manifests transmitted under paragraph (b)(1)(ii)(A) and (B) of this section, no later than 30 minutes prior to the securing of the aircraft;

ii. For manifest information transmitted under paragraph (b)(1)(ii)(C) of this section, no later than the securing of the aircraft; and

iii. For an aircraft operating as an air ambulance in serice of a medical emergency, no later than 30 minutes after departure.

The various mysterious paragraphs and bracketed ellipses all refer to minutiae about batch reporting and the like. The bottom line is you have to submit a crew and passenger manifest and CBP has a few extra steps to follow before approving your arrival. Once again this is broken down into English, as follows .

Departure Process (In English)

Ensure that an APIS manifest is submitted to CBP. The pilot is responsible for the submission of an accurate manifest submission and validating APIS data for travelers departing the United States. APIS manifests must be submitted no later than 60 minutes prior to the flight's departure.

Receive an electronic clearance response from DHS. You should get a confirmation e-mail receipt from APISConfirmNoReply@dhs.gov within a few seconds saying your manifest was successfully processed and cleared as expected, or

CBP was unable to systematically clear your manifest.

If your manifest was not processed successfully, you'll be given instructions on how to contact a DHS representative to assist with the flight's clearance.

You are clear to depart without further interaction unless CBP or another DHS agency contacts you and instructs you to report for an outbound inspection. In that case, you must present the aircraft, yourself, and all travelers for inspection just as he would for an inspection upon arrival in to the United States.

You should keep a copy of the eAPIS e-mail during the flight.

Changes: you must submit another manifest in eAPIS if: additional travelers are added; you can resubmit the previous manifest if the pilot has not changed, the date of travel has changed, the aircraft changes.

Changes: you do not make change in eAPIS if: the travel time on the same day changes; just notify the CBP airport of arrival, the port changes; just notify the original and new CBP, passengers or crew do not fly; you don't need to do anything if the pilot is the same.

Part 135 Caveat

The process for eAPIS under 14 CFR 135 is similar to 14 CFR 91 but the system goes through extra steps that can create a few problems:

If you are departing and arriving on the same day using the same flight number, the system may only keep the data for the second flight. You may need to change the flight number of one of the flights or delay submitting the eAPIS for the second flight.

If you depart under 14 CFR 91 and return under 14 CFR 135 the steps of the system used to record commercial flights gets bypassed and the return flight could set up a few alarms. If you plan on returning 14 CFR 135 you need to depart 14 CFR 135 as well.

The Actual Mechanics

The eAPIS system is accessed through https://eapis.cbp.dhs.gov.

You will need to enroll in the system and learn through trial and error. There used to be an online tutorial, in fact the website still makes reference to it. But it is not there any more.

Chapter 18

Equal Time Points

*A*n Equal Time Point (ETP) is not a "time" at all, it is a position in space between two remote points. When you get to that point, you will have an equal time between going back or going ahead in various conditions. For example, if you lose an engine over the North Atlantic at your computed ETP, it will take you just as long to turn around and head to your alternate in Canada with the forecast headwind, as it will to continue to Ireland with the forecast tailwind. But there are other ETP situations too, such as what happens if you lose pressurization? Or what if you are able to maintain speed and altitude but have to land as soon as possible for a medical emergency? That's why we need ETPs. Your flight planning service provider can do them for you automatically, but you need to know how to compute one manually to make sure they chose the ETP airports wisely and to compute your own if they didn't. The KBED - LSGG example used in the Tutorial Section is used here as well.

Equal Time Points for Navigators

Back in the days a navigator was needed to cross oceans, the Air Force used Manual 51-40 for this type of thing. The lessons remain valid today.

[AFM 51-40, page 24-9.] The equal time point is a point along the route from which it takes the same amount of time to return to departure as it would to continue to destination. The ETP is not necessarily the midpoint in time from departure to destination. Its location is somewhere near the midpoint of the route, however, and it dependent upon the wind factor.

A wind factor is a headwind or tailwind component which is computed by comparing the average groundspeed (GS) to the true airspeed (TAS). To do this, algebraically subtract the TAS from the GS. When the wind factor is a minus value (GS less than TAS), it is called a head wind factor; when it is a plus value (GS greater than TAS), it is a tail wind factor. When computing ETP, obtain a wind factor for each half of the route.

Use the following formula to compute a ETP:

$$\frac{\text{Total Distance}}{GS_R + GS_C} = \frac{\text{ETP (in nm from } GS_R)}{GS_R}$$

Total distance is the number of nautical miles from departure to destination. Since ETP is most significant for the overwater portion of a flight, the ETP should be determined from coastal departure points and for alternate landing points. GS_R is the groundspeed to return to departure from the ETP. Compute it for the first half of the route by applying the wind factor with the sign reversed to the TAS. GS_C is the GS to continue from the ETP to destination. Determine it by applying the wind factor for the second half of the route to the TAS.

Equal Time Points for Pilots

The navigator formula is not very useful to a pilot, but we can fix that with a little algebra.

The following formula is used to calculate the ground distance from the departure airport to ETP:

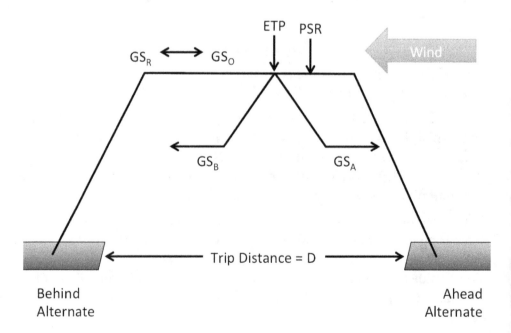

$$\text{Ground distance to ETP} = \frac{(D)\,(GS_B)}{GS_A + GS_B}$$

Where:

D = Total Trip Distance

GS_A = Ground speed to continue to "Ahead" airport at altitude to be flown

GS_B = Ground speed to return to "Behind" airport at altitude to be flown

In most navigator and pilot ETP versions the terms "departure" and "destination" are used when in fact they should refer to the alternate airports "ahead" and "behind." You will seldom opt return to your departure point or continue to your destination, though it could happen. Regardless, you will often see "GS_R" to denote your groundspeed while returning and "GS_C" to denote your groundspeed while continuing.

The terms GS_O and GS_R are for the Point of Safe Return (PSR), which is sometimes called the "Point of No Return" (PNR). See the Appendices, Chapter 29, Point of Safe Return.

In our example flight from KBED to LSGG we have plotted one equal time point around 37° West:

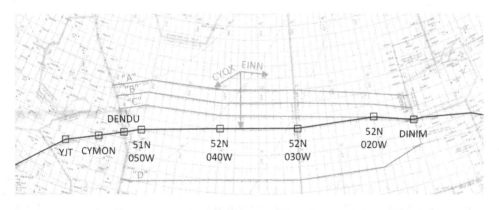

Equal Time Points provide pilots with decision making aids in the event the airplane needs to proceed to a landing airport as soon as possible. An ETP is a geographic location along the route of flight where the time to return to an airport behind the aircraft is equal to the time to proceed to an airport in front of the aircraft.

For some routes, a series of ETP location sets may be called for. In the example problem, ETPs between CYQX and EINN are used. In the event of a problem before the ETP, the airplane would turn back to CYQX. Beyond this point, the airplane would continue eastbound and a diversion to CYQX would be called for.

At least three types of ETPs should be considered . . .

Loss of Engine ETP

In the event of an engine loss, driftdown procedures are normally used and the airplane may be required to turn to either Loss of Engine ETP.

This ETP can have other names, "1E INOP" in the example shown, but normally means you have lost an engine and must descend and slow down.

In our example this ETP occurs at N52°05.0' / W037°17.3' which is 1,510 nm along the route of flight from the takeoff point. (This is a useless number when talking ETPs, but four lines later we see the ETP is 686 nm from CYQX.) In the event of an engine loss, the fuel and time are based on descending to FL300 after reversing course to CYQX or FL310 pressing forward to EINN. In either case, it will take around 2 hours 36 or 37 minutes at the recommended engine out speed.

```
LAT/LONG       N52 05.0/W037 17.3            CYQX
TIME TO ETP DIVRSN PT          02.51
DIST TO ETP DIVRSN PT          01510
FUEL TO ETP DIVRSN PT/RMNG     010177 /18923
FL/BURN/TIME TO ETP AP         300/05553/02.36
TAS/ETA/DIST TO ETP AP         340/2227/000686
MAG CRS/AVG WIND COMP TO ETP AP    271/M076
ISA TEMP DEV TO ETP AP                    M000
TOTAL FUEL TO ETP AP /RMNG         15730/13366
```

Loss of Level ETP

In the event of the loss of pressurization or other problem requiring a rapid descent without an engine loss, the airplane may be required to turn to either Loss of Level ETP. Most flight planning programs compute a rapid descent to 10,000 or 15,000 feet, depending on user preferences. A descent to 10,000 feet permits all occupants to breathe without the use of supplemental oxygen. A descent to 15,000 feet permits passengers to breathe without the use of supplemental oxygen, requires the flight crew to remain on supplemental oxygen, but provides greater endurance.

This ETP can also be called "Depressurization" or some variation leading to the idea the airplane must descend.

In our example this ETP occurs just after the Engine-Out ETP, at 1,541 nm along the route of flight from our takeoff point. In the event of loss of pressurization, the aircraft would descend to 15,000' and either turn back or continue east. In either case, it will take around 3 hours at the recommended speed.

```
LAT/LONG        N52 05.8/W036 28.0              CYQX
TIME TO ETP DIVRSN PT           02.55
DIST TO ETP DIVRSN PT           01541
FUEL TO ETP DIVRSN PT/RMNG  010347 /18753
FL/BURN/TIME TO ETP AP          150/11951/03.00
TAS/ETA/DIST TO ETP AP          278/2254/000717
MAG CRS/AVG WIND COMP TO ETP AP     271/M046
ISA TEMP DEV TO ETP AP                  M016
TOTAL FUEL TO ETP AP /RMNG          22298/06779
```

Maintain Level ETP

In the event of a need to land as soon as possible without the need to descend, such as a medical emergency, the airplane may be required to turn to either Maintain Level ETP.

This ETP can also be called "Medical" or some variation leading to the idea that the airplane must divert but not need to descend or decelerate. But some vendors do select what appears to be an arbitrary descent and you may need to request a change from your vendor or compute your own.

In our example the vendor decided a medical ETP requires a descent to FL200 to make the ETP about the same as what they call the 1E INOP (Loss of Engine) and DEPRESS (Loss of Level) ETPS. This makes flight planning and plotting easier but it is not entirely accurate. Fortunately, with the information they've given us, we can come up with a better answer. See Computing ETPs / Manually, below.

```
MEDICAL
LAT/LONG        N52 05.3/W037 00.9        CYQX                EINN
TIME TO ETP DIVRSN PT           02.52
DIST TO ETP DIVRSN PT           01521
FUEL TO ETP DIVRSN PT/RMNG  010234 /18866
FL/BURN/TIME TO ETP AP          200/11482/02.49    200/11505/02.48
TAS/ETA/DIST TO ETP AP          302/2241/000697    304/2240/001027
MAG CRS/AVG WIND COMP TO ETP AP     271/M060        105/P057
ISA TEMP DEV TO ETP AP                  M012             M010
TOTAL FUEL TO ETP AP /RMNG          21716/07361     21739/07361
```

Selecting ETP Airports

The oceanic or remote area route of flight should be examined and suitable diversion airports identified based on aircraft requirements, airport capability, and weather. The airport must meet the weather requirements for filing as an alternate and if operating under 14 CFR 135, the aircraft must have the performance to fly en route and hold at least 1,500 feet above all obstacles. [14 CFR 135.381]

If using a computerized flight planning service, always look at the selected ETP airports with a eye towards judging its common sense. The flight planner may have made the airport selections prior to a significant change in winds and it may become obvious the selected airports are no longer viable. You may also receive a routing change that negates the previously selected ETP airports.

Multiple ETP location sets may be advantageous when the route of flight is near multiple airport options.

Computing ETPs

Computer Flight Plans

Computer ETP Computations are generally superior to manually calculated ETPs because they consider a greater number of wind points and will yield more accurate ETPs. But, as we've seen with this vendor's "DIST TO ETP DIVRSN PT," you need to carefully consider what the data means before making any assumptions.

Manually

As shown above, ETPs can be computed manually if the ground speed ahead and behind are known. To manually calculate an ETP:

$$\text{Ground distance to ETP} = \frac{(D)\,(GS_B)}{GS_A + GS_B}$$

All you really need is the wind factor, TAS, and distance between the behind and ahead airports. Remember that GS_B = TAS + Wind and GS_A = TAS + Wind, and the wind factor is positive if behind you and negative if in front of you.

We see from our plotting chart that D = 1722 nm.

Master Document

```
FLIGHTPLAN N7700    KBED TO LSGG  GLF4  M80 /F  IFR  24DEC13   -- AB
COMPUTED 0054Z FOR ETD 1700Z   PROGS 231800Z              WGT IN LBS

            FUEL   TIME   DIST ARRIVE TAKEOFF  LAND    AV PLD  OPNLWT
DEST LSGG  016917 05:56   3295  2256Z  065825  048908  000000  043908
RESV       001921 00:45
ALTN       000000 00:00   0000  0000Z
HOLD       000000 00:00
REQD       018838 06:41                        ES ZFW    MX ZFW
TAXI       000400                               43908     49000
XTRA       003079 01:12                        ES LNDG   MX LNDG
TOTL        22317 07:53                         48908    058500

KBED DCT PSM ENE J573 EBONY N81B YQX KOBEV 5050N 5040N 4930N 4920N
NERTU ETIKI UN480 REGHI UN482 DEGEX UN490 TERPO UM616 NTS UP860
RUBLO UZ87 BELUS BELU1S LSGG

WIND P105    MXSH  7/KBED      AVG WIND 268/106
TAS 458      FL 410  REGHI 430 DEGEX 410 BEBIX 400 VALKU 390
```

We can also see that our average wind factor during the oceanic portion of the flight is P062 and our average TAS is 451, as shown on the master document. The TAS may be different and our winds could be wildly inaccurate for the pertinent portion of the flight so it pays to scan the oceanic portion to make sure.

CPT	FLT	T	WIND	S	TAS	AWY		MH	DST	ETE	ETR	FU	FR	FF/E
FREQ	TRO	TDV	COMP		GRS			MCRS	DSTR	ATE	ATR	AFU	AFR	
LAT	LONG													
DENDU	390	-52	288105	7	463	DCT		083	0123	014	0435	698	22176	1531
	36	P04	P075		538			090	2315					
N50302	W052041													
5150N	390	-50	288090	4	465	DCT		095	0084	009	0426	485	21690	1531
	36	P06	P067		531			097	2231					
N51000	W050000													
5240N	390	-50	276063	2	466	DCT		106	0379	043	0343	2204	19487	1516
	52	P07	P060		527			104	1851					
N52000	W040000													
5230N	410	-51	252054	1	465	DCT		103	0371	043	0300	2076	17411	1445
	52	P06	P051		516			100	1481					
N52000	W030000													
5220N	410	-53	241060		464	DCT		124	0371	043	0217	2026	15385	1407
	31	P05	P051		515			117	1110					
N52000	W020000													
DINIM	410	-55	236069	1	462	DCT		102	0197	024	0153	1081	14305	1377
	36	P03	P040		502			097	0913					
N51000	W015000													

The oceanic legs reveal a better average TAS would be 463 and wind factors of P075, P067, P060, P051, P051, and P040. Rather than use a wind factor of 62 throughout, as the flight plan would suggest, we'll use P067 for our return scenario and P051 for the continue option:

GSB = TAS + WF = 463 + (-67) = 396

GSA = TAS + WF = 463 + (+51) = 514

Therefore:

Ground Distance to ETP = (D)(GSB) / (GSA+GSB) = nm

Ground Distance to ETP = (1722)(396) / (514 + 396) = 749 nm

Our manually computed ETP is 52 nm further east than the computerized version because the vendor selected a descent to lower the TAS in an attempt to make the three provided ETPs about the same. If your decision is based on really staying at flight level, the actual ETP is the one we computed, 52 nm east.

Circular Slide Rule

With a circular slide rule, place the Total Distance (D) on the outer scale opposite the added groundspeeds (GSB + GSA), and place the sliding index over the return groundspeed (GSB) on the inner scale. The ETP will appear on the outer scale under the sliding index:

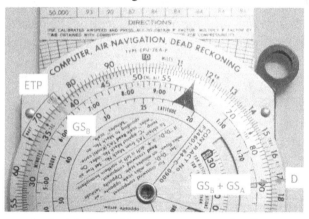

The technique works but it introduces an opportunity for error and has been relegated to the "You can, but why would you?" category.

Three Airport Example

There are times when a third airport may become advantageous. (This occurs frequently in the North Atlantic when the route of flight is near Iceland.) For this example, we will compute only the Maintain Level ETP between EINN-BIKF and BIKF-CYQX to illustrate the positioning of the ETP on the route of flight. (The process of checking the Loss of Level and Loss of Engine ETPs is the same, using the appropriate groundspeeds for those scenarios.)

Maintain Level ETP (EINN-BIKF). Using our FMS or by measuring the distance on the plotting chart, we see the distance between EINN and BIKF is 798 nm. For the example our True Airspeed is 492 knots but this time our winds will be out of the west at 20 knots.

ETP (EINN-BIKF) = (798 x 512) / (512 + 472) = 415 nm from EINN

Maintain Level ETP (BIKF-CYQX). Using our FMS or by measuring the distance on the plotting chart, we see the distance between BIKF and CYQX is 1367 nm. Once again our True Airspeed is 492 knots but this time our winds will be out of the west at 10 knots.

ETP (BIKF-CYQX) = (1367 x 502) / (502 + 482) = 697 nm from BIKF

Each of these points are plotted on straight lines between airports. A line is then drawn from these points at a right angle towards the actual aircraft route of flight. Where the lines intersect are the appropriate equal time points:

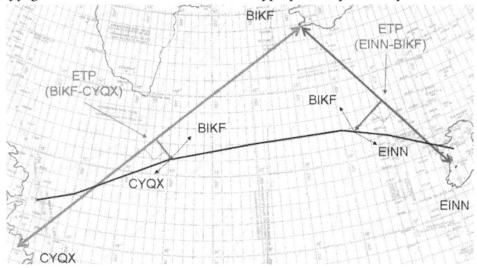

In this example, the emergency options will be to turn back to EINN before the first ETP, to divert north to BIKF between the first and second ETPs, and finally to press on to CYQX after the second ETP.

If the winds were especially strong up north and the route of flight was further south, we could see a case where it is never advantageous to proceed to one of the three ETP choices. In the example shown below, the flight time to either EINN or CYQX is always shorter than BIKF:

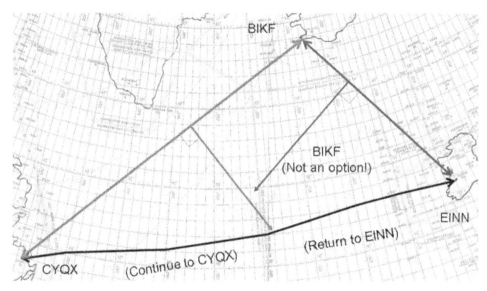

Plot ETPs

If a plotting chart is required the ETPs should be noted along the route of flight. See Part II, Chapter 6, Plotting.

A perpendicular line pointing to the route and arrows pointing to the ETP airports will allow rapid and easy identification of a course of action if a diversion decision becomes necessary.

If a plotting chart is not used, another means of identifying the ETP should be employed. A pencil mark on the en route chart is normally sufficient. Some FMS units allow an electronic display of a non-flight plan point that allows easy reference.

CAUTION: Do not enter the ETP into the FMS as a waypoint. The FMS will fly a great circle route to and from this point and can result in a significant off-course error.

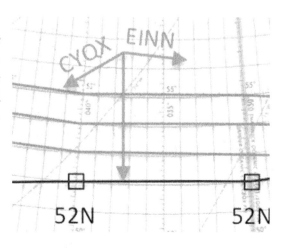

Chapter 19

Extended Operations (ETOPS)

*A*s turbine engines have become more and more reliable the definition of what constitutes extended operations has changed. What remains constant is confusion among many pilots as to what it means, who it impacts, and how to "comply."*

- *What it means, for most aircraft, is any operation that is beyond 180 minutes with one engine inopearative from a suitable airport.*

- *Who it impacts are commercial operators, 14 CFR 121 and 135.*

- *How to comply is quite complicated, involves many steps for pilots, mechanics, the airplane and the operator.*

This isn't an article about becoming ETOPS eligible, it is an article on how to fly just about everywhere in the world without having to become ETOPS certified.

Under 14 CFR 135, to fly without ETOPS certification, you need to demonstrate that the aircraft can make it to a suitable airport in under 180 minutes, using engine-out altitudes and airspeeds of your choosing. You do not need to use Equal Time Point (ETP) altitudes and speeds. If you have the fuel and performance to do this, the rule book is satisfied. Under real engine-out situations, the actual altitudes and airspeeds are up to you and you need not do this in under 180 minutes.

None of this make sense to you? If you fly more than 3 hours from the nearest airport under 14 CFR 135, you need to understand ETOPS. If you fly a Challenger or Boeing it may not impact how you fly over water at all, but you need to know why. If you fly a Gulfstream, however, ETOPS may impact your fuel loading.

Location

To find out where your aircraft can operate and remain within the 180-minute ETOPS criteria, you figure your airplane's expected engine-out speed, multiple that by 3, and draw distance rings around all suitable airports. You can also do this manually, for example using 360 KTAS on a GV:

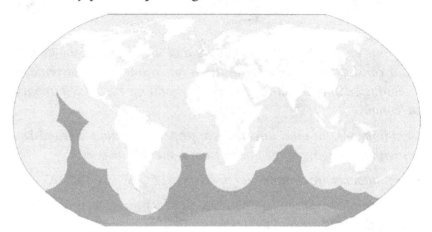

Figure: GV 360 KTAS ETOPS (world map courtesy Gustav Giradeli)

To fly a GV in the shaded area under 14 CFR 135, you would need to be certified for ETOPS. So long as you stay out of these areas, you are good to go without ETOPS certification.

[14 CFR 135, §135.364 Maximum flying time outside the United States.] After August 13, 2008, no certificate holder may operate an airplane, other than an all-cargo airplane with more than two engines, on a planned route that exceeds 180 minutes flying time (at the one-engine-inoperative cruise speed under standard conditions in still air) from an Adequate Airport outside the continental United States unless the operation is approved by the FAA in accordance with Appendix G of this part, Extended Operations.

If you are flying under 14 CFR 135 and your planned range exceeds 14 CFR § 135.364 criteria, you and your airplane have to meet 14 CFR 135 Appendix G requirements. This is an expensive and time-consuming process. Aircraft not under an ETOPS program must be able to return to an acceptable airport within 180 minutes (in still air) in the event of an engine failure.

Accuracy / Performance Standards

Refer to 14 CFR 135 Appendix G to determine your 180-minute engine out qualification:

- 14 CFR 135.98, Operations in the North Polar Area
- 14 CFR 135.364, Maximum Flying Time Outside the United States
- 135.411, Maintenance Requirement Applicability
- 135 Appendix G, ETOPS

Most aircraft are grand fathered into a 180-minute engine-out capability, which means they may fly as far as 180 minutes from the nearest suitable airport engine-out, no wind, but no further. For example, a GIV, V, 450, and 550 are all 180-minute engine-out qualified. They can qualify for ETOPS, which extends that range to either 207 or 240 minutes, but the process is so time consuming and expensive, I've not heard of a single operator who has bothered.

Documentation / Certification

To be ETOPS qualified, 14 CFR 135 operators must have Operations Specification B342 and B344, as detailed under FAA 8900.1, Volume 4, Chapter 6.

If you plan all of your 14 CFR 135 operations to be within 180 minutes, engine-out of a suitable airport, you do not need ETOPS certification.

Example: Is a Gulfstream V Impacted by ETOPS?

The Gulfstream V is a good aircraft for an ETOPS case study because it has an incredibly long range and is impacted in two out of the three scenarios presented here.

North Atlantic Example: No Issues

If your Equal Time Points (ETPs) come to less than 180 minutes, you know without further research that the aircraft can lose an engine at the furthest point and make a suitable airport. A GV, for example, can easily make the hop from the east coast of the United States to Europe and never be more than 180 minutes from the nearest suitable airport, even flying at single-engine endurance speeds.

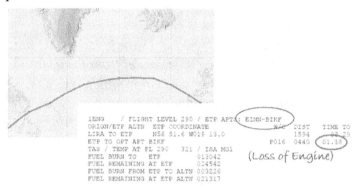

```
1ENG    / FLIGHT LEVEL 290 / ETP APTS: EINN-BIKF
ORIGN/ETP ALTN  ETP COORDINATE            W/C  DIST    TIME TO
LIPA TO ETP      N56 51.6 W019 13.0            1594     07 29
ETP TO OPT APT BIKF                       P016 0440    01.18
TAS / TEMP AT FL 290    321 / ISA M01
FUEL BURN TO     ETP          013042            (Loss of Engine)
FUEL REMAINING AT ETP         024542
FUEL BURN FROM ETP TO ALTN 003226
FUEL REMAINING AT ETP ALTN 021317
```

East Pacific: Some Thought Required

A Challenger 604 can make the hop from KSFO to PHNL with suitable fuel reserves, but just barely. A Gulfstream GV can make the same trip and fly back all on the same tank of gas. And yet only the GV has an ETOPS issue for the KSFO-PHNL city pair. Why?

The ETPs between KSFO and PHNL flying a Challenger 604 will probably be less than 180 minutes, so no ETOPS issues when flying 14 CFR 135. This isn't the case for a GV.

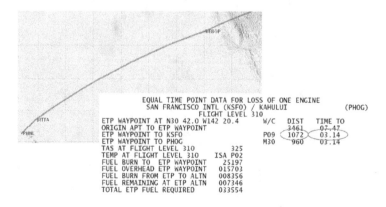

```
         EQUAL TIME POINT DATA FOR LOSS OF ONE ENGINE
         SAN FRANCISCO INTL (KSFO) / KAHULUI        (PHOG)
                   FLIGHT LEVEL 310
ETP WAYPOINT AT N30 42.0 W142 20.4    W/C   DIST   TIME TO
ORIGIN APT TO ETP WAYPOINT                  3461   07.47
ETP WAYPOINT TO KSFO                  P09   1072   03.14
ETP WAYPOINT TO PHOG                  M30    960   03.14
TAS AT FLIGHT LEVEL 310         325
TEMP AT FLIGHT LEVEL 310     ISA P02
FUEL BURN TO  ETP WAYPOINT    25197
FUEL OVERHEAD ETP WAYPOINT   015703
FUEL BURN FROM ETP TO ALTN   008356
FUEL REMAINING AT ETP ALTN   007346
TOTAL ETP FUEL REQUIRED      033554
```

Using standard drift down procedures, if you lose thrust on an engine you set the operating engine to its maximum continuous setting, allow the airplane to decelerate to an optimum speed, and then you allow the airplane to drift down to an altitude it can sustain on one engine. Most flight plan providers know this and program the equal time point calculations to do just that.

A normal airplane—one with more fuselage than wing—will have to drift down to the middle twenties and fly a speed around 250 or so. The Challenger 604, for example, may end up at 27,000 feet and 240 KIAS, which equates to 370 nautical miles per hour true airspeed. The airplane can make it to its divert airport in 2 hour 53 minutes, though it will be right at its minimum fuel.

31,000 feet	218 KCAS	352.1 KTAS	0.1317 NAM/LB fuel
29,000 feet	228 KCAS	355.1 KTAS	0.1266 NAM/LB fuel
27,000 feet	238 KCAS	358.2 KTAS	0.1214 NAM/LB fuel

Table: Example GV Engine-out Drift Down

With its massive wing, the Gulfstream V, only needs to descend to 31,000 feet and can slow down to 218 KCAS. It doesn't have to fly that slowly, but the chart says it can. So flight planners use these numbers; a higher altitude translates to a lower true airspeed, as does the lower calibrated airspeed. The airplane, if flown at this altitude and speed, makes it to the divert airport in 3 hours and 14 minutes. An FAA examiner who doesn't understand the topic well will go ballistic and start the violation paperwork. The pilot needs to understand why the flight planning software is wrong.

In this example, the pilot need only select an altitude 4,000 feet below optimum and a little faster to beat the 3 hour stop watch:

$$Time = 1072 / 358.2 = 179\ minutes.$$

The lower altitude will cost extra fuel, but the airplane has that to spare. So long as the pilot ensures there is fuel to do this, the aircraft doesn't need ETOPS certification.

Southeast Pacific: A Show Stopper

While not a common flight, a trip from New Zealand to Chile is well within the range of a GV but cannot be made under 14 CFR 135 because of ETOPS-180 requirements. The total flight time is under 10 hours and not much over 5,100 nm. There is only one suitable alternate between Christchurch, New Zealand (NZCH) and Santiago, Chile (SCEL): the Isle de Pascua (SCIP).

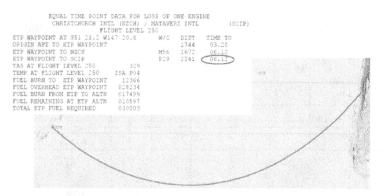

The engine-out ETP is already calculated at an optimal altitude in terms for producing the highest available TAS, but even if the TAS is increased to the aircraft's maximum capable, the time to the ETP airport cannot be reduced to under 180 minutes. This flight cannot be accomplished in a GV under 14 CFR 135.

Section VIII - Appendices

Chapter 20

Flight Operations Checklist

Whenever you fly internationally there are a host of things you need to consider that may not be of primary concern when operating closer to home. You should develop a checklist that covers all the bases for your operation and run that checklist before you start international operations and at least once every year to make sure everything is up-to-date and nothing has changed in the list of requirements. Here is my checklist to give you a head start.

Aircraft Equipment

There are things you are required to have by regulation and others that you should have, depending on where you are going.

- Aircraft tow bar or at least the tow head.

  If you are going someplace that regularly handles your aircraft type, and all of your alternate, ETP, and ETOPS airports too, then maybe you don't need this. Otherwise, you should consider bringing one.

- Emergency locator transmitter. [AC 91-70A, ¶3-2.e.]
- First-aid kit. [ICAO Annex 6, Part II, Chapter 2.4, ¶2.4.2.2.]
- Fire extinguisher, portable. [ICAO Annex 6, Part II, Chapter 2.4, ¶2.4.2.2.]
- Fuel sample kit.

  If your location will be dispensing fuel from 50-gallon drums or a fuel truck caked in rust, you may want a fuel sample kit.

- Headphones, microphones.

  These are no longer mandated but remain "should" items for the cockpit voice recorder. [ICAO Annex 6, Part II, ATT 3, ¶2.2.2.]

- High frequency radios. [AC 91-70A, ¶3-3.c.] [ICAO Annex 2, ¶3.6.5.1.]

You have CPDLC and SATCOM and both can be used to make position reports. But you still need an HF radio. See Part III, Chapter 2, High Frequency Radios.

- Life rafts, vests of sufficient quantity. [AC 91-70A, ¶3-2.e.]

- Pyrotechnic signaling devices. [AC 91-70A, ¶3-2.e.]

- SATCOM.

  SATCOM might be required in some regions when using Controller Pilot Data Link Communications. See Part IV, Chapter 5, CPDLC.

- SELCAL.

  Certainly not required, but nice to have.

- Survival equipment appropriate to route. [AC 91-70A, ¶3-2.e.]

- VHF 8.33 kHz. Required in various parts of Europe. [ICAO Doc 7030, Chapter EUR, ¶2.1.8.]

There may be other regional requirements, such as Mode S Transponders, a minimum level of TCAS software version, or even FM immunity. ICAO Doc 7030 may specify some of these and other requirements.

Aircraft Documentation

The documentation required for a trip will obviously vary by location and route of flight. Here are a few things you should consider for every trip:

- Air carrier certificate (14 CFR 135 operations). [ICAO Annex 6, Part I, ¶4.2.1.1] An operator shall not engage in commercial air transport operations unless in possession of a valid air operator certificate issued by the State of the Operator.

- Aircraft flight manual and systems manuals. [ICAO Annex 6, Part II, ¶2.4.2.2.]

- Aircraft noise compliance certificates. [ICAO Annex 6, Part I, ¶2.4.9.] An aeroplane shall carry a document attesting noise certification.

- Aircraft registration. [AC 91-70A, ¶3-1.u.]

  The advisory circular notes "a temporary registration certificate is not acceptable for international travel," but some countries will accept a "fly wire," or equivalent. You have to ask to find out.

- Airframe and engine logs. [AC 91-70A, ¶3-1.u.]

  The aircraft's most recent flight and aircraft log usually suffices, but some countries may require much more. Once again, you need to ask.

- Airworthiness certificate. [AC 91-70A, ¶3-1.u.]

- Authorization letters from the operating company or owner, if applicable. [AC 91-70A, ¶3-1.u.]

  Not many countries require this but some do. If you aren't traveling with the person who owns the aircraft or is somehow identified on the registration, you might need to consider this.

- Cargo manifest, if applicable. [AC 91-70A, ¶3-1.u.]

- Certificates of insurance. [AC 91-70A, ¶3-1.u.] The operator is responsible for ensuring the need for airframe logbooks, the engine logbooks, and insurance certificates. For additional details for operations of corporate aircraft, contact the company's aviation underwriter. In operations of private aircraft, if the owner is the pilot or is onboard the aircraft, there are usually no insurance difficulties. However, if a private aircraft owner is not onboard the aircraft, many countries require a letter from the owner that authorizes international flight in that specific country before they will allow operations within their country (you can find specific information on this letter and other requirements in the AIPs of the countries concerned).

  Insurance paperwork can be problematic; you ask prior to travelling any place new. See the Appendices, Chapter 23, Insurance.

- Customs decals, receipts. [http://www.cbp.gov/xp/cgov/trade/basic_trade/uftd_info.xml] Decals are stickers that are placed on all private aircraft and private vessels (30 feet or more in length) as proof that the User Fee for entry into the U.S. has been paid for the calendar year. Any arriving vessel or aircraft that does not have an annual decal is required to pay a non-refundable per arrival User Fee of $27.50, and complete an application, which will be forwarded to the processing center.

- Import papers for aircraft of foreign manufacture. [AC 91-70A, ¶3-1.u.]

- Journey log book for the aeroplane. [ICAO Annex 6, Part II, Chapter 2.4, ¶2.4.2.2.]

This requirement comes from the 1944 Chicago Convention and is further explained in ICAO Annex 6, Part I and ICAO Annex 6, Part II. A journey logbook could be your aircraft flight and maintenance log, provided it contains all the necessary items. See the Appendices, Chapter 24, Journey Logbook.

- LOAs/MSpecs/OpSpecs for Special Areas of Operation, if applicable. [AC 91-70A, ¶3-1.u.]

- Minimum Equipment List. [AC 91-70A, ¶3-1.u.]

  If you operate with an MEL or MMEL, you need to have them on board.

- Navigation charts suitable for the route and divert locations. [ICAO Annex 6, Part II, Chapter 2.4, ¶2.4.2.2.]

- Operator's manual. [AC 91-70A, ¶3-1.u.]

- Passenger manifest. [AC 91-70A, ¶3-1.u.]

- Radio licenses. [AC 91-70A, ¶3-1.u.]

- Weight and balance manual. [AC 91-70A, ¶3-1.u.]

Operational Approvals

Depending on where you are flying, you may need:

- Automatic Dependent Surveillance-Broadcast (ADS-B) Out

  You can think of ADS-B Out as a higher-tech replacement of your transponder, it sends your GPS position and other data to ATC and other aircraft equipped with ADS-B In.

  ◊ Where — It is becoming required in parts of the world, but work arounds are readily available. You can expect delays and reroutes if you are not equipped and authorized.

  ◊ Authorization — 14 CFR 91: Letter of Authorization required, 14 CFR 135: Operations Specification required.

  See Part V, Chapter 2, ADS-B Out.

- Automatic Dependent Surveillance-Contract (ADS-C)

  You can think of ADS-C as a high tech form of "radar contact."

  ◊ Where — Optional in much of the world's oceanic and remote regions, is also used domestically in various regions.

◊ Authorization — 14 CFR 91: Letter of Authorization required, 14 CFR 135: Operations Specification required.

See Part V, Chapter 3, ADS-C.

- Basic Area Navigation (B-RNAV)

B-RNAV is not RNP-5 but the term has been "grand fathered" and will continue to mean the ± 5 nm standard without the performance monitoring requirements in a true Performance Based Navigation standard.

◊ Where — Most of Europe.

◊ Authorization — Statement in AFM required.

See Part III, Chapter 6, Basic Area Navigation (B-RNAV).

- Controller Pilot Data Link Communications (CPDLC)

You can think of Controller Pilot Data Link Communications (CPDLC) as a replacement for your HF when oceanic and VHF over some domestic areas. It is far superior to your HF and has distinct advantages over VHF.

◊ Where — Optional in much of the world's oceanic and remote regions, is also used domestically in various regions.

◊ Authorization — 14 CFR 91: Letter of Authorization required, 14 CFR 135: Operations Specification required.

See Part IV, Chapter 5, Controller Pilot Data Link Communications (CPDLC).

- Extended Operations of Multi-engine Airplanes (ETOPS)

ETOPS does not apply to 14 CFR 91 operators and only constrains 14 CFR 121 and 135 operators from flying in the most remote regions of the world. If you want to fly in those regions, the requirements are daunting and probably beyond what most corporate commercial operators want to do.

◊ Where — Any place beyond 3 hours of a suitable airport with an engine failed.

◊ Authorization — 14 CFR 135: Operations Specification required.

See the Appendices, Chapter 19, Extended Operations of Multi-engine Airplanes (ETOPS).

- High Latitude and Northern Domestic Airspace

  Operating in what many simply call "polar ops" requires special certification under 14 CFR 135 and special procedures for anyone venturing the high latitude regions.

  ◊ Where — High latitude operations occur in areas above 78°N, below 60°S, the northern and southern poles, and the Canadian Northern Domestic Area (NDA). The NDA includes the Northern Control Area (NCA), the Arctic Control Area (ACA) and the Area of Magnetic Unreliability (AMU). The NDA, NCA and ACA are depicted on Canadian HI en route charts and encompass the northernmost Canadian airspace.

  ◊ Authorization — 14 CFR 135: Operations Specification required.

  See the Appendices, Chapter 22, High Latitude and Northern Domestic Airspace.

- Minimum Navigation Performance Specifications (MNPS)

  We tend to think of "NAT/MNPS" as a single thought, the North Atlantic Minimum Navigation Performance Specification, but it isn't that at all. MNPS applies to more than the NAT, and parts of the NAT are changing to more than just a navigation accuracy area.

  ◊ Where — Most of the North Atlantic and the Canadian Arctic Control Area

  ◊ Authorization — 14 CFR 91: Letter of Authorization required, 14 CFR 135: Operations Specification required.

  See Part III, Chapter 7, Minimum Navigation Performance Specifications (MNPS).

- Precision Area Navigation (P-RNAV)

  P-RNAV is giving way to RNAV-1 and has many similarities: it is used to fly RNAV departure and arrival procedures, requires high-integrity navigation databases, can be flown with GPS, and requires the aircraft stay within 1 NM of course. There are differences which are transparent to most high tech aircraft.

  ◊ Where — European Civil Aviation Conference countries (most of Europe) and some other areas throughout the word, i.e., Hong Kong. Terminal procedures will have "P-RNAV Required" annotated.

◊ Authorization — 14 CFR 91: Letter of Authorization required, 14 CFR 135: Operations Specification required.

See Part III, Chapter 8, Precision Area Navigation (P-RNAV).

- Reduced Vertical Separation Minimum (RVSM)

While RVSM is now the standard just about everywhere, there are country-specific rules for flight level selection and contingency procedures.

◊ Where — Just about everywhere in the world.

◊ Authorization — 14 CFR 91: Letter of Authorization required, 14 CFR 135: Operations Specification required.

See Part II, Chapter 7, Reduced Vertical Separation Minimum (RVSM).

- Required Navigation Performance-4 (RNP-4)

The Required Navigation Performance-4 (RNP-4) standard is performance based, requiring on-board performance monitoring and alerting. This is as opposed to the older RNAV systems which are an equipment-based standard that do not require on-board performance monitoring and alerting. So, you might say, your airplane and crew are RNAV-1 qualified, one is more accurate than four, so you are good to go! Wrong! RNP-4 almost always requires CPDLC while RNAV-1 does not.

◊ Where — Parts of Australia, New Zealand, and Japan list RNP-4 as a requirement but allow RNP-10 as a substitute. In theory, ATS can monitor aircraft with RNP-4 more closely and will have traffic priority.

◊ Authorization — 14 CFR 91: Letter of Authorization required, 14 CFR 135: Operations Specification required.

See Part III, Chapter 9, Required Navigation Performance-4 (RNP-4).

◊ Required Navigation Performance-10 (RNP-10)

RNP-10 is an exception to the rule that all Required Navigation Performance (RNP) standards are performance based, requiring on-board performance monitoring and alerting. "RNP-10" was adopted by many parts of the world when that really meant "RNAV 10."

◊ Where — The Central East Pacific (CEP) between Hawaii and the west coast of the United States, and portions of the North Pacific (NOPAC) require RNP-10. There are other areas of the world that have adopted RNP-10, such as parts of Africa, the Indian Ocean, Australia, New Zealand, Tahiti, and some parts of South America near Recife.

◊ Authorization — 14 CFR 91: Letter of Authorization required, 14 CFR 135: Operations Specification required.

See Part III, Chapter 10, Required Navigation Performance-10 (RNP-10).

Crew Qualification and Training

Each of the operational approvals shown above have specific training requirements and some countries and airports have their own specific training requirements. You need to check with the country's Aeronautical Information Publication, the Jeppesen Airway Manual, or with your international service handler to be sure. Also consider:

- Aircrew ID cards.
- FAA Airman's Certificates. [ICAO Chicago Convention, Article 29.]
- FAA Medical Certificates. [AC 91-70A, ¶3-1.d.]
- FCC Radiotelephone License. [AC 91-70A, ¶3-1.r.]
- Immunization Records.
- Pilot's proof of qualification. [AC 91-70A, ¶12-1.]
- Passports. [ICAO Chicago Convention, Article 13.]
- Proof of Citizenship.

Chapter 21

Flight Plans

*T*he international flight plan has always been a little more involved than
the U.S. version, even after the FAA standardized its codes with the ICAO.
But it is still a mess. Ordinarily the only time you have to worry about this is
when you set up an account with a flight planning service. But there are times
in some locations you will have to fill one of these out manually, or check the
work of a handler who did that for you.

General

[ICAO Doc 4444, Amendment 1] All clock times are in four figures, UTC.
All estimated elapsed times are in four figures (hours and minutes). Area
preceding Item 3 is to be completed by ATS and COM services.

If called upon to fill out an International Flight Plan you may wish to copy the
filed flight plan portion of your computer flight plan as a guide.

Instructions for Items 7 through 19

7. **Aircraft Identification.** Normally the aircraft call sign, if used, or
    the registration marking of the aircraft. (i.e., "TAG5")

8. **Flight Rules.** "I" for IFR, "V" for VFR.

    Type of Flight. "N" for non-scheduled air transportation operation,
    "G" for general aviation.

9. **Number of Aircraft.** Leave blank for one aircraft only.

    Type of Aircraft. Designator as specified in ICAO Doc 8643. (i.e.,
    "GLF5")

    Wake Turbulence Category. "H" if aircraft MTOW is greater than
    136,000 kg, "M" if less than 136,000 kg but more than 7,000 kg, "L"
    if less than 7,000 kg.

U.S. Department of Transportation
Federal Aviation Administration

International Flight Plan

PRIORITY ADDRESSEE(S)

<=FF <=

FILING TIME ORIGINATOR <=

SPECIFIC IDENTIFICATION OF ADDRESSEE(S) AND / OR ORIGINATOR

3 MESSAGE TYPE 7 AIRCRAFT IDENTIFICATION 8 FLIGHT RULES TYPE OF FLIGHT

<=(FPL — — — <=

9 NUMBER TYPE OF AIRCRAFT WAKE TURBULENCE CAT. 10 EQUIPMENT

— / — / <=

13 DEPARTURE AERODROME TIME

— <=

15 CRUISING SPEED LEVEL ROUTE

—

<=

TOTAL EET

16 DESTINATION AERODROME HR MIN ALTN AERODROME 2ND ALTN AERODROME <=

18 OTHER INFORMATION

—

<=

SUPPLEMENTARY INFORMATION (NOT TO BE TRANSMITTED IN FPL MESSAGES)

19 ENDURANCE EMERGENCY RADIO

HR MIN PERSONS ON BOARD UHF VHF ELT

—E/ P/ R/ U V E

SURVIVAL EQUIPMENT JACKETS

POLAR DESERT MARITIME JUNGLE LIGHT FLUORES UHF VHF

/ P D M J / L F U V

DINGHIES

NUMBER CAPACITY COVER COLOR

D / C <=

AIRCRAFT COLOR AND MARKINGS

A/

REMARKS

N / <=

PILOT-IN-COMMAND

C/)<=

FILED BY ACCEPTED BY ADDITIONAL INFORMATION

Figure: International Flight Plan, FAA Form 7233-4

10. **Equipment.**

Left of Slash (Often called 10a):

- S VHF, VOR, ILS
- A GBAS Ldg System
- B LPV (APV with SBAS)
- C LORAN C
- D DME
- E1 FMS WPR ACARS
- E2 D-FIS ACARS
- E3 PDC ACARS
- F ADF
- G GNSS
- H HF
- I IRS
- J1 CPDLC ATN VDL Mode 2
- J2 CPDLC FANS 1/A HFDL
- J3 CPDLC FANS 1/A VDL Mode A
- J5 CPDLC FANS 1/A SATCOM (INMARSAT)
- J6 CPDLC FANS 1/A SATCOM (MTRSAT)
- J7 CPDLC FANS 1/A SATCOM (Iridium)
- K MLS
- L ILS (Unless "S" specified)
- M1 ATC SATCOM (INMARSAT)
- M2 ATC (MTSAT)
- M3 ATC (Iridium)
- O VOR (Unless "S" specified)
- R PBN (requires remark in block 18)
- T TACAN
- U UHF

- V VHF (Unless "S" specified)
- W RVSM
- X MNPS
- Y VHF with 8.33 spacing
- Z Other Com, Nav, or Dat (requires remark in block 18)

Right of Slash (Often called 10b):

- A Mode A trasnponder 4 digits
- C Mode C transponder and Mode C transponder
- E Mode S trasnponder with Flt ID, pressure altitude, and extended squitter (ADS-B)
- H Mode S transponder with Flt ID, pressure altitude, enhanced surveillance
- I Mode S transponder with Flt ID, but no pressure altitude capability
- L Mode S transponder with Flt ID, pressure altitude, extended squitter (ADS-B), enhanced surveillance
- P Mode S transponder with pressure altitude but no Flt ID
- S Mode S transponder including both pressure altitude and Flt ID capability
- X Mode S transponder with neither Flt ID nor pressure altitude
- B1 ADS-B out via 1090 MHz
- B2 ADS-B out and in via 1090 MHz
- D1 ADS-C via FANS 1/A
- G1 ADS-C with ATN
- U1 ADS-B out via UAT
- U2 ADS-B out and via UAT
- V1 ADS-B out via VDL Mode 4
- V2 ADS-B out and in via VDL Mode 4

Block 10a/10b on a Gulfstream G-450 with enhanced navigation, for example:
SBDE2E3FGHIJ3J5M1RWXYZ/SD1

13. **Departure Aerodrome.**

The four letter identifier of the departure airport, or "ZZZZ" if no identifier (then specify in Item 18 with "DEP/" followed by name).

15. **Speed.**

Cruising Speed. Enter the "N" followed by four figures to specify true airspeed in knots (e.g., "N0485"), or "M" followed by three figures to specify true Mach Number (e.g., "M083")

Cruising Level. Enter "F" followed by three figures to specify a flight level (e.g., "F450"), or "A" followed by three figures to specify altitude in hundreds of feet (e.g., "A100")

Route.

Flights along designated ATS routes. Insert the route designator if the departure airport is located on the route, otherwise insert "DCT" followed by the point of joining the first ATS route, followed by the designator of the route. Then, insert each point at which either a change of speed or level, a change of ATS route, and/or a change of flight rules is planned. Followed in each case by the designator of the next route segment, even if same as the previous one, or by "DCT" if the next point will be outside a designated route, unless both points are specified by geographic coordinates.

Flights outside designated ATS routes. Insert points normally not more than 30 minutes flying time or 200 nm apart, including each point at which a change of speed or level, a change of track, or a change of flight rules is planned. Insert "DCT" between successive points unless both points are defined by geographic coordinates or by bearing and distance.

ATS routes. The coded designator (2 to 7 characters), i.e., "UB10".

Significant points. The coded designator (2 to 5 characters) of the assigned point, i.e., "HADDY". Degrees only (7 characters) will be two figures describing latitude in degrees followed by "N" or "S" and three figures describing longitude in degrees followed by "E" or "W", i.e., "46N078W". Degrees and minutes (11 characters) will be four figures describing latitude in degrees and minutes followed by "N" or "S" and five figures describing longitude in degrees and minutes followed by "E" or "W", i.e., "4620N07805W". Bearing and distance from a navigation aid will be described by two or three characters, then the bearing in three figures (degrees magnetic), then the distance in three figures (nautical miles), i.e., "DUB180040".

Change of speed or level (maximum 21 characters). The point at which a change of speed (5% TAS or 0.01 Mach or more) or a change of level is planned will be followed by an oblique stroke and both the cruising speed and cruising level without a space. I.e., "DUB180040/M082F330".

16. **Destination Aerodrome.** The four letter ICAO location identifier or "ZZZZ" if no identifier (then specify airport in Item 18 with "DEST/" followed by name).

Total Elapsed Time. In four digits (hours and minutes).

Alternate Aerodrome. The four letter ICAO identifier or "ZZZZ" if no identifier (then specify in Item 18 with "ALTN/" followed by name).

18. **Other Information.** As necessary.

"EET/" (Significant points or FIR boundary designators and accumulated estimated elapsed time to such points.)

"REG/" (Registration markings of the aircraft, if different from Item 7 aircraft identification.)

"SEL/" (SELCAL code)

"OPR/" (Name of operator, if not obvious from Item 7.)

"NAV" Codes

RNV   RNAV

A1   RNAV 1 arrival procedures

D1   RNAV 1 departure procedures

E2   RNAV 2 routes

LPV   LPV approach

"PBN/" Performance Based Navigation codes:

A1   RNAV 10, RNP 10

B2   RNAV 5 via GNSS

B3   RNAV 5 via DME/DME

B4   RNAV 5 via VOR/DME

C1   RNAV 2 via all permitted sensors

D1   RNAV 1 via all permitted sensors

L1   RNP 4 operations permitted

O1   RNP 1 via all permitted sensors

S2   GNSS Approach using Baro-VNAV

T1   RNP AR Approach authorized

"DAT/"

S   Datalink via SATCOM

V   Datalink via VHF

"RMK/" (plain language remark.)

For a G450 with enhanced navigation:

PBN/A1B2B3B4C1D1O1S2 COM/INMARSAT NAV/RNVD1E2A1

Supplementary Information.

Endurance. Four figures (hours and minutes) of fuel on board.

Persons on Board.

Emergency and survival equipment. Cross out those items not carried.

Chapter 22

Fueling

*B*efore you let the fuel truck pull away, in fact before you allow the truck to hook up, there are two critical questions you need to ask:

- *Is the amount of fuel coming out of the truck the same as what the engines are expecting?*

- *Is the fuel containated?*

The reason we measure fuel in the cockpit by weight and not volume is that is how the engines burn fuel. The pump sends a volume of fuel but the engine consumes less fuel when it is dense, more when it isn't. This density equation works out so that if we think of the engine burning pounds (or kilos) of fuel versus gallons (or liters), we are better off. So you need to understand variations in fuel density around the world.

We tend to rely on the FBO for fuel quality testing but sometimes you aren't familiar with the FBO, sometimes the fuel truck causes you to wonder if those engines will keep running once full thrust is added on takeoff. In either case, you may want to sump and test the fuel in your tanks. There are commercially available fuel test kits that can detect some contaminants and some amounts of water. While they are not as good as a lab test, they are certainly better than relying on the word of the guy doing the pumping. But what if you don't have a fuel test kit available? There are two other options.

Fuel Density Variations

We often think of fuel density as a function only of temperature, but temperature isn't the largest factor in determining how much "bang" you get per drop of fuel. To understand what is, consider this riddle. Why can a Gulfstream V almost always fly from San Francisco to Tokyo non-stop even with a headwind, but sometimes not be able to make the return trip, even with a tailwind?

As it turns out, fuel density in California is about the highest in the world while density in Japan is about the lowest. If you are planning on flying to the airplane's maximum range you need to understand fuel density, especially if operating out of Asia.

[PetroValue, ¶1.6]

- Scientific definition of density: density (ρ) of a body is the ratio of its mass (m) to its volume (V).

- Density of fuel is "the mass of fuel per unit volume".

- In some cases the density is expressed as a specific gravity or relative density, in which case it is expressed in multiples of the density of some other standard material, usually water or air.

- Reference: ASTM D1655 specification, Jet A-1 fuel has a density of between 775.0 and 840.0 kg/m3. Density ranging from 37 to 51 °C API corrected to 15 °C or 60 °F.

When it comes to fuel, higher density means more "bang for the buck." The density is determined by the quality of the crude used to produce the fuel and the refining process.

Jet-A fuel density limits are established by the American Society for Testing and Materials (ASTM) Specification D1655. At 60°F the density limits are from 6.46 to 6.99 lbs/gallon.

In a G-450, this equates to a range of:

- *28,230 lbs at 6.46 lbs/gallon*

- *30,546 lbs at 6.99 lbs/gallon*

A variation of 2,316 lbs.

Fuel Contamination

If you are flying out of a major international airport with a reputable fuel dealer, you probably have nothing to worry about. What about those lesser travelled destinations? Perhaps a fuel contamination test kit is in order.

White Bucket Test

[PetroValue]

The white bucket is a simple but reliable test for detection of significant amounts of water and particulates. Water occurs in different forms in the fuel;

- Dissolved in the fuel, normally this water can not be removed from the fuel.

- Suspended or entrained in the fuel. Entrained water can be detected with the naked eyes. The fine droplets of water in fuel reflect light and in high concentration give the fuel a cloudy or hazy appearance.

- Water in high quantity into fuel may be caused by leakage into storage tanks, delivery of water-laden fuel, condensation or the coalescence and subsequent settling of entrained water.

Particulate or dirt is normally found in fuel in the form of rust, scale, lint, dust, particles from gaskets and hoses which have been released from the side of the tanks, piping and transportation vehicles.

A bucket, white porcelain lined or stainless steel of a capacity of seven liters (7 L) and with a bonding cable (a separate cable if not equipped, must be provided). A shiny coin with well-defined feature is an additional tool.

Bucket must be clean and dry.

- A static bonding cable must be connected between bucket and the source of sample container, pipe or valve as required.

- Take a sample at system operating pressure (except samples from a storage tank or transport trailer). Fuel in the drain or line should be removed or displaced before taking sample. Valve should be completely open without causing spill.

- Fill bucket at least 15 cm of its depth.

- Place bucket on a level surface and allow it to stand for few minutes to settle sample to ensuring no air bubbles present.

- Visually inspect and observe the fuel sample to determine presence of free water, particulates, unusual colour, haze, floating material and lacy substance layers.

- Swirling of sample will cause dirt or water to collect at the centre of bucket for easier examination.

- Drop a coin with well-defined features into the fuel sample bucket to assist visual detection of haze.

Evaluation

- Observed colour of jet fuel should be colourless to a light straw. Colour should be similar to previously acceptable test if any.

- A cloudy or haziness condition in appearance of the fuel sample suggests water contamination.

- If sample does not appear cloudy, a drop of food colouring or coffee added to the sample will ensure absence of water when coloured drop settles at the bottom. If it dissolves in the sample the fuel is not pure and contaminated with unacceptable amount of water.

- Slime on the bottom surface of container or lacy substance is an indication of Microbiological Contamination.

Clear and Bright Test

[PetroValue]

Delivered fuel must be clean, bright and not contaminated with free water.

"Clear" is a visual condition of fuel with the absence of cloud, emulsion, visible particulate matter or entrained water. "Bright" is the quality of fuel refers to the shiny and sparkling appearance of clean and dry fuel.

The "bright and clear" condition of the fuel is not dependent on the natural colour of the fuel.

The "Clear and Bright" test is a visual check and conducted to detect water or other solid contaminants in the fuel. An evidence of external contaminants renders the fuel as "not suitable for use" and points to a requirement of further laboratory analysis.

Glass Jar – a wide mouth glass jar of 7.5 cm (3 in.) in diameter or other similar transparent container. A white paper sheet or light background surface material is a great tool to enhance detection of contaminants.

Evaluation is completed as given earlier, in the White Bucket Test.

Contaminants found in fuel sample would suggest a need to inspect the source of contaminants and could also be attributed to the failure of equipment or procedures.

Free water contamination in fuel can go undetected using visual test methods. There are number of free water detection kits available for field use such as the Velcon Hydrokit® and the Shell Water Detector®. A water sensitive chemical product is used with the fuel sample which reacts with the suspended water content in the fuel by changing its color.

Other Contaminants

There are several other worrisome contaminants that may escape visual detection. Unfortunately, you are pretty much at the mercy of the fuel provider to do the necessary tests. It is to your advantage to make sure the fueler is busy; there is no better reassurance than knowing airplanes have been successfully flying using the same fuel all day. Here are a few things to worry about and a thought or two about each.

[Fuel Handling Jet Quality and Test Procedure, ¶1.3] Rust is generally the leading source of particulate contamination. Frequently the sand or dust could also be present. The main source of this kind of contamination is erosion and corrosion of container surfaces, pipes, fittings, pumps cavity erosion and any other source which come in contact with the fuel.

The best test is force fuel under pressure through a filter membrane with pores as small as 0.8 microns. A collection of rust or sand will discolor the membrane. The FBO should be doing this. I don't think any commercially available portable pilot-operated fuel testing kits have this capability.

[PetroValue, ¶1.4] Micro-organisms may enter in aviation fuel in many ways such as air, sea or fresh water, soil or by other means. Micro-organism causes significant damage to the fuel system by means of slime formation, sludge and corrosion.

These micro-organisms feed on the fuel and produced more micro-organisms. Once they've multiplied enough they can be seen in the fuel as a black gelatinous matter. To detect them early, you need a laboratory test. There are commercially available kits but they aren't really suitable for pilot usage on the road.

Chapter 23

High Latitude Operations

If you fly anywhere near the poles under 14 CFR 135, you need to understand everything written below about high latitude operations. It could very well be that you can't legally do what your airplane is physically capable of doing. Flying near the poles under 14 CFR 91? You still need to understand this stuff, but you might not be prevented from doing something stupid. Me? I would make sure we had all our ducks in line first. What follows should help you do just that.

Location

U.S. Regulations

[Advisory Circular 120-42B, ¶601.]

- The North Polar Area is defined as the entire area north of latitude 78° North.

- The South Polar Area is defined as the entire area south of latitude 60° South.

[Advisory Circular 91-70A, ¶ 3-6.w.] Navigation in Areas of Magnetic Unreliability (AMU). The FAA designates Canada's NCA and Arctic Control Area (ACA) as AMUs. Although Canadian publications sometimes refer to it as the area of compass unreliability, they are the same. The magnetic North Pole is at approximately 75°N 100°W and is slowly moving as it circles the true pole every 960 years. This is why we see current navigation charts occasionally changing an instrument landing system (ILS) course by 1°.

1.   Magnetic North Pole. When you approach the magnetic North Pole, horizontal magnetic influences decrease and vertical magnetic influences increase to a point where the compass is no longer reliable (the magnetic pole is below the aircraft). It is common to see the compass drifting aimlessly or tilting in its case due to the vertical

component even when hundreds of miles from the magnetic North Pole. The better the magnetic compass, the closer to the magnetic pole it will operate. Within about 250 miles of the magnetic pole, all aircraft magnetic compasses will be useless. As a result, some VORs, runways, and radar vectors in Canada's NCA and ACA are oriented to true north.

2. AMU. When operating in the AMU, move the HDG REF switch to TRUE when the Canada HI 4 chart defines the course with a °T. Add two additional items to the master flight plan checklist: TRUE HDG adjacent to the first true heading leg and MAG HDG at the end of the AMU. This will serve as a reminder to return to a normal heading reference. The primary reason for selecting TRUE HDG in the NCA and ACA is to provide a more realistic navigation display (ND) heading presentation, thus avoiding rapidly changing heading indications. This will help with radar vectors in TRUE and comply with Canadian Air Regulations.

The worst magnetic compass performance is probably in the center of the Northern Control Area, home to the magnetic north pole. This position creates a notch in the circle of magnetic unreliability, often called a "key hole." Charts should be checked for the presence of a "T" denoting the use of True Heading instead of Magnetic. Some aircraft automatically switch to True based on airway designation or latitude.

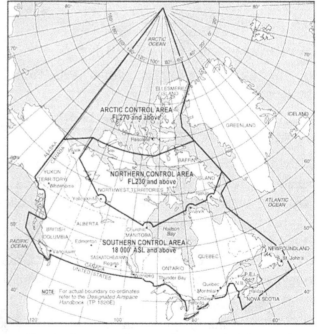

Figure: Southern, Northern, and Arctic Control Areas, from Transport Canada Aeronautical Information Manual, Figure 2.3.

Canadian Regulations

[Transport Canada Aeronautical Information Manual, ¶ 2.6] Controlled airspace within the High Level Airspace is divided into three separate areas. They are the Southern Control Area (SCA), the Northern Control Area (NCA) and the Arctic Control Area (ACA).

Pilots are reminded that both the NCA and the ACA are within the Northern Domestic Airspace; therefore, compass indications may be erratic, and true tracks are used in determining the flight level at which to fly. In addition, the airspace from FL330 to FL410 within the lateral dimensions of the NCA, the ACA and the northern part of the SCA has been designated CMNPS airspace.

What we used to call "polar ops" is now "high latitude operations."

- *The northern and southern poles.*

- *The Canadian Northern Domestic Area (NDA). The NDA includes the Northern Control Area (NCA), the Arctic Control Area (ACA) and the Area of Magnetic Unreliability (AMU). The NDA, NCA and ACA are depicted on Canadian HI en route charts and encompass the northernmost Canadian airspace.*

Documentation / Certification

[14 CFR 135, §135.98 Operations in the North Polar Area.] After February 15, 2008, no certificate holder may operate an aircraft in the region north of 78° N latitude ("North Polar Area"), other than intrastate operations wholly within the state of Alaska, unless authorized by the FAA. The certificate holder's operation specifications must include the following:

- The designation of airports that may be used for en-route diversions and the requirements the airports must meet at the time of diversion.

- Except for all-cargo operations, a recovery plan for passengers at designated diversion airports.

- A fuel-freeze strategy and procedures for monitoring fuel freezing for operations in the North Polar Area.

- A plan to ensure communication capability for operations in the North Polar Area.

- An MEL for operations in the North Polar Area.
- A training plan for operations in the North Polar Area.
- A plan for mitigating crew exposure to radiation during solar flare activity.
- A plan for providing at least two cold weather anti-exposure suits in the aircraft, to protect crewmembers during outside activity at a diversion airport with extreme climatic conditions. The FAA may relieve the certificate holder from this requirement if the season of the year makes the equipment unnecessary.

[FAA Order 8900, Volume 4, Chapter 1, §5, ¶4-102.E.] All approvals for operations into AMUs are granted by issuing OpSpec paragraph B040, Operations in Areas of Magnetic Unreliability, and by adding that area of en route operation to paragraph B050 of the standard OpSpecs. A checklist for operations in AMUs is available in the guidance subsystem in association with OpSpec paragraph B040.

Crews operating under 14 CFR 135 require operations specification approval (B040 and B050).

Crews operating under 14 CFR 91 should consider the many challenges involved and the potential safety risks illustrated below.

Equipment

[Advisory Circular 135-42, Appendix 3, ¶3.f.] Certificate holders must have at least two cold weather anti-exposure suit(s) for the crewmembers on the airplane if outside coordination by a crewmember at a diversion airport with extreme climatic conditions is determined to be necessary. The certificate holder may be relieved of this requirement based on seasonal temperatures that would render the use of such suits unnecessary. This determination must be made with concurrence of the CHDO.

This isn't much of a list; you would be wise to consider adding the requirements of Advisory Circular 120-42B, which do not restrict 14 CFR 135 and 91, but offer sound operating practices.

[Advisory Circular 120-42B, ¶603.b.(5)]

- Fuel quantity indicating system (FQIS), including the fuel tank temperature indicating system;

- APU (when the APU is necessary for an airplane to comply with ETOPS requirements), including electrical and pneumatic supply to its designed capability,

- Autothrottle system;

- Communication systems relied on by the flight crewmember to satisfy the requirement for communication capability; and

- Except for all-cargo operations, an expanded medical kit to include automated external defibrillators (AED).

Navigation Equipment

[Order 8900, Volume 4, Chapter 1, §5, ¶4-102.C.]

1. Special navigation equipment, techniques, and/or procedures are critical to operate safely in polar areas, including the two AMUs. Operations based solely on magnetic references within AMUs are unsafe, unacceptable, and shall not be approved. Operations within these areas can only be conducted safely if the primary heading reference is derived from sources other than magnetic.

2. All INS/IRS/IRU are capable of calculating true North independently from other aircraft systems. INS/IRS/ IRU can be approved and safely used for operations in AMUs and polar areas provided the following conditions are met:

   a. The INS is certified as airworthy for the highest latitude authorized for these operations.

   b. Ground alignment of the INS/IRS/IRU is restricted to those airports where satisfactory alignment has been demonstrated or otherwise approved.

   c. The operator's training programs and crew procedures provide acceptable techniques and methods for the following:

      i. Approaches and departures using appropriate heading references other than magnetic.

      ii. The use of ground-based NAVAIDs, which are oriented to appropriate directional references other than magnetic.

MEL

[Advisory Circular 135-42, Appendix 3, ¶3.c.] Before receiving approval to conduct polar operations, a certificate holder must review their MEL for such operations and should amend their MEL. The following systems and equipment should be addressed in the MEL based on specific needs applicable to this operation.

- Fuel Quantity Indicating System (to include a fuel tank temperature indicating system).
- Communication system(s) needed for effective communications by the flight crewmember while in flight.
- Expanded medical kit.

Training

[Advisory Circular 135-42, Appendix 3, ¶3.e.] Before conducting polar operations, certificate holders must ensure that flight crewmembers are trained on any applicable passenger recovery plan used in this operation. Certificate holders should also ensure that flight crewmembers are trained on the following items, which should be included in a certificate holder's approved training programs:

- Atmospheric pressure at Field Elevation/Barometric pressure for Local Altimeter Setting and meter/feet conversion issues (flight crewmember training).
- Training requirements for fuel freeze (maintenance and flight crewmember training).
- General polar-specific training on weather patterns and aircraft system limitations (flight crewmember training).
- Proper use of the cold weather anti-exposure suit, if required (flight crewmember training).
- Radiation exposure (see AC 120-61A, In-Flight Radiation Exposure).

[Order 8900, Volume 4, Chapter 1, §5, ¶4-103.D.] The following must be in the approved training programs:

- Training on Barometric pressure for Standard Altimeter Setting (QNE)/ Barometric pressure for Local Altimeter Setting (QNH) and meter/feet issues is required for flight crew and dispatcher training.

- Training on fuel freeze (included in maintenance, dispatch, and flight crew training (special curriculum segments.))

- General area and route-specific training on weather patterns and aircraft system limitations.

- Training on special considerations, such as diversion decision-making into austere airport environments to include aircraft performance, crash, fire, and rescue availability, and passenger support.

- Flight crew training in the use of the cold weather anti-exposure suit.

Communications Issues

VHF

There is some VHF radio coverage, denoted on en route charts.

HF

HF Frequencies and CPDLC addresses also appear on en route charts.

[Order 8900, Volume 4, Chapter 1, §5, ¶4-103.B.(2)] High frequency (HF) voice has been considered the primary communications medium in the North Polar Area. However, other mediums may be used as a supplemental means in accordance with the applicable policy. For example, although HF voice remains primary for communications with Anchorage Center, in areas where there is satellite coverage, satellite communication (SATCOM) voice may be used as a back-up to communicate with ARINC Radio and in non-routine situations to establish direct pilot-controller voice communications.

I am told the HF quality is generally good, though signals may be impacted by solar activity. You may need to use either AM, USB or LSB to achieve the best clarity.

SATCOM / CPDLC

[Order 8900, Volume 4, Chapter 1, §5, ¶4-103.B.(3)] In areas of satellite coverage, Controller-Pilot Data Link Communications (CPDLC) may be used for ATC communications, provided the ATS unit has an approved capability. In addition, provided the capability is approved, HF datalink may also be used to fulfill communications requirements with ATS units having the capability and with airline dispatch. Inspectors must ensure the operators meet the regulatory (14 CFR part 1) and policy requirements for long-range communication systems (LRCS). HF voice capability is always required.

[Order 8900, Volume 4, Chapter 1, §5, ¶4-103.B.(4)]

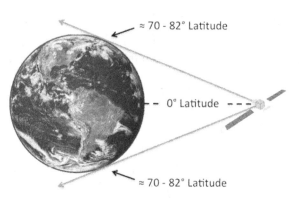

Figure: INMARSAT Line of Sight.

It is recognized that SATCOM may not be available for short periods during flight over the North Pole, particularly when operating on some designated polar routes. Communication capability with HF radios may also be affected during periods of solar flare activity. For each dispatched polar flight, the operator must take into consideration the predicted solar flare activity and its effect on communication capability.

Because INMARSAT satellites are in geostationary orbits over the equator, the curvature of the earth limits their use at the poles. It is said that SATCOM is available for voice and datalink up to 82°N.

As in other remote areas, do not enter holding for lack of further clearance or radio contact at the FIR. Continue on your cleared route and altitude while trying pass a position report through the appropriate agency or a relay by another aircraft that you might raise on guard or on the air-to-air frequency 123.45 MHz. In the event of a total loss of communications, fly your flight plan. See Part VI, Chapter 2, Lost Communications.

Navigation Issues

Magnetic Variation and Convergence of the Meridians

[Order 8900, Volume 4, Chapter 1, §5, ¶4-102.]

- Conventional magnetic compasses sense magnetic direction by detecting the horizontal component of the earth's magnetic field. Since this horizontal component vanishes near the magnetic poles, magnetic compasses are highly unreliable and unusable in an area approximately 1,000 nm from each magnetic pole. Within these areas, air navigation tasks are further complicated by very rapid changes in magnetic variation over small distances. For example, when flying between the magnetic North Pole and the true North Pole, a heading of true North results in a magnetic heading of South (a magnetic variation of 180 degrees).

- Since these two major AMUs also occur near the earth's geographic poles, the convergence of the meridians also presents additional directional complications. When flying "great circle" courses at latitudes greater than 67 degrees, convergence of the meridians can create rapid changes in true headings and true courses with small changes in aircraft position. As a result, relatively small errors in determining the aircraft's actual position can produce very large errors in determining the proper heading to fly and maintain the assigned flight path. When even small errors occur, very large navigation errors can develop over extremely short distances. An extreme example of this phenomenon occurs at the earth's geographic North Pole. Flight in any direction from the exact pole is initially due South (that is, the direction to Russia or the United States is South).

True Heading

Navigating near the poles presents several issues not found anywhere else in the world. Because of these issues, the only acceptable method of navigating through the NCA and high latitude region is through the use of long-range navigation systems using inertial and GPS based FMS systems referenced to True North only.

Other methods of navigation in the NCA are impractical or unreliable because of the inherent limitations of magnetic compasses near the magnetic and geographic north poles, and because of the geometric problem caused by meridian convergence.

Some aircraft make the switch automatically by reference to latitude or airway, while for other the switch must be made manually.

GPS Navigation

Each GPS satellite traces a track over the earth from 55° North to 55° South every twelve hours. At their maximum latitudes they are actually "looking down" on the poles:

Height Above Pole = 10998 cos 55 − 6887 = 2122

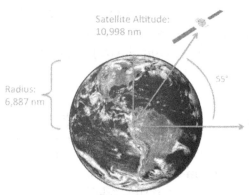

Of course you have no guarantee you will have at least one satellite that high in its orbit. In order to have line of sight on the pole, a satellite would have to be at least 39° latitude:

Figure: GPS Satellite Line of Sight.

Minimum Latitude to See Pole = arcsin(6887 / 10998) = 39

I've not found anything in writing that tells you there will always be at least four satellites above 39° North and 39° South, but it appears so. You should have a good GPS position at either pole. See Part II, Chapter 8, GNSS.

Temperature Issues

Tropopause Height and ISA

[Geerts and Linacre] The height of the tropopause depends on the location, notably the latitude, as shown in the figure on the right (which shows annual mean conditions). It also depends on the season.

At latitudes above 60°, the tropopause is less than 9-10 km above sea level; the lowest is less than 8 km high, above Antarctica and above Siberia and northern Canada in winter. The highest average tropopause is over the oceanic warm pool of the western equatorial Pacific, about 17.5 km high, and over Southeast Asia, during the summer monsoon, the tropopause occasionally peaks above 18 km. In other words, cold conditions lead to a lower tropopause, obviously because of less convection.

Deep convection (thunderstorms) in the Intertropical Convergence Zone, or over mid-latitude continents in summer, continuously push the tropopause upwards and as such deepen the troposphere.

On the other hand, colder regions have a lower tropopause, obviously because convective overturning is limited there, due to the negative radiation balance at the surface. In fact, convection is very rare in polar regions; most

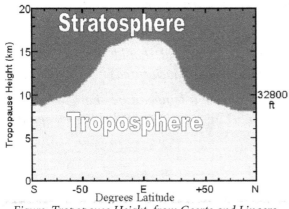

of the tropospheric mixing at middle and high latitudes is forced by frontal systems in which uplift is forced rather than spontaneous (convective). This explains the paradox that tropopause temperatures are lowest where the surface temperatures are highest.

Figure: Tropopause Height, from Geerts and Linacre.

The tropopause at the poles is lower than at the equator; that means the altitudes where most polar-capable aircraft cruise is warmer. Knowing this, altitude selection may not be straightforward.

Surface Temperatures

If a descent into lower altitudes is required, fuel freezing and other aircraft systems limitations can become issues. If an emergency landing is required, surface temperatures can be life threatening.

Fuel Freezing

[Advisory Circular 135-42, Appendix 3, ¶3.c.] Fuel Freeze Strategy and Monitoring Requirements for Polar Operations. Certificate holders must develop a fuel freeze strategy and procedures for monitoring fuel freezing for operations in the North Polar Area. A fuel freeze analysis program in lieu of using the standard minimum fuel freeze temperatures for specific types of fuel may be used. In such cases, the certificate holder's fuel freeze analysis and monitoring program for the airplane fuel load must be acceptable to the FAA Administrator. The certificate holder should have procedures for determining the fuel freeze temperature of the actual fuel load on board the airplane. These procedures relative to determining the fuel freeze temperature and monitoring the actual temperature of the fuel on board should require appropriate levels of coordination between maintenance and the flight crewmember.

Should fuel temperatures approach the aircraft's freezing limit you should consider:

- *Climbing or descending into a level of warmer air,*
- *Altering the route into a region of warmer air, and/or*
- *Increasing cruise airspeed (Fuel temperatures should increase approximately one degree for every .02 increase in Mach speed)*

Your flight planning vendor should provide a temperature chart to help you plan for these contingencies. Remember, any changes in flight level, speed or route must be coordinated with ATC.

Polar Radiation

[Advisory Circular 120-61A, ¶6.] Radiation received on a lower-latitude flight will be lower because of the greater amount of radiation shielding provided by the earth's magnetic field. This shielding is maximum near the equator and gradually decreases to zero as one goes north or south. Radiation levels over the polar regions are about twice those over the equator at the same altitudes.

[NASA Study, Michael Finneran] Space radiation on the ground is very low, but increases significantly with altitude. At 30,000 to 40,000 feet, the typical altitude of a jetliner, exposure on a typical flight is still considered safe – less than a chest X-ray.

Exposure is considerably higher, however, over the Earth's poles, where the planet's magnetic field no longer provides any shielding. And with a thousand-fold rise in commercial airline flights over the North Pole in the last 10 years, exposure to radiation has become a serious concern.

A study by Mertens of polar flights during a solar storm in 2003 showed that passengers received about 12 percent of the annual radiation limit recommended by the International Committee on Radiological Protection. The exposures were greater than on typical flights at lower latitudes, and confirmed concerns about commercial flights using polar routes.

People who work on commercial airline flights are technically listed as "radiation workers" by the federal government – a classification that includes nuclear plant workers and X-ray technicians. But unlike some others in that category, flight crews do not quantify the radiation they are exposed to.

Flights in the Polar Region at typical business jet operating altitudes are well above the tropopause where much of the atmospheric protection from solar storms is lost, increasing crew and passenger exposure to solar radiation.

For example, one New York-Tokyo flight during a solar storm could expose the passengers and crew to the normal annual exposure (1mSv) of someone who remained on the surface. If an S4 solar storm is active or predicted, polar operations are generally considered not suitable at any altitude, while operations at FL310 or below are considered acceptable in S3 storm conditions.

Some flight plan vendors will include predicted solar activity for flights through the high latitude airspace. Additionally, Space Weather Now from the NOAA and spaceweather.com are useful when planning a polar flight.

Alternate Airports

[Advisory Circular 135-42, Appendix 3, ¶3.a.] Before each flight, certificate holders must designate alternate airports that can be used in case an en route diversion is necessary. The airplane should have a reasonable assurance that the weather during periods when the certificate holder would need the services of the airport are within the operating limits of the airplane. The airplane should be able to make a safe landing and maneuver off the runway at the diversion airport. In addition, those airports identified for use during an en route diversion should be capable of protecting the safety of all personnel by allowing:

- Safe offload of passengers and crewmember during possible adverse weather conditions;

- Providing for the physiological needs of the passengers and crewmember until a safe evacuation is completed; and

- Safe extraction of passengers and crewmember as soon as possible (execution and completion of the recovery should be within 12 to 48 hours following landing).

[Order 8900, Volume 4, Chapter 1, §5, ¶4-103.E.] Operators are expected to define a sufficient set of polar diversion alternate airports, such that one or more can be reasonably expected to be suitable and available in varying weather conditions (AC 120-42A, Extended Range Operation With Two-Engine Airplanes (ETOPS), provides additional guidance for two-engine airplanes).

[Order 8900, Volume 4, Chapter 1, §5, ¶4-103.G.] A recovery plan is required that will be initiated in the event of an unplanned diversion. The recovery plan should address the care and safety of passengers and flight crew at the diversion airport and include the plan of operation to extract the passengers and flight crew from that airport.

The requirements for the passenger recovery plan are quite extensive and must be detailed for each airport listed as a possible alternate airport. More on this: Advisory Circular 135-42, Appendix 3, ¶3.b.

There aren't many airports with paved runways in the Arctic, and many of those do not have regular airline service or customs. If you are flying under 14 CFR 135 your Operations Specification approval will require a list of alternates and a plan for getting passengers from the alternates within 48 hours.

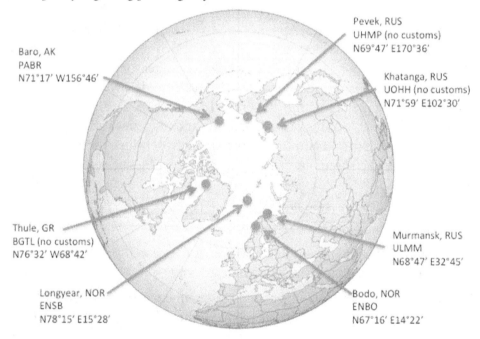

Pevek, RUS
UHMP (no customs)
N69°47' E170°36'

Baro, AK
PABR
N71°17' W156°46'

Khatanga, RUS
UOHH (no customs)
N71°59' E102°30'

Thule, GR
BGTL (no customs)
N76°32' W68°42'

Murmansk, RUS
ULMM
N68°47' E32°45'

Longyear, NOR
ENSB
N78°15' E15°28'

Bodo, NOR
ENBO
N67°16' E14°22'

Chapter 24

Insurance

Your insurance paperwork needs to be in order whenever you depart for foreign shores, there are places where they will be asking to see them.

Documentation of Insurance

[AC 91-70A, ¶3-1.d.] Operators should ensure that all required entry documents are available for presentation upon arrival and may need multiple copies of the following documents:

- Ownership papers.
- Management specifications (MSpecs)/operations specifications (OpSpecs)/letters of authorization (LOA).
- General declarations.
- Passenger and cargo manifests.
- Licenses.
- Crewmember certificates. Logbooks.
- Radio licenses.
- Detailed insurance information.

[McLaren, "Insurance Considerations For Overseas Missions"] A copy or a certified copy of your policy is usually sufficient, but not always.

[McLaren, "Dealing With the New Rules of Worldwide Documentation"] Insurance requirements can be persnickety at some locations. The European Union (EU) has special insurance mandates, liability limits and formats that must be followed. Mexico, in most cases, requires liability policies from providers in Mexico and these documents must be in Spanish. Hong Kong is particularly obsessive in terms of insurance requirements, liability limits and specific wording/format of policies. "We had a case of a Hong Kong landing permit request denied because one comma was missing on the insurance policy."

You will sometimes find airport-specific insurance requirements in a country's Aeronautical Information Publication (AIP). The United Kingdom AIP, for example, lists insurance minimums for Belfast International, Blackpool Airport, Chichester/Goodwood, and Norwich. So where do you find what insurance is required at your international destinations and what kind of proof do you need? There is no "go to" source, you need to ask a handling agent with local and recent knowledge.

Worldwide Coverage

[McLaren, "Insurance Considerations For Overseas Missions"] You can't always get by with standard worldwide coverage. Examples:

- Ascension requires coverage for emergency medical evacuation of passengers and crew while visiting the island.
- Brazil requires you carry an original copy of your policy.
- Greenland requires you have insurance coverage for search and rescue even when overflying their airspace.
- Hong Kong requires specific wording in policies and routinely rejects landing permits for the smallest formatting or wording error.
- Mexico requires you provide both a standard worldwide insurance policy and a Mexican insurance policy drawn on a Mexican insurance company.
- United Kingdom joint use civil/military airports require "Crown indemnity waiver" language in policies.

EU Requirements

[European Regulation No. 859/2008, ¶OPS 1.125 (a)] An operator shall ensure that the following documents or copies thereof are carried on each flight:

1.   The Certificate of Registration;

2.   The Certificate of Airworthiness;

3.   The original or a copy of the Noise Certificate (if applicable), includ-

ing an English translation, where one has been provided by the Authority responsible for issuing the noise certificate;

4.   The original or a copy of the Air Operator Certificate;

5.   The Aircraft Radio Licence; and

6.   The original or a copy of the Third party liability Insurance Certificate(s).

[NBAA, "Flying to Europe? Think Again"] European Union Regulation 785-2004 of the European Parliament sets out mandatory liability limits (inclusive of war risk) in respect of passengers, cargo, baggage and third parties and will affect almost all aircraft carriers and operators, both commercial and private, operating flights within, into, out of, or over the territory of an EU Member State. The regulation sets out minimum coverage requirements for personal and third-party liability. Each EU member state has the right to inspect aircraft landing in that state, and may require verification of compliance with the new insurance regulation. A current insurance certificate showing the necessary coverages should be carried on board the aircraft in order to evidence compliance and avoid unexpected and expensive delays and possible refusal of the right to land in EU territory.

War Risk Insurance

The insurance mandated by European Union Regulation 785-2004 must include coverage for war, terrorism, hijacking, sabotage, unlawful seizure of aircraft, and civil commotion. In addition, the third party element of the cover must be on an 'each accident, each and every aircraft' basis.

["Flying to Europe? Think Again"] There are no war risk insurance requirements in the United States but if you fly internationally you need to check. For example, Germany requires €60,000,000, China (Hong Kong) requires $200,000,000, and Poland requires €60,000,000.

Incognito LLC
Flight / Maintenance Log

Aircraft Reg: **7700C** Log Number: _____

Oil
L:
R:

Crew, Duty Times, PIC Signature

Crew, Duty Times, PIC Signature	On Duty	Off Duty	Total
PIC			
SIC			
ACM			
Signature			

Flight Log

Leg	Z-Date	From / To	Out / In	Block Time	NM Distance	Off / On	Flight Time	Crew L	Crew R	T/O D	T/O N	Landing D	Landing N	Apchs P	Apchs NP	Inst Time Hrs	PF	Night
1																		
2																		
3																		
4																		
5																		

Totals This Log

	Aircraft	Left Engine		Right Engine		APU			
	Hours	Landings	Hours	Cycles	Hours	Cycles	Hours		
Log						03-08 → 0.1	33-38 → 0.6		
Fwd						09-14 → 0.2	39-44 → 0.7		Station
Tot						15-20 → 0.3	45-50 → 0.8	Type	VOR #1
						21-26 → 0.4	51-56 → 0.9		VOR #1
						27-32 → 0.5	57-02 → 1.0		VOR #2

VOR Check

VOR Check		RVSM Altimeter Check
Station		
Type		Left
Right		Stby
		Right

Fuel/Passenger Data

Leg	Uploaded	Start (#)	End (#)	Pax	T/O Wt	Max Wt
1						
2						
3						
4						
5						

Weight and Balance

Fwd Limit	T/O CG	Aft Limit	

Discrepancy Report

I certify that this aircraft has been inspected in accordance with the inspection program identified in 14 CFR 91.409 and was determined to be in airworthy condition with respect to the work performed and is approved for return to service.

Discrepancy Report	Corrective Action	Sign/Certificate Number
No:		
Leg:		Type Inspection
Z-Date:		
Signature:		

Discrepancy Report	Corrective Action	
No:	Mechanic	
Leg:	Cert	Date

Discrepancy Report	Corrective Action	
No:	Mechanic	
Leg:	Cert	Date
Z-Date:		
Signature:		

White Copy - Operations / Yellow Copy - Maintenance / Pink - Remains With Aircraft

Sample Flight and Maintenance Logbook

450

Chapter 25

Journey Logbook

*T*here was once a huge controversy over what exactly constitutes a journey logbook. Everybody agreed you had to have one, but what is it? The original requirement was set out in 1944 without a precise definition. ICAO Annex 6 changed all that a few years ago, but we are still left with a decision on where the book should be kept.*

The only document we have that comes even close to satisfying all the requirements is the Flight and Maintenance Log that we complete for every flight. You will have to examine your version to see if it also satisfies the ICAO.

As for how long you need to keep it on the aircraft, that's where it gets tricky. More on that below.

Where (and when) it all started . . .

[1944 ICAO Chicago Convention, Article 34] There shall be maintained in respect of every aircraft engaged in international navigation a journey log book in which shall be entered particulars of the aircraft, its crew and of each journey, in such form as may be prescribed from time to time pursuant to this Convention.

Updated Guidance for Commercial Operators

[ICAO Annex 6 Part I]

11.4.1. The aeroplane journey log book should contain the following items and the corresponding roman numerals:

I.   Aeroplane nationality and registration.

II.   Date.

III.   Names of crew members.

IV.   Duty assignments of crew members.

V.   Place of departure.

VI.   Place of arrival.

VII.   Time of departure.

VIII.   Time of arrival.

IX.   Hours of flight.

X.   Nature of flight (private, aerial work, scheduled or non-scheduled).

XI.   Incidents, observations, if any.

XII.   Signature of person in charge.

11.4.2 Recommendation.— Entries in the journey log book should be made currently and in ink or indelible pencil.

11.4.3 Recommendation.— Completed journey log book should be retained to provide a continuous record of the last six months' operations.

Paragraph 11.4.3 recommends the journey log book be "retained" but doesn't say it has to be on the aircraft. I think if you have electronic access to them you should be okay.

[EASA Acceptable Means of Compliance (AMC) to Annex III - Part-ORO] §AMC1 ORO.MLR.110]

a.   The aircraft journey log, or equivalent, should include the following items, where applicable:

1.   aircraft nationality and registration,

2.   date,

3.   name(s) of crew member(s),

4.   duty assignments of crew member(s),

5.   place of departure,

6.   place of arrival,

7.   time of departure,

8.   time of arrival,

9.   hours of flight,

10.   nature of flight (scheduled or non-scheduled),

11.   incidents, observations, if any,

12.   signature of person in charge.

b.   The information, or parts thereof, may be recorded in a form other than on printed paper. Accessibility, usability and reliability should be assured.

c.   'Journey log, or equivalent' means that the required information may be recorded in documentation other than a log book, such as the operational flight plan or the aircraft technical log.

d.   'Series of flights' means consecutive flights, which begin and end:

1.   within a 24-hour period;

2.   at the same aerodrome or operating site or remain within a local area specified in the operations manual; and

3.   with the same pilot-in-command/commander of the aircraft.

Updated Guidance for General Aviation

[ICAO Annex 6 Part II]

2.8.2 A journey log book shall be maintained for every aeroplane engaged in international air navigation in which shall be entered particulars of the aeroplane, its crew and each journey.

2.8.2.2. Recommendation.—The aeroplane journey log should contain the following items:

a.   aeroplane nationality and registration;

b.   date;

c.   crew member names and duty assignments;

d.   departure and arrival points and times;

e.   purpose of flight;

f.   observations regarding the flight; and

g.   signature of the pilot-in-command.

[European Union Regulation No 965/2012, §ORO.MLR.110] Particulars of the aircraft, its crew and each journey shall be retained for each flight, or series of flights, in the form of a journey log, or equivalent.

[AC 91-70A, ¶2-3.p.] Article 34 of the Chicago Convention determined that it was extremely important that each aircraft have a journey logbook. Annex 2 requires this standard for operations engaged in international aviation. The aircraft should carry a journey logbook containing the particulars of the aircraft, crew, reporting points, communication problems, and any unusual circumstances surrounding the flight. Note: An electronic version of the journey logbook is acceptable but you should retain the data at least 90 days for support in the event of an oceanic error.

We scan every flight log and have it electronically available at our home base on a full time, secured, network drive. We can download any log from anywhere with an Internet connection. We only carry enough past flight logs on the aircraft to prove a maintenance airworthiness release, a valid VOR check, and an RVSM check. Will this pass muster? I think so. I have been SAFA ramp checked and the subject never came up.

If you would like an example of a Flight and Maintenance Log that I believe satisfies all these Journey Logbook requirements, look at the first page of this chapter.

Section VIII - Appendices

Chapter 26

Mach Number Technique

It is called "Mach Number Technique" but it is actually "Mach Number Procedure" because if you don't follow it you could lose your oceanic pilot's privileges. The procedure is required around much of the world, though the ICAO manual description is rather sparse.

If you have auto throttles you are pretty much set. Tune those puppies to the filed oceanic Mach and leave them there. If your ETA to the next waypoint varies by the required tolerance, 3 minutes or more for most of the world, update your ETA. Do not change your target Mach. Why? Read on . . .

Mach Number Technique Defined

[ICAO NAT Doc 007, ¶7.1.1.] The term 'Mach Number Technique' is used to describe a technique whereby subsonic turbojet aircraft operating successively along suitable routes are cleared by ATC to maintain appropriate Mach Numbers for a relevant portion of the en route phase of their flight.

Objective

[ICAO NAT Doc 007, ¶7.2.1.] The principal objective of the use of Mach Number Technique is to achieve improved utilisation of the airspace on long route segments where ATC has no means, other than position reports, of ensuring that the longitudinal separation between successive aircraft is not reduced below the established minimum. Practical experience has shown that when two or more turbojet aircraft, operating along the same route at the same flight level, maintain the same Mach Number, they are more likely to maintain a constant time interval between each other than when using other methods. This is due to the fact that the aircraft concerned are normally subject to approximately the same wind and air temperature conditions, and minor variations in ground speed, which might increase and decrease the spacing between them, tend to be neutralised over long periods of flight.

455

Longitudinal Separation

[ICAO Doc 4444, ¶5.4.2.1.1.] Longitudinal separation shall be applied so that the spacing between the estimated positions of the aircraft being separated is never less than a prescribed minimum. Longitudinal separation between aircraft following the same or diverging tracks may be maintained by application of speed control, including the Mach number technique. When applicable, use of the Mach number technique shall be prescribed on the basis of a regional air navigation agreement.

[ICAO NAT Doc 007, ¶7.3.] The Oceanic Clearance includes the assigned (True) Mach Number which is to be maintained. It is therefore necessary that information on the desired Mach Number be included in the flight plan for turbojet aircraft intending to fly in NAT oceanic airspace. ATC uses Mach Number together with pilot position reports to calculate estimated times for significant points along track. These times provide the basis for longitudinal separation between aircraft and for coordination with adjacent ATC units.

ATC will try to accommodate pilot/dispatcher requested or flight planned Mach Numbers when issuing Oceanic Clearances. It is rare that ATC will assign a Mach Number more than 0.01 faster or 0.02 slower than that requested. The prescribed longitudinal separation between successive aircraft flying a particular track at the same flight level is established over the oceanic entry point. Successive aircraft following the same track may be assigned different Mach Numbers but these will be such as to ensure that prescribed minimum separations are assured throughout the oceanic crossing. Intervention by ATC thereafter should normally only be necessary if an aircraft is required to change its Mach Number due to conflicting traffic or to change its flight level.

It is, however, important to recognise that the establishment and subsequent monitoring of longitudinal separation is totally reliant upon aircraft providing accurate waypoint passing times in position reports. It is therefore essential that pilots conducting flights in MNPS Airspace utilise accurate clocks and synchronise these with a standard time signal, based on UTC, prior to entering MNPS Airspace. It should be noted that some aircraft clocks can only be re-set while the aircraft is on the ground.

[ICAO Annex 2, ¶3.6.2.2. c)] Change in time estimate: if the time estimate for the next applicable reporting point, flight information region boundary or destination aerodrome, whichever comes first, is found to be in error in excess of 3 minutes from that notified to air traffic services, or such other period of time as is prescribed by the appropriate ATS authority or on the basis of air navigation regional agreements, a revised estimated time shall be notified as soon as possible to the appropriate air traffic services unit.

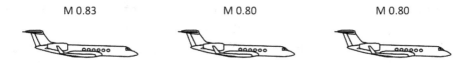

M 0.83   M 0.80   M 0.80

Chasing ETA's

Imagine in the drawing you are the airplane in the middle. Your spacing is designed with the varying speeds taken into consideration. If all three airplanes are hit with less than forecast headwinds, all three airplanes will start arriving at their waypoints early. If you, in the middle, slow down to arrive at your waypoint on time while the faster airplane behind you correctly maintains his Mach number, you could have loss of separation. If the other two airplanes update their ETA's and you don't, it will be obvious to ATC who gets the violation.

The correct procedure:

- *Fly the assigned Mach Number if at all possible, if your ETA varies by 3 minutes or more, inform ATC.*

- *If you cannot maintain the assigned Mach Number for any reason (performance, turbulence, etc.), inform ATC before making an adjustment. If you cannot get clearance first, consider broadcasting your actions on 123.45 and 121.5 to ensure aircraft ahead and behind you are aware.*

Mach Number Tolerances

[ICAO NAT Doc 007, ¶7.2.2.] For many aircraft types the cockpit instrument displays the True Mach being flown. However, for some types the AFM notes a correction that must be made to the Indicated Mach to provide the True Mach. It is important to recognise that the maintenance of longitudinal separations depends upon the assumption that the ATC assigned Mach numbers maintained by all aircraft are True Mach numbers. Pilots must therefore ensure that any required corrections to indicated Mach are taken into account when complying with the True Mach number specified in the ATC clearance.

[ICAO NAT Doc 007, ¶7.3.4.] In the application of Mach Number Technique, pilots must adhere strictly to their assigned True Mach Numbers unless a specific re-clearance is obtained from the appropriate ATC unit. However, as the aircraft weight reduces it may be more fuel efficient to adjust the Mach Number. Since the in-trail and crossing track separations between individual aircraft are established on the basis of ETAs passed to, or calculated by, ATC, it is essential that ATC approval is requested prior to effecting any change in cruise Mach Number. Such approval will be given if traffic conditions permit. Pilots must recognise that adherence to the assigned Mach Number is essential. No tolerance is provided for. Pilots must not utilise Long Range Cruise or ECON FMC modes when transiting NAT MNPS airspace. If an immediate temporary change in the Mach Number is essential, e.g. due to turbulence, ATC must be notified as soon as possible. Pilots with experience of flying in oceanic airspaces other than the North Atlantic, may be familiar with a procedure in those areas which permits pilots to unilaterally elect to change their cruising Mach number by up to 0.02M, without prior ATC approval. This is not the case in the North Atlantic MNPS airspace.

Before the adoption of Mach Number Technique requirements, there was indeed a 0.02 tolerance on Mach Number. Those days are gone. Remember you want to fly a constant True Mach Number. If your cockpit doesn't present True Mach Number, you need to make the adjustment. If your auto throttles tend to fly slow or fast, you need to make the adjustment. In the case of the G450, for example, the cockpit instrument shows True Mach Number and the auto throttles do a pretty good job of bracketing the set number. We set the auto throttles on the correct Mach Number and leave them alone.

Climbs

[ICAO NAT Doc 007, ¶7.3.4.] Pilots should maintain their last assigned Mach Number during step-climbs in oceanic airspace. If due to aircraft performance this is not feasible ATC should be advised at the time of the request for the step climb.

If you can't make the climb at your filed Mach number, you shouldn't be making the climb.

Procedures After Leaving Oceanic Airspace

[ICAO NAT Doc 007, ¶7.4.] After leaving oceanic airspace pilots must maintain their assigned Mach Number in domestic controlled airspace unless and until the appropriate ATC unit authorises a change.

Where Mach Number Technique is Used

The Mach Number Technique is required in various parts of the world, for example:

- Africa (Canarias, Dakar, Recife, Sal Oceanic FIRs, and designated RNP-10 routes): [ICAO Doc 7030, ¶AFI 6.2.2.]

- Caribbean (specified areas in Houston Oceanic, Merida and Monterrey CTAs, Miami Oceanic, San Juan CTA, and New York Oceanic): [ICAO Doc 7030, ¶CAR 6.2.2.]

- Middle East/Asia (specified routes): [ICAO Doc 7030, ¶MID/ASIA 2.1.11.]

- North America (Anchorage Arctic CTA): [ICAO Doc 7030, ¶NAM 6.2.2.]

- North Atlantic: [ICAO Doc 7030, ¶NAT 6.2.2.]

- Pacific (Anchorage and Oakland Oceanic FIRs): [ICAO Doc 7030, ¶PAC 6.1.1.]

- South America (Dakar, Recife, and Sal Oceanic FIRs): [ICAO Doc 7030, ¶SAM 6.2.2.]

ICAO Doc 7030 is rarely updated and airspace around the world is getting more crowded so you can expect to see the use of Mach Number Technique expand. It might not be a bad idea to use it everywhere when not in radar contact.

Oceanic Checklist and RVSM/NAV Performance Log

Preflight

☑ Label one copy of the computer flight plan "Master Document"
☑ Plot route over Class II airspace and any relevant tracks
☑ Add ETPs (loss of pressurization, all-engine cruise, loss of engine) if required
☑ Position Check: Ramp (GPS) N/S 42°27.6   E/W 71°17.4

IRS #1	IRS #2	IRS #3	GPS #1	GPS#2
Diff 0.0	Diff 0.0	Diff 0.0	Diff 0.0	Diff 0.0

☑ Altimeter Check: QNH 2992 Pilot's 120 Stby 130 Copilot's 120
☑ Time Check: Source (circle) WWV/GPS/ATC +/- 10 sec ✓
☑ Compare Master Document course/distance with plotting or en route chart, circle waypoint
☑ Compare Master Document course/distance with FMS, draw diagonal over waypoint
☑ Record fuel onboard on the Master Document

Coast Out

☑ Check both HFs, check SELCAL prior to entering oceanic airspace
☑ Nav Accuracy Check:

RAW: Fix YQX   Radial 270   Distance 113
FMS: Fix YQX   Radial 270   Distance 112

☑ Altimeter Check: QNH 2992 Pilot's 41000 Stby 40900 Copilot's 41020
☑ Record oceanic clearances on the Master Document

At Each Waypoint

☑ Record ATA, fuel remaining, winds/temperature (if required), next ETA, HF frequencies, three altimeters on Master Document
☑ Make the position report, draw a second diagonal over waypoint on Master Document
☑ Check distance, time, heading, and fuel remaining to the next waypoint against the Master Document
☑ Plot aircraft position approximately 10 minutes after waypoint passage

Coast In

☑ Nav Accuracy Check:

RAW: Fix CRK   Radial 240   Distance 130
FMS: Fix CRK   Radial 240   Distance 129

Post-flight

☑ Position Check: Ramp (GPS) N/S 46°13.0   E/W 06°06.4

IRS #1	IRS #2	IRS #3	GPS #1	GPS#2
Diff 0.4	Diff 0.2	Diff 1.2	Diff 0.0	Diff 0.0

☑ Altimeter Check: QNH 1010 Pilot's 1410 Stby 1440 Copilot's 1430

Figure: Completed Oceanic Checklist and RVSM/NAV Performance Log

Section VIII - Appendices

Chapter 27

Navigation Accuracy Check

*I*t's getting harder and harder to justify the need for a navigation accuracy check, with GPS redundancy and hybrid IRS, ADS, and all the rest. Most of these techniques came from the days where flying without a navigator was an act of faith and have stubbornly remained. The book — AC 91-70A — still says you have to do these and I think it is a good idea.

I was starting to soften on my evangelical quest to get every international pilot to do nav accuracy checks but, in April of 2014, I heard of a rash of gross navigation errors after the North Atlantic adopted half-degree spacing on some of its tracks. Pilots have been blindly inputting ARINC-424 codes and ending up 30 miles off course. N4550 and 4550N, for example, are 30 nautical miles apart. More about this: International Operations / ARINC 424 Shorthand. They could have all been saved by, first, being more careful with the FMS inputs, and second, using navigation accuracy checks. Besides, what else you got to do when oceanic?

The Requirement

Coast-Out Navigation Accuracy Check.

[AC 91-70A, Appendix 2, ¶2.f.(1)] Gross Error Accuracy Check. Before oceanic entry, check the accuracy of the LRNS against a ground-based NAVAID. Record the results of the accuracy check with the time and position. A large difference between the ground-based NAVAID and the LRNS may require immediate corrective action. Operators should establish a gross error check tolerance based on the type of LRNS. It is not advisable for crews to attempt to correct an error by doing an air alignment or by manually updating the LRNS since this has often contributed to a gross navigation error (GNE).

Before you stray out of ground-based NAVAID range — sooner actually, before you leave the service volume of an appropriate NAVAID — you need to compare what it is telling you versus what your FMS is telling you. The procedure

461

can be checking a VOR Radial/DME plot versus your FMS latitude/longitude on your plotting chart, or using an FMS "Cross Points" function versus the VOR Radial/DME.

Coast-in Navigation Accuracy Check.

[AC 91-70A, Appendix 2, ¶2.l.(1)] Compare Ground-Based NAVAID to LRNS. When departing oceanic airspace and acquiring ground-based NAVAIDs, crews should note the accuracy of the LRNS by comparing it to those NAVAIDs. Note any discrepancy in the maintenance log.

The coast-in navigation accuracy check is conducted in the same manner as for coast-out, except that the earliest possible navigation aid is sought for the first opportunity to check navigation performance, keeping in mind the service volume of the navaid is limited.

Post-Flight.

[AC 91-70A, Appendix 2, ¶2.n.(1)] Navigation Accuracy Check. When arriving at the destination gate, crews should note any drift or circular error in the LRNS. A GPS primary means system normally should not exceed 0.27 NM for the flight. Some inertial systems may drift as much as 2 NM per hour. Because the present generation of LRNSs is highly accurate, operators should establish a drift tolerance which, if exceeded, would require a write-up in the maintenance log. Required Navigation Performance (RNP) requirements demand close monitoring of drift.

The latest generation of hybrid IRS, such as those in the G450, will may do this for you automatically.

Techniques

The navigation accuracy check compares FMS position against a ground-based navigation aid and can be accomplished in several ways, depending on aircraft avionics. Depending on aircraft FMS capabilities, the following methods are presented in order of probable accuracy.

FMS Cross-Points

Some FMS installations include a "cross points" function that computes the position of the aircraft relative to a waypoint or VOR. The applicable VOR is inputted and compared to a raw data instrument tuned to the same VOR.

Photos: G450 PPOS page and Electronic Bearing/Distance Indicator.

In the example photo, we see that we are on the 270° radial, 112 NM from YQX.

Tuning the YQX VOR we can see the raw data on the EBDI.

In the example photo, we see that we are on the 270° radial, 113 NM from YQX.

Of course the raw data distance is greater than the actual distance because it is the slant range.

FMS Bearing/Distance

Some FMS installations can provide a course and distance to fly to a selected waypoint. The applicable VOR is inputted and the reciprocal of the course is compared to a raw data instrument tuned to the same VOR.

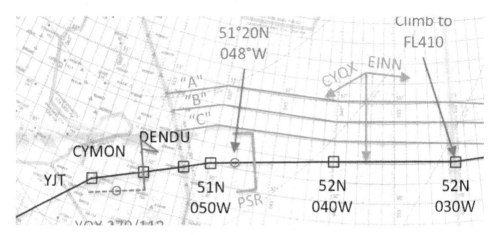

FMS Lat/Long Plotting versus NAVAID Plotting

If the FMS doesn't provide a means for providing a track and distance to a VOR, the check can still be accomplished by recording the VOR radial and DME and the primary FMS latitude/longitude.

For example, the Gander VOR can be used for a coast-out NAV accuracy check.

The VOR should be drawn on the plotting chart with a magnetic north flag which would be drawn in this case 22° to the west. (This flag points to magnetic north and can be labeled "360°M / 348°T")

The latitude and longitude from the FMS is plotted directly on the chart. A compass plotter measures the angle from the magnetic north flag to determine the aircraft is on a 270° radial and the distance is measured to be 112 nm. (We were cleared direct 51°N 050°W so didn't overfly YJT, CYMON, or DENDU.)

Overhead VOR Fix

If the route of flight is directly over a VOR, the FMS latitude and longitude can be checked against the VOR latitude and longitude when directly overhead. This method is not as accurate as a radial/dme fix because of the geometric error associated with an overhead passage.

Radar Fix

If all other means are unavailable and the aircraft is still under radar contact, ATC may be able to provide a radar fix in terms of a radial/dme from a known NAVAID which can be plotted or compared to an FMS cross points solution.

Chapter 28

Navigation Worksheet

*I*f *you get a re-clearance that is significantly different than what is on your master document, you will need to update the master document, get a new one sent to you, or you will have to compute a new one on your own. The math isn't that hard, but you are likely to be in a rush when this happens and that means you will be prone to making math errors. You should carry a supply of blank navigation worksheets on every oceanic flight. You can find a blank navigation worksheet at the end of this chapter. Now that you have the worksheet, here are your options:*

- *If you have an Internet connection and a printer, have your flight planning service send you a new flight plan and print it out. Even without a printer, you can at least transpose the information onto the navigation worksheet.*

- *If you have a fax machine, have them fax it to you.*

- *Got a phone? Have them read off the pertinent information. You don't need the entire flight plan, just the oceanic portion that has changed.*

- *Failing all that, get your trusty calculator and plotter and be careful.*

The Requirement

[AC 91-70A, ¶3-6.z.] Scrutiny groups determined that a re-clearance scenario is the greatest contributor to an oceanic error (e.g., GNE, Large Height Deviation (LHD)). Experience suggests that when ATC issues a clearance involving rerouting and new waypoints, the risk of error increases. The procedures used to copy the ATC clearance, load and check the waypoints, verify the flight plan information, and prepare a new plotting chart should be the same as the procedures for beginning a flight. Designate one pilot to fly the aircraft while the other pilot reprograms the navigation systems and amends the cockpit documents. In the event that a re-clearance involves a direct routing, retain the data relevant to the original route in case ATC requires the aircraft to return to its original course.

[AC 91-70A, Appendix 2, ¶2.f.(5)] A re-clearance (that is different from the oceanic route requested with the filed flight plan) is the number one scenario which leads to a GNE. Crews must be particularly cautious when receiving a re-clearance. Both pilots should receive and confirm the new routing and conduct independent crosschecks after updating the LRNS, Master CFP, and plotting chart. It is critical that crews check the magnetic course and distance between the new waypoints as noted in PREFLIGHT under the paragraph "LRNS Programming."

[AC 91-70A, Appendix 2, ¶2.c. LRNS Programming] (4) Track and Distance Check. To minimize oceanic errors, it is important to conduct a magnetic course and distance check from oceanic entry to oceanic exit. Operators should establish a tolerance such as + 2° and + 2 nm. The course and distance check comparing the Master CFP against the LRNS are critical in detecting errors you may not have noticed by simply checking coordinates. A difference of more than 2° between waypoints may be due to a difference of the magnetic variation in the database versus the variation used in the Master CFP. Recheck and verify any difference outside the + 2° or + 2 nm.

Navigation Worksheet

Navigation Worksheet

Date: _____

From: _____

To: _____

Time Off: _____

Time On: _____

Waypoint	Route	FL	Wind	TC / Var	MC / Drift	MH / GS	Fuel Est / Fuel Act	Est T Rem / Act T Rem	Leg Dist / Tot Dist	Leg Time / Tot Time	ETA / ATA	Time Dif

Oceanic Checklist and RVSM/NAV Performance Log

Preflight

- [ ] Label one copy of the computer flight plan "Master Document"
- [ ] Plot route over Class II airspace and any relevant tracks
- [ ] Add ETPs (loss of pressurization, all-engine cruise, loss of engine) if required
- [ ] Position Check: Ramp (GPS) N/S _____ E/W _____

IRS #1	IRS #2	IRS #3	GPS #1	GPS#2
Diff _____	Diff _____	Diff _____	Diff _____	Diff _____

- [ ] Altimeter Check: QNH _____ Pilot's _____ Stby _____ Copilot's _____
- [ ] Time Check: Source (circle) WWV/GPS/ATC +/- 10 sec _____
- [ ] Compare Master Document course/distance with plotting or en route chart, circle waypoint
- [ ] Compare Master Document course/distance with FMS, draw diagonal over waypoint
- [ ] Record fuel onboard on the Master Document

Coast Out

- [ ] Check both HFs, check SELCAL prior to entering oceanic airspace
- [ ] Nav Accuracy Check:

RAW: Fix _____ Radial _____ Distance _____

FMS: Fix _____ Radial _____ Distance _____

- [ ] Altimeter Check: QNH _____ Pilot's _____ Stby _____ Copilot's _____
- [ ] Record oceanic clearances on the Master Document

At Each Waypoint

- [ ] Record ATA, fuel remaining, winds/temperature (if required), next ETA, HF frequencies, three altimeters on Master Document
- [ ] Make the position report, draw a second diagonal over waypoint on Master Document
- [ ] Check distance, time, heading, and fuel remaining to the next waypoint against the Master Document
- [ ] Plot aircraft position approximately 10 minutes after waypoint passage

Coast In

- [ ] Nav Accuracy Check:

RAW: Fix _____ Radial _____ Distance _____

FMS: Fix _____ Radial _____ Distance _____

Post-flight

- [ ] Position Check: Ramp (GPS) N/S _____ E/W _____

IRS #1	IRS #2	IRS #3	GPS #1	GPS#2
Diff _____	Diff _____	Diff _____	Diff _____	Diff _____

- [ ] Altimeter Check: QNH _____ Pilot's _____ Stby _____ Copilot's _____

Oceanic Checklist and RVSM/NAV Performance Log

*Y*ou can make your oceanic checklist as detailed as you wish or fit just the important things on one page. If you are new to this, you should start out with details and start paring down as you become comfortable with the procedures.

If you have datalink, don't forget to include those operations or keep a CPDLC checklist handy too. See Section IV, Chapter 6, CPDLC Checklist.

Over the years I've settled on the oceanic checklist on the facing page.

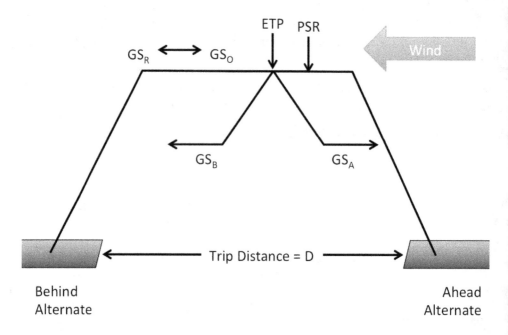

Figure: Equal Time Point and Point of No Return.

Section VIII - Appendices

Chapter 30

Point of Safe Return (PSR)

*T*he Point of Safe Return is seldom discussed because it is rarely critical with modern aircraft designed for oceanic travel. It is, however, applicable even with lots of range and reliability.

You may need a PSR if you think your passengers may, for some reason, need to cancel their plans across the pond and return immediately. Of course this may not be possible because the skies are filled with airplanes behind you who may object. But, in case you need one, here's how to do that.

PSR Explained

The Point of Safe Return (PSR) provides the pilot with the farthest point to which the aircraft can go and be able to return safely to the departure point with adequate holding, approach, landing, and alternate fuel. It is normally used when flying to remote island destinations with no diversion possibilities en route but can be useful even when alternates are available.

Point of Safe Return, The Math

The diagram on the facing page describe both Equal Time Points (ETPs) and the Point of Safe Return (PSR).

- *Unlike the ETP, the Point of Safe Return should be based on your original departure airport, since that is where you are likely to want to go if it becomes an issue.*

- *The terms GS_A, GS_B, and ETP are for the "Equal Time Point." See the Appendices, Chapter 18, Equal Time Points.*

The following formula is used to calculate the ground distance from the departure airport to the Point of Safe Return:

$$\text{Ground distance to PSR} = \frac{(\text{Endurance}) (\text{GS}_R) (\text{GS}_O)}{\text{GS}_O + \text{GS}_R}$$

Where:

Endurance = Total Fuel Quantity / Average Fuel Flow

GS_O = Normal Outbound Ground Speed at Cruise Altitude

GS_R = Return Ground Speed at Normal Cruise Altitude

Example PSR

Figure: Master Document Example, PNR.

The example flight used in Part VII, Tutorial, is from KBED to LSGG on a G450 which has more than ample range. The flight planning service automatically computed a "PNR" which came to 1,161 nm from KBED.

```
                    CRITICAL FUEL SUMMARIES

PNR
LAT/LONG      N51 26.5/W046 36.0             KBED
TIME TO ETP DIVRSN PT          02.11
DIST TO ETP DIVRSN PT          01161
FUEL TO ETP DIVRSN PT/RMNG     008170 /20930
FL/BURN/TIME TO ETP AP         200/20928/04.46
TAS/ETA/DIST TO ETP AP         308/2357/001141
MAG CRS/AVG WIND COMP TO ETP AP    262/M072
ISA TEMP DEV TO ETP AP                 M003
TOTAL FUEL TO ETP AP /RMNG         29098/00001
```

If any of our passengers, for some reason, decide they need to go back to our departure airport (KBED), the last moment you can do this without having to make a fuel stop if you haven't passed the Point of Safe Return. Keep in mind that if you return at this point, you will need to fly direct to the airport, the PSR does not use normal routings that anyone less than an emergency aircraft will be offered.

Chapter 31

Post-Position Plot

A *post-position plot is simply a check made after enough time has elapsed since crossing the waypoint to detect a navigation error, but soon enough to fix things before a loss of separation with other traffic occurs.*

We started doing these after inertial reference systems replaced our navigators, and started wondering about the requirement when we installed our first GPS. Well here we are years later and guys are still getting violated even with hybrid IRUs and six satellites hooked up to two GPS. We still need to do these.

The rules were originally written to say 10 minutes after passing an oceanic waypoint. Many of us decided it was easier and more accurate to pick an even longitude going east or west so we adopted a 2° check. This simply eliminates having to interpolate twice. The Feds adopted this a few years back but failed to note this only works when the course is more or less east or west. If you are flying north or south make sure you get some kind of post position plot around 10 minutes after waypoint passage.

Requirement

[AC 91-70A, Appendix 2, ¶2.j.] Approximately 10 minutes after passing an oceanic waypoint, crews should plot the latitude, longitude and time on the plotting chart. It is advisable to plot the non-steering LRNS. A 10-minute plot can alert the crew to any lateral deviation from their ATC clearance prior to it becoming a GNE. A good crosscheck for the position of the 10-minute plot is that it is approximately 2° of longitude past the oceanic waypoint.

[ICAO NAT Doc 007, ¶8.4.20.] A position check should be made at each waypoint and the present position plotted 10 minutes after passing each waypoint. For a generally east-west flight, this 10 minute point will be approximately 2 degrees of longitude beyond the oceanic waypoint. It may therefore in fact be simpler to plot a present position 2 degrees of longitude after each 10 degree waypoint. There may be circumstances, (e.g. when, due to equipment failure, only one LRNS remains serviceable) in which additional plots midway between each waypoint may be justified.

The "non-steering LRNS" may not apply to many aircraft, since triple FMS with hybrid IRUs tend to blend everything together. The point, however, is to plot the aircraft's position after about ten minutes to ensure the next waypoint wasn't entered in error. If, for example, the flight plan download (or manual entry) entered the next waypoint as 51N 040W, one degree south of the clearance, it would look perfectly normal on the cockpit displays but plotting the position would alert the crew that something is amiss, as shown on the figure.

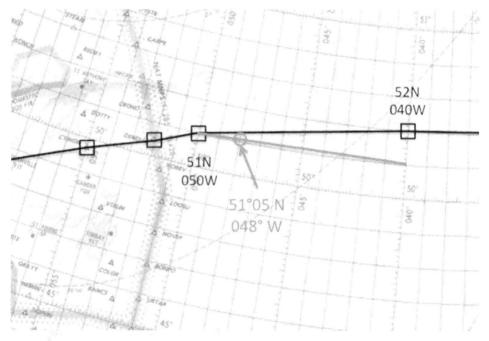

Figure: Two Degree Check Error Example.

Chapter 32

Reroute

*I*t is a common fear of inexperienced oceanic travelers: the FMS is programmed, the charts are plotted, and you are wondering what to do with
yourself for the next three hours. Then the oceanic clearance comes in and it
doesn't look anything like what you had planned; you have been rerouted. You
know a reroute is an invitation to a gross navigational error so you obviously
want to take all of this seriously and if you ever needed to do navigation accuracy checks, the time is now. But how you are you going to do all this without
a computer flight plan?

*I used to wax poetic about how now is the time to get out your plotter and
a sharp pencil and get to work. But these days you are better off picking up
the phone and calling your flight planning service provider. See the "Preferred
Method," below.*

*If you can't do that for some reason, there is still no reason to panic. You can
get this done manually. You really ought to practice this once or twice. What
follows is a walk through on how we used to do this routinely.*

Preferred Method: Fax, E-mail, Phone

The easiest and most accurate method is to pick up the inflight phone and
call your flight planning service and ask them to run the flight plan using the
reroute points. If you have the technology you can have them fax or e-mail
the flight plan. Even if you don't, just have them read you the particulars for
the oceanic legs that matter.

As is true with your original flight plan, you should understand which legs
the numbers apply to and if they are based on initial or midpoint course
lines. Many of the default formats provided by international flight plan services do not arrange each item on a line of the flight plan as you would expect. See Part II, Chapter 3, Initial vs. Midpoint Course.

With this example:

- The data given on a particular line are the numbers needed to fly from the previous line.

- The course line is measured from the midpoint.

- Specifically: Flying between 55°N 050°W and 58°N 040°W will require a true course of 062° as measured at 045°W (the midpoint) and is 378 nautical miles in length.

At this point, if you have the hard copy sent to you and printed, you should plot the new course and you are ready to continue as before. If you can't print it, you really ly should transpose the data to a navigation worksheet, shown below, as a part of your master document. If you don't have the data, you will have to compute it on your own. Read on . . .

```
M83      / FLIGHT LEVEL 450 / ETP APTS: BIKF-EINN
ORIGIN/ETP ALTN   ETP COORDINATE            W/C    DIST     TIME TO
KASH TO ETP        N58 16.6 W015 46.5              2274     04.52
ETP   TO OPT APT EINN                        M008   0408    01.03
TAS / TEMP AT FL 450    400 / ISA M10
FUEL BURN TO    ETP           014428
FUEL REMAINING AT ETP         010072
FUEL BURN FROM ETP TO ALTN 002188
FUEL REMAINING AT ETP ALTN 007884

CPT    FLT OAT WIND  TAS MCS  TCS  ZDST  ZT  FF/E  ZFU   EFR   ETA
FREQ    TP  DEV S    GRS MH   TH   DSTR  CT  LB/NM CFU   AFR   ATA
                                         ETR
------------------------------------------------------------------
MHT    ... ... .....  ... 066M 051T 0008  002 .... 00218 24282 .....
114.40 ... ... 01     ... 064M 048T 2929 00.02 ... 00218 ..... .....
                                         06.24

ENE    ... ... .....  ... 061M 045T 0047  008 .... 00976 23306 .....
117.10 ... ... 01     ... 055M 038T 2882 00.10 ... 01194 ..... .....
                                         06.16

BGR    450 -61 30055 474 058M 041T 0113  018 3029 01832 21474 .....
114.80 383 M05 01     480 053M 035T 2769 00.28 078 03026 ..... .....
                                         05.58

TOPPS  450 -57 30033 475 076M 058T 0057  007 1386 00323 21151 .....
       376 M01 01     487 073M 055T 2712 00.35 171 03349 ..... .....
                                         05.51

STEAM  450 -55 31016 478 063M 042T 0614  078 1362 03506 17645 .....
       353 P02 00     477 061M 040T 2098 01.53 175 06855 ..... .....
                                         04.33

OYSTR  450 -52 16008 481 083M 059T 0100  012 1355 00554 17091 .....
       354 P04 00     482 084M 059T 1998 02.05 177 07409 ..... .....
                                         04.21

55050  450 -52 14010 481 094M 069T 0187  024 1323 01035 16056 .....
       346 P04 00     478 096M 070T 1811 02.29 182 08444 ..... .....
                                         03.57

58040  450 -51 11012 479 087M 062T 0378  047 1294 02048 14008 .....
       345 P03 00     478 088M 063T 1420 03.16 185 10492 ..... .....
                                         03.10

59030  450 -58 19010 474 081M 079T 0320  040 1254 01674 12334 .....
       385 M01 02     480 104M 083T 1120 03.56 189 12166 ..... .....
                                         02.30

59020  450 -63 22023 469 087M 090T 0310  039 1221 01564 10770 .....
       411 M06 02     484 110M 092T 0025 04.35 192 13730 ..... .....
                                         01.51
```

Figure: Example Flight Plan (GV)

Classic ("Back in the Old Days") Method

If you can't get a hard, printed copy of the reroute using the preferred method, above, you will have to write one of your own. You should keep a number of blank navigation worksheets for just this purpose. Copies are available in the Appendices, Chapter 27, Navigation Worksheet. It isn't hard if you are methodical about it.

Step 1: Plot the New Oceanic Points

Plot the new points on your existing chart unless it would be too hard to read, in which case you should get a fresh chart. See Part II, Chapter 5, Plotting.

Figure: Reroute plotted.

Step 2: Enter Known Data

You can guess the winds from your existing flight plan or download them from data link if available. The variation can be read directly from the en route chart. Note that the chart's plotted variation lines are likely to be out of date, your FMS may provide more timely variation data.

Navigation Worksheet

Date: Oct 8, 2007

From: KASH

To: EGGW

Time Off: 1220 Z

Time On:

Waypoint	Route	FL	Wind	TC	MC	MH	Fuel Est	Est T Rem	Leg Dist	Leg Time	ETA	Time Off
				Var	Drift	GS	Fuel Act	Act T Rem	Tot Dist	Tot Time	ATA	
55N 50W	D	450	140/10	+24								
58N 40W	D	450	140/10	+23								
59N 30W	D	450	190/20	+19								
59N 20W	D	450	220/20	+14								
LOMUP	D	450	250/10	+8								

Figure: Navigation Worksheet (known data entered).

Step 3: Determine True Courses

Using 10 Degree Tables

Using True Course 10 Degree tables you can find courses and distances between major latitudes and longitudes. A major latitude is one to a whole degree and a major longitude is one to the nearest 10 degrees. See the Appendices, Chapter 34, True Course 10 Degree Tables.

In the example we see that flying from 55°N 050°W to 58°N 040°W will require a true course of 062° as measured from the midpoint and a distance of 376 nautical miles. (The 050°W and 040°W are not needed in the table, the answer will be the same at any pair of latitudes 55° - 58°N in the world, so long as the longitudes are 10 degrees apart.)

From 55° Latitude

To determine the average true course and distance between two points which are ten degrees apart in longitude:

1. Find the table with the starting latitude (North or South doesn't matter)
2. Find the corresponding latitude in the second column. (If there are two choices, the latitude on top is in the same hemisphere (North or South))
3. Read the true course underneath the desired hemisphere and direction of travel (east or west)
4. Read the distance in the last column

To Latitude	Northern Hemisphere East	Northern Hemisphere West	Southern Hemisphere East	Southern Hemisphere West	Distance (nm)
65	027	333	153	207	669
64	030	330	150	210	618
63	033	327	147	213	570
62	037	323	143	217	523
61	042	318	138	222	479
60	047	313	133	227	440
59	054	306	126	234	405
58	062	298	118	242	376
57	070	290	110	250	356
56	080	280	100	260	345
55	090	270	090	270	344
54	100	260	080	280	353
53	109	251	071	289	372
52	117	243	063	297	399
51	124	236	056	304	433
50	129	231	051	309	472
49	134	226	046	314	515
48	138	222	042	318	561
47	142	218	038	322	610
46	145	215	035	325	660
45	147	213	033	327	712

Figure: 55° True Course 10° Table, from the Appendices, Chapter 34, True Course 10 Degree Tables / 55°.

Using a Chart and Plotter

If you do not have 10-degree tables or if your waypoints are not covered in the tables, you can determine the courses and distances right off the chart.

In our example we measure a course of 062° and a distance of around 375 nautical miles.

In our example we've used a plotter and the en route chart to find our course and distances for each point through GOMUP.

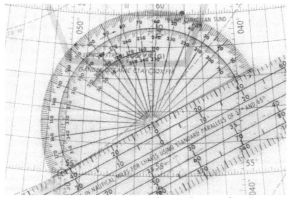

Figure: Reroute en route chart, plotting first leg.

Navigation Worksheet

Date: _Oct 8, 2007_

From: _KTASH_

To: _EGGW_

Time Off: _1220 Z_

Time On: _____

Waypoint	Route	FL	Wind	TC / Var	MC / Drift	MH / GS	Fuel Est / Fuel Act	Est T Rem / Act T Rem	Leg Dist / Tot Dist	Leg Time / Tot Time	ETA / ATA	Time Dif
55N 50W	D	450	140/10	+24								
58N 40W	D	450	140/10	062 +23					376			
59N 30W	D	450	190/20	079 +19					319			
59N 20W	D	450	220/20	090 +14					309			
60 NUP	D	450	250/10	112 +8					335			

Figure: Navigation Worksheet (true courses and distances added).

Step 4: Determine Magnetic Courses

Compute each leg's magnetic course by adding the magnetic variation to the true course. Westerly variation is added, easterly is subtracted.

The navigation worksheet now includes magnetic courses based on the variation we provided. (The plotting chart was a few years out of date and some of the variation figures were off by a few degrees. We need to keep that in mind when checking navigation performance.)

Navigation Worksheet

Date: Oct 8, 2007

From: KASH

To: EGGW

Time Off: 1220 Z

Time On:

Waypoint	Route	FL	Wind	TC / Var	MC / Drift	MH / GS	Fuel Est / Fuel Act	Est T Rem / Act T Rem	Leg Dist / Tot Dist	Leg Time / Tot Time	ETA / ATA	Time Dif
55N 50W	D	450	140/10	+24								
58N 40W	D	450	140/10	062 +23	085				376			
59N 30W	D	450	190/20	079 +19	098				319			
59N 20W	D	450	220/20	090 +14	104				309			
60 MUP	D	450	250/10	112 +8	120				335			

Figure: Navigation Worksheet (mag courses added).

Step 5: Determine Drift, Heading, and Ground Speed

The higher your TAS in relation to your wind speed the less of a factor it will be, in fact the harder it will be to visualize on a wind computer such as the Jeppesen CR-2. For the purpose of demonstrating the method, we will use the highest wind in the example, on the leg to 59°N 020°W: 220/20. The method is similar for each leg.

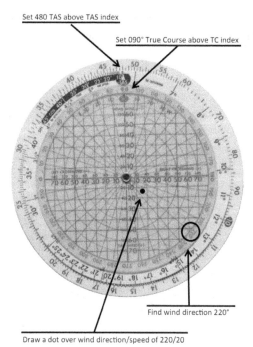

Set 480 TAS above TAS index

Set 090° True Course above TC index

Find wind direction 220°

Draw a dot over wind direction/speed of 220/20

- Set the true airspeed (i.e., 480) under the TAS index.

- Set the true course (i.e., 090°) under the TC index.

- Find the wind direction (i.e., 220°) on the wind slide.

- Draw a dot over the windspeed on the wind direction line. You may have a choice of scales. In our case, we use the largest scale available for ease of legibility.

- Draw a line from the wind dot parallel to the horizontal scale to read the tailwind on the vertical scale (i.e., 12 knots, which means our groundspeed will be 490 + 12 = 492 knots)

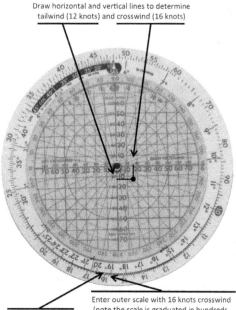

Draw horizontal and vertical lines to determine tailwind (12 knots) and crosswind (16 knots)

- Draw a line from the wind dot parallel to the vertical scale to read the crosswind on the horizontal scale (i.e., 16 knots)

- Find the crosswind, in knots, on the outer scale. Remember that since we entered this outer scale with 480 knots, our 16 knot crosswind is actually 1.6 when read against the 16 number.

- Read the drift angle on the inner scale. (i.e., 1.9°)

- Since true course = 090° and magnetic variation = +14°, magnetic course = 090 + 14 = 104°. Adding drift angle gives us a magnetic heading of 104 + 2 = 106°)

Result is 1.9° from inner scale (divided by ten)

Enter outer scale with 16 knots crosswind (note the scale is graduated in hundreds, since we started with 480 knots so our drift angle will have to be divided by ten)

The navigation worksheet now includes drift and groundspeed. We can then figure magnetic heading by adding the drift to magnetic course.

Navigation Worksheet

Date: _Oct 8, 2007_

From: _KASH_

To: _EGGW_

Time Off: _1220 Z_

Time On: _____

TAS 480

Waypoint	Route	FL	Wind	TC / Var	MC / Drift	MH / GS	Fuel Est / Fuel Act	Est T Rem / Act T Rem	Leg Dist / Tot Dist	Leg Time / Tot Time	ETA / ATA	Time Dif
55N 50W	D	450	140/10	+24								
58N 40W	D	450	140/10	062 +23	085 +1	086 480			376			
59N 30W	D	450	190/20	079 +19	098 +2	100 485			319			
59N 20W	D	450	220/20	090 +14	104 +2	106 490			309			
GOMUP	D	450	250/10	112 +8	120 +3	123 495			335			

Figure: Navigation Worksheet (drfit, heading, ground speed added).

Note: Each step of this process involves the width of your pencil on the wind side of the circular computer and small errors early magnify themselves. This navigation worksheet will get you in the ballpark.

Safety Assessment of Foreign Aircraft (SAFA)

*T*he idea here is to beat the European Aviation Safety Agency (EASA) at their own game and to sail through their ramp checks, known as Safety Assessment of Foreign Aircraft (SAFA), as quickly and painlessly as possible. You can do that if you know what they are looking for and have it ready for them in a binder organized exactly the same as their inspection checklist.

I recommend you keep two binders on the airplane. The first is dedicated to aircraft documentation and will have all the necessary original documents that aren't required to be elsewhere, such as the aircraft registration. The second we'll call the "SAFA Inspection Binder" and will be organized with all 54 items on the inspector's checklist organized precisely the same way. What follows are some background material and a shell of both binders. In italics you will see notes on how to add to your binder for maximum impact. (An impressed inspector is a happy inspector.)

Background

Members

In 1994 members of the European Civil Aviation Conference (ECAC) decided ICAO standards were not being applied by all and that something had to be done about it. In 1996 they adopted the SAFA program which included ramp checks on a voluntary basis until 2006 and mandatory thereafter. These checks would be administered by "safety third country aircraft using community airports," in other words, an N-number aircraft could only be ramp checked outside the U.S. and by inspectors other than the country being visited.

The SAFA Directive, 2004/36/CE, applies to all aircraft involved in "commercial operation" as well as aircraft over 5,700 KGS (12,500 lbs) in "non-commercial" operations — that means you.

You are liable for a SAFA check at any of the following countries:

- EU: Austria, Belgium, Bulgaria, Cyprus, Czech Republic, Denmark, Estonia, Finland, France, Germany, Greece, Hungary, Ireland, Italy, Latvia, Lithuania, Luxembourg, Malta, Netherlands, Poland, Portugal, Romania, Slovak Republic, Slovenia, Spain, Sweden, United Kingdom

- EASA and EU: Iceland, Norway, Switzerland

- Other Participating States: Albania, Armenia, Azerbaijan, Bosnia & Herzegovina, Croatia, FYROM, Georgia, Moldova, Monaco, Serbia & Montenegro, Turkey, Ukraine

The Inspection

[SAFA Ramp Inspections Guidance Material, ¶3.1]

a. The SAFA Ramp Inspection should preferably be performed by at least 2 inspectors. The main elements of the inspection, the visual inspection of the aircraft exterior, the inspection on the flight deck and the inspection of the passenger cabin and/or cargo compartments can be divided among the inspectors.

b. Inspectors are entitled to perform a SAFA inspection and search the aircraft according to Article 16 of the Convention on International Civil Aviation (search of aircraft): "...the appropriate authorities of each of the contracting States shall have the right...to search aircraft of other contracting States...".

c. Should an operator refuse to permit the performance of a SAFA inspection without a valid reason, the competent authority should consider the detention of the aircraft (provided that the national legislative framework allows for this). In such a case, the competent authority must immediately inform the State of oversight.

d. Departure delay of an aircraft should be avoided. However, when an inspector discovers an issue which may have a major effect on flight safety or requires further investigation to be clarified, a delay may be justified, for example:

　　1. the tyres appear to be worn beyond the limits (central groove no longer visible), however reference must be made to the applicable AMM to determine the actual limit;

　　2. an oil leakage (e.g. 5 drops/minute) must be checked against

the applicable AMM to determine the actual limit;

3.   a flight crew member cannot produce his/her licence. Clarification must be sought from the operator to confirm that the flight crew member has a valid licence by requesting, for instance, a copy of the licence to be sent to the inspectors for verification.

[SAFA Ramp Inspections Guidance Material, ¶3.3] Depending on the items to be inspected, a SAFA Ramp Inspection may be performed on landing or on departure of the aircraft. Fuel remaining and cargo area (overloading, restraining, segregation, etc.), are examples of items that could be checked on landing. Flight preparation and storage of baggage in the cabin could be checked on departure. However, inspectors should be aware of the following constraints; an inspection after landing should not jeopardise the total resting time of the flight crew and an inspection prior to departure should not lead to a departure delay unless there is a good reason.

Preparation

There are various one-page "SAFA Inspection Checklist" cheat sheets out there that don't really help you. What you really want is a peek at what the inspector is using. It is called the "EASA Approvals & Standardization Directorate SAFA Ramp Inspections Guidance material." You can often find it by typing the title into an Internet Search Engine but its location tends to jump around. Section D, below, duplicates all 54 items.

Post-Inspection Actions

The ramp inspector can pat you on the back or cite you as in violation of an ICAO standard with minor, significant, or major action:

Class 1

[SAFA Ramp Inspections Guidance Material, ¶6.1.1] Class 1 action: information to the captain. A class 1 action is to be taken after each inspection, and consists of providing information about the results of that SAFA inspection, regardless of whether findings have been identified or not. In accordance with article 6.3 of the before mentioned Annex, this is achieved by a verbal debriefing and the delivery of the Proof of Inspection (POI) to the aircraft commander (or, in his/her absence, to another member of the flight crew or the most senior representative of the operator).

The inspection ends with the inspector telling you what he thinks.

Class 2

[SAFA Ramp Inspections Guidance Material, ¶6.1.2] Class 2 action: Information to the authority and the operator. Category 2 and 3 findings are considered to have a significant and major influence on safety. Therefore, when category 2 and/or 3 findings have been raised, written communications must be made in accordance – with Article 6.4 of the above mentioned Annex – to both:

- The operator: The communication should request that corrective actions are taken (or alternatively the provision of a corrective action plan) and evidence supporting the corrective actions taken; in case of no focal point is known for the inspected operator, its Quality department might be the most suitable point of contact.

- The state of oversight: The communication shall contain, where appropriate, a request for confirmation that they are satisfied with the corrective actions taken by the operator.

The inspector tells you to fix something and sends a letter to your base and the FAA.

Class 3

[SAFA Ramp Inspections Guidance Material, ¶6.1.3]

A class 3 action follows a category 3 finding which are considered to have a potential major effect on the safe operation of the aircraft. For that reason, Article 6.5 of the said Annex requires that action(s) need to be taken before the departure of the aircraft. On the ramp inspection report only the actions required/imposed by the inspector should be mentioned.

If the operator voluntary corrected a cat. 1 or 2 finding before the flight, this should not be reported as a class 3b action. Instead, such voluntary action should be mentioned in the "Additional information box".

If the category 3 (major) findings that have been established during the SAFA Ramp Check concern damage of a nature such that the aircraft is no longer airworthy, this has to be communicated immediately to the State responsible for overseeing the airworthiness of the aircraft. Although the first contact may be, as a matter of urgency, accomplished by telephone, it is advisable to use written communication procedures. For ICAO guidance on this matter, refer to ICAO Annex 8 Part II Chapter 3.5 – Temporary Loss of Airworthiness.

The class 3 action is divided into 4 sub-actions:

- Class 3a. Restriction on the aircraft flight operation. The inspector(s) performing the ramp inspection have concluded that, as a result of some deficiencies identified during the inspection, the aircraft may depart only under certain restrictions.

- Class 3b. Corrective actions before flight. The ramp inspector(s) have identified some deficiencies that require corrective action(s) before the intended flight.

- Class 3c. Aircraft detained by inspecting National Aviation Authority. An aircraft is grounded in a situation where the category 3 (major) findings are not corrected by the operator before flight. Because the safety of the aircraft and its occupants is at stake, the aircraft has to be prevented from resuming its flight and has to be 'grounded' until the safety hazard is removed. This class of action should be imposed only if the crew refused to take the necessary corrective actions or to respect the restrictions on the aircraft flight operation. A class 3c action would also be appropriate when an operator refuses to permit the performance of a SAFA inspection without a valid reason (see paragraph 3.1 c), provided that the Inspecting NAA has set forth provisions in its national regulation covering this case.

- Class 3d. Immediate operating ban. In case of an immediate and obvious safety hazard a competent authority may react by imposing an operating ban on an operator or an aircraft.

Aircraft Documentation Binder

We keep an aircraft documents binder as a handy place to keep things we know we will be needing for various purposes, including the SAFA inspection. But this is not the SAFA Inspection Binder, which follows in the next section.

Here are the contents of our aircraft documents binder. Of course yours may differ depending on what region of the world you frequent, the number of pilots, and so forth.

Aircraft Documentation — N_____

Original copies in this book, unless otherwise noted.

- Aircraft Australian Security Program Letter
- Aircraft Certificate of Airworthiness (Copy; original in placard behind pilot's seat)
- Aircraft Certificates of Insurance
- Aircraft FAA Letters of Authorization
- Aircraft Lease Agreement
- Aircraft "No Single Failure" Exemption
- Aircraft Noise Certificates
- Aircraft Radio License
- Aircraft Registration (Copy; original in placard behind pilot's seat)
- Aircraft RVSM Monitoring Proof
- Aircraft Safety Management System Certificates
- Aircraft US Customs Decal (Copy; original on aircraft)
- Aircraft US Customs Overflight Exemption Letter
- Aircraft US Customs Visa Waiver Program Letter
- Pilot _____ Documents
  - ◊ Licenses (Copy)
  - ◊ Medical Certificates (Copy)
  - ◊ Passport (Copy)
  - ◊ Radio Operator Permit (Copy)
  - ◊ Training Certificates (Copy)
- Pilot _____ Documents
  - ◊ Licenses (Copy)
  - ◊ Medical Certificates (Copy)
  - ◊ Passport (Copy)
  - ◊ Radio Operator Permit (Copy)
  - ◊ Training Certificates (Copy)

SAFA Inspection Binder

The SAFA binder has 54 tabs, each marked with the label from the EASA SAFA Inspection Guidance. In each tab is chapter and verse of what they are looking for. In some cases, the actual document is in the binder. In other cases, the tab points to where the inspector can find the item. Do you have to go through all this trouble? No, but it will make your life easier the day an inspector shows up on the ramp. It works well for an FAA inspector too.

The language in the SAFA binder comes straight out of the EASA SAFA Guidance, to make it easier for the inspector. The references are given in the same code they use, which uses:

- *"A" to denote an ICAO Annex, such as [A6-I-4.3.1] to mean Annex 6, Part I, Chapter 4.3.1*

- *"CC" to mean an article of the Chicago Convention, such as [CC29] to mean Article 29 of the Chicago Convention*

- *"EUR" to mean the ICAO Doc 7030, such as [EUR 2.1.6.2] to mean ICAO Doc 7030, chapter 2.1.6.2*

In some cases there is no reference given; it appears the inspector has wide latitude. As with many things when it involves an aviation inspector, there is much to be lost and little to be gained.

A note about the pages that follow.

The following pages are meant to provide a template for your own SAFA Inspection Binder. The items that appear in normal text come straight from the EASA Guidance. Many of these items are followed by comments in italics explaining how we satisfied the requirements. Quite often we offer a brief explanation and say "see photo which follows" or "see manual extract which follows." In our actual SAFA Inspection Binder we will include the photos and manual extracts. For the purpose of this Appendix, those have been deleted.

SAFA Inspection Preparation Checklist — N_____

Operator: _____

The following checklist was prepared to follow the 2012 European Aviation Safety Agency Approvals & Standardisation Directorate SAFA Coordination Section "SAFA Ramp Inspections Guidance material Version 2.0" Each tab contains answers to the indicated SAFA Inspection Checklist inspection item in the form of: (1) The actual requested document, (2) Location of a requested document, (3) A photo, diagram, or description answering the inspection item, or (4) A narrative answer to the inspection item.

SAFA Ramp Inspection Procedures

Guidance material

Insp. Item	Insp. Item Description
A	**Flight Deck**
A01	General Condition
A02	Emergency Exit
A03	Equipment
A04	Manuals
A05	Checklists
A06	Radio Navigation Charts
A07	Minimum Equipment List
A08	Certificate of Registration
A09	Noise certificate
A10	AOC or equivalent
A11	Radio license
A12	Certificate of Airworthiness
A13	Flight Preparation
A14	Weight and balance sheet
A15	Hand fire extinguishers
A16	Life jackets/flotation device
A17	Harness
A18	Oxygen equipment
A19	Flash light
A20	Flight crew license
A21	Journey log book
A22	Maintenance release
A23	Defect notification and rectification
A24	Preflight inspection

B	**Safety/Cabin**
B01	General Internal Condition
B02	Cabin Attendant's Station/Crew Rest Area
B03	First Aid Kit/Emergency Medical Kit
B04	Hand fire extinguishers
B05	Life jackets/Flotation devices
B06	Seat belt and seat condition
B07	Emergency exit, lightning and marking, Torches
B08	Slides/Life Rafts, ELT
B09	Oxygen Supply
B10	Safety instructions
B11	Cabin crew members
B12	Access to emergency exits
B13	Safety of passenger baggage
B14	Seat capacity
C	**Aircraft Condition**
C01	General External Condition
C02	Doors and Hatches
C03	Flight Controls
C04	Wheels, tyres and brakes
C05	Undercarriage, skids/floats
C06	Wheel well
C07	Powerplant and Pylon
C08	Fan blades
C09	Propellers, rotors (main/tail)
C10	Obvious repairs
C11	Obvious unrepaired damage
C12	Leakage
D	**Cargo**
D01	General Condition of Cargo Compartment
D02	Dangerous Goods
D03	Safety of Cargo on Board
E	**General**
E01	General

The flight crew is eager to cooperate with the EASA SAFA inspection team and demonstrate full compliance with ICAO standards. If you cannot find what you are looking for, please ask! Thank you.

SAFA Inspection Preparation — Flight Deck (A01)

Tab A01 General Condition

1. Stowage of interior equipment, suitcases, navigation chart cases, etc.

    We do not require navigation chart cases because most of our charts are electronic. The few charts and manuals that we do keep are secured in provided holders, bins, and cabinets. (See photos which follow)

2. Means to monitor the door area from either pilot seat. [A6-I-13.2.3]

    (See photos which follow)

3. Condition of flight deck windows.

    (See photos which follow)

4. The number and composition of the flight crew shall not be less than that specified in the operations manual. [A6-I-9.1.1]

    G450 AFM 1-01-10 specifies a pilot and copilot is the minimum crew. (Extract follows)

5. An operator shall formulate rules to limit flight time and flight duty periods. A6-I-2.2.10.2.

    Our Company Operations Manual specifies these limits. (Extract follows)

SAFA Inspection Preparation — Flight Deck (A02)

Tab A02 Emergency Exit

1. Check whether access to emergency exits is restricted or impeded. [A8-IIIA-4.1.7.3]

    (See photos which follow)

2. Prescribed safety and survival equipment that the crew or passengers are expected to use or operate at the time of an emergency shall be reliable, readily accessible and easily identified, and its method of operation shall be plainly marked. [A8-IIIA-8.3]

    (See photos which follow)

3. Facilities shall be provided for the rapid evacuation of the aeroplane in conditions likely to occur following an emergency landing. Such

facilities shall be related to the passenger and crew capacity of the aeroplane and shall be shown to be suitable for their intended purpose. [A8-IIIB-4.6.2]

Four emergency escape exits, and alternate routes are shown in the Aircraft Flight Manual 4-19-30. (See extract which follow)

SAFA Inspection Preparation — Flight Deck (A03)

Tab A03 Equipment

1. TAWS (E-GPWS): Check if installed and serviceable. If unserviceable check if properly deferred and check if still within MEL dispatch limits. Verify that the installed GPWS has a forward looking terrain avoidance function. If the terrain database is found to be expired, verify against the MEL the dispatch conditions. When an operational test can be performed by the pilot, it should be requested. [A6-I-6.15.8]

    The test procedure is in the Gulfstream G450 Aircraft Operating Manual, §2B-20-140 §3. (See test procedure, which follows)

2. ACAS II (TCAS): Check if installed and serviceable. If unserviceable check if properly deferred (reported in the ATLB) and check if still within MEL dispatch limits. When an operational test can be performed by the pilot, it should be requested. [A6-I-6.18.2] (See test procedure, which follows)

    The test procedure is in the Gulfstream G450 Aircraft Operating Manual, §2A-34-60 §3.C. (See test procedure, which follows)

3. RVSM. [A6-I-7.2.1] (LOA in Aircraft Documents Book, Tab 7)

4. B-RNAV. [A6-I-7.2.1] (LOA in Aircraft Documents Book, Tab 7)

5. P-RNAV. [A6-I-7.2.1] (LOA in Aircraft Documents Book, Tab 7)

6. MNPS. [A6-I-7.2.1] (LOA in Aircraft Documents Book, Tab 7)

7. 8.33 kHz Spacing. [EUR 3.2.1]

    Three VHF radios with 8.33 kHz spacing are installed. (See operating manual extract which follows)

8. A CVR capable of retaining the information recorded during at least the last two hours of its operation. [A6-I-6.3.2.1.4]

A description of the CVR can be found in the Gulfstream G450 Aircraft Operating Manual, §2B-23-60. (See extract which follows)

SAFA Inspection Preparation — Flight Deck (A04)

Tab A04 Manuals

1.   Check for presence of Aircraft Flight Manual. [A6-I-6.2.3ab]

   The AFM is in the manuals closet, aircraft right, just forward of the interior cabin door. (See photo at Tab A01 in this binder)

2.   Check for presence of Operations Manual. [A6-I-6.2.3ab]

   Electronically held in aircraft EFB. (See photo which follows)

3.   An operator shall formulate rules to limit flight time and flight duty periods and for the provision of adequate rest periods for all its crew members. [A6-I-2.2.10.2]

   (Our Company Operations Manual specifies these limits, extract follows.)

4.   An operator shall provide, for the use and guidance of operations personnel concerned, an operations manual in accordance with Appendix 2. [A6-I-4.2.3.1]

   Electronically held in aircraft EFB. (See photo which follows)

5.   The operator shall provide such information in the Operations Manual as will enable the flight crew to carry out its responsibilities with regard to the transport of dangerous goods and shall provide instructions as to the action to be taken in the event of emergencies arising involving dangerous goods. [A18-9.2]

   Electronically held in aircraft EFB. (See photo which follows)

SAFA Inspection Preparation — Flight Deck (A05)

Tab A05 Checklists

1.   Check if checklists are available and easily accessible. [A6-I-4.2.6]

   Checklists available electronically in aircraft avionics, electronically on 'EFB, and in a Quick Reaction Handbook in cockpit. (See photo of EFB contents at Tab A04)

2.   Check if the OPS Manual contains the required checklists. Compare the version in OPS Manual with the ones available to the crew. Check if their content is in compliance with the operating manual covering all flight phases, in normal and emergency operations. [A6-I-4.2.6]

The operations manual is held electronically in the EFB and issued by Gulfstream, as are all other checklists on the aircraft. (See photo of EFB contents at Tab A04)

3.   Check if the checklists are identical for all members of the flight crew. [A6-I-4.2.6]

There is only one copy of each checklist type in the cockpit.

SAFA Inspection Preparation — Flight Deck (A06)

Tab A06 Radio Navigation Charts

1.   Check if the required departure, en-route, approach and aerodrome charts are available, within reach, up-to-date to the latest AIRAC amendments, including those for the alternate aerodromes. [A6-I-6.2.3c]

All departure, en route, approach, and aerodrome charts are held electronically in the aircraft avionics suite. The revision dates can be found on a display unit accessing the CMC function. (See photo which follows)

2.   Check the validity of the FMS/GPS database; in case of expiration, check the MEL. [A6-I-7.4.2]

FMS/GPS database revision dates can be found on a display unit accessing the CMC function as well as any MCDU. (See photo which follows)

3.   An aeroplane shall carry: current and suitable charts to cover the route of the proposed flight and any route along which it is reasonable to expect that the flight may be diverted. [A6-I-6.2.3c]

Route charts are held electronically in the aircraft avionics suite as well as paper route charts held in binders in the aircraft publication cabinet just aft of the cockpit throttle quadrant and in the publications cabinet on the aircraft right just forward of the interior cabin door. (See photo at Tab A01 of this binder)

SAFA Inspection Preparation — Flight Deck (A07)

Tab A07 Minimum Equipment List

1.	Check if the MEL is available. [A6-I-6.1.3]

	MEL is held electronically in EFB. (See photo of EFB at Tab 04)

2.	Check if the MEL is not less restrictive than MMEL. [A6-I-6.1.3]

	MEL was written by and with approval of aircraft manufacturer and found to be compliant.

SAFA Inspection Preparation — Flight Deck (A08)

Tab A08 Certificate of Registration

1.	Check Certificate of Registration Check for presence and accuracy. In the case where only a photocopy is on board a finding should be made against "No valid CofR or cannot be shown by crew". Check if its format and content are in accordance with the requirements and whether translated into the English language. [A7-7.1]

	Original in holder behind pilot's seat, copies in Documents Binder Tab 12. (Copy follows in this tab)

2.	Check for fireproof identification plate (usually near the left forward door). Compare the data on the plate with that on the C of R. Note: Annex 7 requires that a fireproof plate needs to be installed near the main entrance. It is often found that the plate is located somewhere else on the aircraft. Although it is not compliant to the requirements, the safety relevance is rather low and therefore no finding should be raised. [A7-8]

	(See photo which follows)

SAFA Inspection Preparation — Flight Deck (A09)

Tab A09 Noise certificate

1.	Noise Certificate: Check for presence, accuracy (e.g. cross check MTOM, S/N with the ones specified in the C of R) of the document attesting noise certification and whether translated in English language. [A16-I-II-1.4]

The original noise certificates are in Aircraft Documents Binder Tab 10. (Copies follow in this tab)

SAFA Inspection Preparation — Flight Deck (A10)

Tab A10 AOC or equivalent

1. An operator shall not engage in commercial air transport operations unless in possession of a valid air operator certificate issued by the State of the Operator. [A6-I-4.2.1.5/ A6-I-4.2.1.6/ A6-I-4.2.1.7]

    NOT APPLICABLE: We are not a commercial operator

2. Commercial air transport operators shall carry a certified true copy of the air operator certificate specified and a copy of the operations specifications relevant to the aeroplane type, issued in conjunction with the certificate. [A6-I-4.2.1.6]

    NOT APPLICABLE: We are not a commercial operator

SAFA Inspection Preparation — Flight Deck (A11)

Tab A11 Radio license

1. Radio License: Check for presence and accuracy. Check for the correct name/call sign. Note: Following the Articles 29e and 30 of the Chicago Convention, a radio license is a license to install radio transmitting apparatus. ICAO does not specify the information to be mentioned on the Radio License. The requirement to have a radio license is originating from Article 18 of the Radio Regulations from the International Telecommunications Union, which requires the issuing State to include, besides the name/call sign, "the general characteristics of the installation" into the license. However, the exact content of such a license is only given by the ITU as a recommendation only (Recommendation 7 Rev. WRC-97). Therefore no finding should be raised on the content of the radio license, unless the mentioned information is incorrect. [CC-29e]

    Original is the Aircraft Documents Binder Tab 11. (Copy follows in this tab)

SAFA Inspection Preparation — Flight Deck (A12)

Tab A12 Certificate of Airworthiness

1.   Certificate of Airworthiness: Check for presence, accuracy and validity. [A8-II-3.3.1]

Original in document holder behind pilot's seat, copies are in the Aircraft Documents Binder Tab 2. (Copy follows in this tab)

SAFA Inspection Preparation — Flight Deck (A13)

Tab A13 Flight Preparation

1.   An operational flight plan shall be completed for every intended flight. The operational flight plan shall be approved and signed by the pilot-in-command and, where applicable, signed by the flight operations officer/flight dispatcher, and a copy shall be filed with the operator or a designated agent, or, if these procedures are not possible, it shall be left with the aerodrome authority or on record in a suitable place at the point of departure. [A6-I-4.3.3.1]

Our international flight plans are signed electronically with and held by Rockwell Collins (Air Routing), +1-713-430-7200.

2.   Check for proper filing system (retaining of all relevant flight preparation documents).

Flight plans are retained for 6 months at the base of operations.

3.   Check for proper performance and fuel calculation.

The aircraft performance computer makes all necessary calculations.

4.   Check the fuel consumption monitoring of the incoming flight (if required by the OPS manual).

Fuel consumption is monitored and recorded on the master document.

5.   Check if the operator has selected appropriate alternate aerodromes (if required).

Alternate aerodromes are declared on the flight plan.

6.   Check if the crew ensured that the weather forecast at the destination or the destination alternate aerodrome is above minima.

Crews do check destination and alternate weather prior to departure.

7.   Check whether the flight crew has reviewed the applicable NOTAMS and/or pre-flight information bulletins (including those for alternate aerodromes).

Flight planning services do include NOTAMS.

8.   Check for the presence and accuracy of the ATC flight plan, including proper equipment codes.

Flight plans are checked for accuracy by Rockwell-Collins (Air Routing) and equipment codes are in accordance with aircraft equipment and qualification. (Equipment code listing follows.)

SAFA Inspection Preparation — Flight Deck (A14)

Tab A14 Weight and balance sheet

1.   A flight shall not be commenced until flight preparation forms have been completed certifying that the pilot-in-command is satisfied that: the mass of the aeroplane and centre of gravity location are such that the flight can be conducted safely, taking into account the flight conditions expected; and that any load carried is properly distributed and safely secured. [A6-I-4.3.1(d)(e)]

Company procedures require the pilot-in-command sign the Flight and Maintenance Log prior to the flight once all preflight inspections have been satisfactorily completed and a maintenance release has been issued. Crews complete a weight and balance calculation prior to every flight and record the aircraft's actual weight, maximum allowable weight, center of gravity, and center of gravity limits. The calculations are made on the EFB with a program specific to that purpose and are recorded on the aircraft flight and maintenance log. (Example follows)

2.   The mass of the aeroplane at the start of takeoff shall not exceed the maximum takeoff mass specified in the flight manual for the pressure-altitude appropriate to the elevation of the aerodrome, and, if used as a parameter to determine the maximum takeoff mass, any other local atmospheric condition. [A6-I-5.2.7]

The maximum takeoff weight is computed in accordance with the Gulfstream G450 Airplane Flight Manual, §Section 5. (Available in aircraft manuals cabinet, aircraft right just forward of the cabin door.)

The aircraft performance computer ensures these maximums are not exceeded.

3.   The mass of the aeroplane for the expected time of landing at the aerodrome of intended landing and at any destination alternate aerodrome shall not exceed the maximum landing mass specified in the flight manual for the pressure altitude appropriate to the elevation of those aerodromes, and if used as a parameter to determine the maximum landing mass, any other local atmospheric condition. [A6-I-5.2.7]

The maximum landing weight is computed in accordance with the Gulfstream G450 Airplane Flight Manual, §Section 5. (Available in aircraft manuals cabinet, aircraft right just forward of the cabin door.) The aircraft performance computer ensures these maximums are not exceeded.

4.   In no case shall the mass at the start of takeoff, or at the expected time of landing at the aerodrome of intended landing and at any destination alternate aerodrome, exceed the relevant maximum masses at which compliance has been demonstrated with the applicable noise certification Standards in Annex 16, Volume I, unless otherwise authorized in exceptional circumstances for a certain aerodrome or a runway where there is no noise disturbance problem, by the competent authority of the State in which the aerodrome is situated. [A6-I-5.2.7]

Crews check departure, destination, and alternate aerodromes against the Gulfstream Noise Information Manual (available in the EFB) for proper noise abatement procedures.

SAFA Inspection Preparation — Flight Deck (A15)

Tab A15 Hand fire extinguishers

1.   An aeroplane shall be equipped with: portable fire extinguishers of a type which, when discharged, will not cause dangerous contamination of the air within the aeroplane. At least one shall be located in: the pilot's compartment; and each passenger compartment that is separate from the pilot's compartment and that is not readily accessible to the flight crew; Note.- Any portable fire extinguisher so fitted

in accordance with the certificate of airworthiness of the aeroplane may count as one prescribed. [A6-I-6.2.2b]

Fire extinguishers are positioned exactly as installed under the original certificate of airworthiness (See location chart which follows)

SAFA Inspection Preparation — Flight Deck (A16)

Tab A16 Life jackets/flotation device

1. When flying over water and at a distance of more than 93 km (50 nm) away from the shore, land planes shall carry life jackets/flotation devices for each person on board, stowed in a position easily accessible from the seat or berth of the person for whose use it is provided. [A6-I-6.5.2.1]

    Life jackets are positioned exactly as installed under the original certificate of airworthiness (See location chart which follows)

SAFA Inspection Preparation — Flight Deck (A17)

Tab A17 Harness

1. An aeroplane shall be equipped with: A safety harness for each flight crew seat. The safety harness for each pilot seat shall incorporate a device, which will automatically restrain the occupant's torso in the event of rapid deceleration. [A6-I-6.2.2.c3]

    Each pilot seat has an appropriate harness exactly as installed under the original certificate of airworthiness. (Drawing follows)

SAFA Inspection Preparation — Flight Deck (A18)

Tab A18 Oxygen equipment

1. All flight crew members of pressurized aeroplanes operating above an altitude where the atmospheric pressure is less than 376 hPa (25,000 feet) shall have available at the flight duty station a quick donning type of oxygen mask which will readily supply oxygen upon demand. [A6-I-4.4.5.2]

    The cockpit has three quick donning oxygen masks exactly as installed under the original certificate of airworthiness. (see illustration which follows)

2. Prescribed safety and survival equipment that the crew or passengers are expected to use or operate at the time of an emergency shall be reliable, readily accessible and easily identified, and its method of operation shall be plainly marked. [A8-IIIA-8.3, A8-IIIB-6.3, A8-V-6.3]

Oxygen masks are readily available, exactly as installed under the original certificate of airworthiness. (See operating manual extract which follows)

3. A flight to be operated at flight altitudes at which the atmospheric pressure in personnel compartments will be less than 700 hPa (10,000 feet) shall not be commenced unless sufficient stored breathing oxygen is carried to supply: a) all crew members and 10 per cent of the passengers for any period in excess of 30 minutes that the pressure in compartments occupied by them will be between 700 hPa (10,000 feet) and 620 hPa (13,000 feet); and b) the crew and passengers for any period that the atmospheric pressure in compartments occupied by them will be less than 620 hPa. [A6-I-4.3.8.1]

Crews normally plan to be able to continue any flight no higher than 10,000 in the event of a pressurization loss and ensure oxygen quantity is sufficient using the chart available in G450-OMS-01, Table III. (See extract, which follows)

SAFA Inspection Preparation — Flight Deck (A19)

Tab A19 Flash light

1. Check that appropriate electric torches are readily available at all crew member stations. Check their condition, serviceability and access. [EASA SAFA Inspector's Guide]

Each pilot seat has an electric flashlight readily available, exactly as installed under the original certificate of airworthiness.. (See photo which follows)

2. All aeroplanes, when operated at night shall be equipped with an electric torch for each crew member station. [A6-I-6.10f]

Each pilot seat has an electric flashlight readily available, exactly as installed under the original certificate of airworthiness. (See photo which follows)

SAFA Inspection Preparation — Flight Deck (A20)

Tab A20 Flight crew license

1. A person shall not act as a flight crew member of an aircraft unless a valid licence is held showing compliance with the specifications of this Annex and appropriate to the duties to be performed by that person. The licence shall have been issued by the State of Registry of that aircraft or by any other Contracting State and rendered valid by the State of Registry of that aircraft. Note.— Article 29 of the Convention on International Civil Aviation requires that the flight crew members carry their appropriate licences on board every aircraft engaged in international air navigation. [A1-1.2.1]

   Each flight crewmember holds the appropriate license on their possession and copies are kept in the Aircraft Documents Binder at Tabs 19 forward, Sub tab A.

2. The flight crew shall include at least one member who holds a valid licence, issued or rendered valid by the State of Registry, authorizing operation of the type of radio transmitting equipment to be used. [A6-I-9.1.2]

   Each flight crewmember holds the appropriate radio operator permit on their possession and copies are kept in the Aircraft Documents Binder at Tabs 19 forward, Sub tab D.

3. A Contracting State, having issued pilot licences, shall not permit the holders thereof to act as pilot-in command of an aircraft engaged in international commercial air transport operations if the licence holders have attained their 60th birthday or, in the case of operations with more than one pilot where the other pilot is younger than 60 years of age, their 65th birthday. [A1-2.1.10.1]

   Our operations require either (a) both pilots be younger than 60 years of age, or (b) one pilot to be younger than 60 if the other pilot is between 60 and 65.

4.   Pilots require a Medical Assessment valid from the date of the medical examination for a period not greater than: 60 months for the private pilot licence, 12 months for the commercial pilot licence, 12 months for the multi-crew pilot licence, 12 months for the airline transport pilot licence; except when the holders of airline transport pilot licences have passed their 40th birthday, the period of validity shall be reduced to six months. [A1-1.2.5.2 Except as provided in 1.2.5.2.1, 1.2.5.2.2, 1.2.5.2.3, 1.2.5.2.4, 1.2.5.2.5 and 1.2.5.2.6]

Each flight crewmember holds the appropriate medical certificate on their possession and copies are kept in the Aircraft Documents Binder at Tabs 19 forward, Sub tab B.

5.   Check for spare correcting spectacles (in case a flight crew member is required to wear corrective lenses).

Crews requiring corrective lenses carry spares.

6.   Check for endorsement of English language proficiency (ELP) in the license.

All pilot's licenses have the ELP.

SAFA Inspection Preparation — Flight Deck (A21)

Tab A21 Journey log book

1.   The pilot-in-command shall be responsible for the journey log book or the general declaration containing the information listed in 11.4.1. [A6-I-4.5.5]

[ICAO Annex 6, Part 1 §11.4]

11.4.1 The aeroplane journey log book should contain the following items and the corresponding roman numerals: I —Aeroplane nationality and registration. II — Date. III — Names of crew members. IV — Duty assignments of crew members. V —Place of departure. VI — Place of arrival. VII — Time of departure. VIII — Time of arrival. IX — Hours of flight. X —Nature of flight (private, aerial work, scheduled or non-scheduled). XI — Incidents, observations, if any. XII — Signature of person in charge.

11.4.2. Recommendation.— Entries in the journey log book should be made currently and in ink or indelible pencil.

11.4.3 Recommendation.— Completed journey log book should be retained to provide a continuous record of the last six months' operations.

All the required information is contained on our "Flight and Maintenance" logs, of which at least the previous six months worth are retained in the aircraft maintenance log.

2.   Every aircraft of a contracting State, engaged in international navigation, shall carry the following documents in conformity with the conditions prescribed in this Convention. d) Its journey log book; [CC-29d]

All the required information is contained on our "Flight and Maintenance" logs, of which at least the previous six months worth are retained in the aircraft maintenance log.

SAFA Inspection Preparation — Flight Deck (A22)

Tab A22 Maintenance release

1.   A flight shall not be commenced until flight preparation forms have been completed certifying that the pilot-in-command is satisfied that: a) the aeroplane is airworthy; c) a maintenance release as prescribed in 8.8 has been issued in respect of the aeroplane; [A6-I-4.3.1(a)(c)] (Section 8.8 requires "a) basic details of the maintenance carried out including detailed reference of the approved data used; b) the date such maintenance was completed; c) when applicable, the identity of the approved maintenance organization; and d) the identity of the person or persons signing the release."

A maintenance release is always obtained after maintenance or at intervals no longer than 20 flight days or 50 flight hours. The maintenance release is contained on a Flight and Maintenance Log, kept in the aircraft Maintenance Logbook. Company procedures require the pilot-in-command sign the Flight and Maintenance Log prior to the flight once all preflight inspections have been satisfactorily completed and a maintenance release has been issued.

SAFA Inspection Preparation — Flight Deck (A23)

Tab A23 Defect notification and rectification

1. The pilot-in-command shall be responsible for reporting all known or suspected defects in the aeroplane, to the operator, at the termination of the flight. [A6-I-4.5.4]

    The pilot-in-command completes a flight and maintenance log at the completion of each flight, to include reporting all known or suspected defects. (Original kept in aircraft maintenance logbook.) The company Director of Maintenance is notified as soon as practical at the completion of each duty day.

2. An operator shall ensure that the following records are kept for the periods mentioned in 8.4.2: a) the total time in service (hours, calendar time and cycles, as appropriate) of the aeroplane and all life-limited components; b) the current status of compliance with all mandatory continuing airworthiness information; c) appropriate details of modifications and repairs; d) the time in service (hours, calendar time and cycles, as appropriate) since the last overhaul of the aeroplane or its components subject to a mandatory overhaul life; compliance with the maintenance programme; and f) the detailed maintenance records to show that all requirements for the signing of a maintenance release have been met. 8.4.2 The records in 8.4.1 a) to e) shall be kept for a minimum period of 90 days after the unit to which they refer has been permanently withdrawn from service, and the records in 8.4.1 f) for a minimum period of one year after the signing of the maintenance release. 8.4.3 In the event of a temporary change of operator, the records shall be made available. [A6-I-8.4 8.4.1]

    The required maintenance records are kept on file for at least 90 days at the aircraft's base of operations. Additionally, a summary of inspections completed and due is kept in the aircraft maintenance logbook.

3. The operator shall include in the operations manual a minimum equipment list (MEL), approved by the State of the Operator which will enable the pilot-in-command to determine whether a flight may be commenced or continued from any intermediate stop should any instrument, equipment or systems become inoperative. Where the State of the Operator is not the State of Registry, the State of the

Operator shall ensure that the MEL does not affect the aeroplane's compliance with the Airworthiness requirements applicable in the State of Registry. [A6-I-6.1.3]

The aircraft MEL is kept on the aircraft EFB.

SAFA Inspection Preparation — Flight Deck (A24)

Tab A24 Preflight inspection

1. A flight shall not be commenced until flight preparation forms have been completed certifying that the pilot-in-command is satisfied that: a) the aeroplane is airworthy; c) a maintenance release as prescribed in 8.8 has been issued in respect of the aeroplane; [A6-I-4.3.1(a)(c)]

    Company procedures require the pilot-in-command sign the Flight and Maintenance Log prior to the flight once all preflight inspections have been satisfactorily completed and a maintenance release has been issued.

SAFA Inspection Preparation — Safety/Cabin (B01)

Tab B01 General Internal Condition

1. Check general condition, including lavatories, general condition and smoke detection systems, the condition of the overhead bins, flammable furnishings. Check the stowage of baggage/equipment, or heavy/hard pointed objects which might be stored in the toilets (waste bags temporarily stowed in a locked toilet is considered acceptable). [EASA SAFA Inspector's Guidance]

    Flight crews make this inspection prior to every flight.

2. The operator shall ensure that all baggage carried onto an aeroplane and taken into the passenger cabin is adequately and securely stowed. [A6-I-4.8]

    The aircraft has a secured baggage compartment, equipped with nets, for this purpose. (See photo which follows)

3. The operator shall include in the operations manual a minimum equipment list (MEL), approved by the State of the Operator which

will enable the pilot-in command to determine whether a flight may be commenced or continued from any intermediate stop should any instrument, equipment or systems become inoperative. Where the State of the Operator is not the State of Registry, the State of the Operator shall ensure that the MEL does not affect the aeroplane's compliance with the airworthiness requirements applicable in the State of Registry.[A6-I-6.1.3]

MEL is held electronically in EFB.

SAFA Inspection Preparation — Safety/Cabin (B02)

Tab B02 Cabin Attendant's Station/Crew Rest Area

1. Check general condition and serviceability of the cabin crew seats. Note: If a cabin crew seat is found unserviceable check against MEL and check if the number of serviceable ones can accommodate the minimum required number of cabin crew members (information available in the Operations Manual). Note: If a cabin crew seat is found not to retract automatically impeding the rapid evacuation of the aeroplane in an emergency, this finding should be addressed under the item B12 – Access to emergency exit. Check presence and condition of the safety harness and/or belt. Note: Aeroplanes for which the individual CofA was issued on or after 1 January 1981 must be fitted with safety harnesses for the use of cabin crew members. Check accessibility of life jackets. Check the serviceability of the communication system (Cockpit to Cabin and Cabin to Cabin). In case of unserviceability, check against the MEL. [EASA SAFA Inspector's Guidance]

   We do not use cabin attendants.

2. Aeroplanes for which the individual certificate of airworthiness is first issued on or after 1 January 1981 All aeroplanes shall be equipped with a forward or rearward facing (within 15 degrees of the longitudinal axis of the aeroplane) seat, fitted with a safety harness for the use of each cabin crew member required to satisfy the intent of 12.1 in respect of emergency evacuation. [A6-I-6.16.1 6.1]

   We do not use cabin attendants.

3. Land planes shall carry the equipment prescribed in 6.5.2.2: a) when

flying over water and at a distance of more than 93 km (50 nm) away from the shore, in the case of land planes operated in accordance with 5.2.9 or 5.2.10; b) when flying en route over water beyond gliding distance from the shore, in the case of all other land planes; and c) when taking off or landing at an aerodrome where, in the opinion of the State of the Operator, the takeoff or approach path is so disposed over water that in the event of a mishap there would be a likelihood of a ditching. 6.5.2.2 The equipment referred to in 6.5.2.1 shall comprise one life jacket or equivalent individual flotation device for each person on board, stowed in a position easily accessible from the seat or berth of the person for whose use it is provided. [A6-I-6.5.2]

We do not use cabin attendants.

SAFA Inspection Preparation — Safety/Cabin (B03)

Tab B03 First Aid Kit/Emergency Medical Kit

1. Check for presence, accessibility, and identification of medical supplies. Note: A First-Aid kit or a Medical kit or a universal precaution kit is only an ICAO recommendation. Note: ICAO does not require First Aid Kits / Emergency Medical Kits/Universal precaution kits to have an expiration (or next check) date. A First Aid Kit, Emergency Medical Kit, Universal precaution kit without a date does not constitute a finding. However, if stated expiry date has been exceeded, then this should be reported as a finding. [EASA SAFA Inspector's Guidance]

    The aircraft has two medical kits, both checked for expiration. (Location on chart which follows)

2. The operator shall inform the passengers of the location and general manner of use of the principal emergency equipment carried for collective use. [A6-I-4.2.12.2]

    Pilots ensure each passenger has received an appropriate briefing the first time on the aircraft and thereafter on request. Additionally, all passengers are briefed if any of the equipment has changed location or function. Passenger briefing cards are provided to new passengers and on request. (See copy which follows) Pilots are provided a "Aircraft

Specific Information Card" to ensure briefings are complete. (See copy which follows)

3.   An aeroplane shall be equipped with: a) accessible and adequate medical supplies; Recommendation.- Medical supplies should comprise: 1) one or more first-aid kits for the use of cabin crew in managing incidents of ill health; and 2) for aeroplanes required to carry cabin crew as part of the operating crew, one universal precaution kit (two for aeroplanes authorized to carry more than 250 passengers) for the use of cabin crew members in managing incidents of ill health associated with a case of suspected communicable disease, or in the case of illness involving contact with body fluids; and. 3) for aeroplanes authorized to carry more than 100 passengers, on a sector length of more than two hours, a medical kit, for the use of medical doctors or other qualified persons in treating inflight medical emergencies. Note.- Guidance on the types, number, location and contents of the medical supplies is given in Attachment B. [6.2.2]

The aircraft has two medical kits, both checked for expiration. (Location on chart which follows)

4.   Prescribed safety and survival equipment that the crew or passengers are expected to use or operate at the time of an emergency shall be reliable, readily accessible and easily identified, and its method of operation shall be plainly marked. [A8-IIIA-8.3 A8-V-6.3 A8-IIIB-6.3]

The aircraft has two medical kits, both checked for expiration. (Location on chart which follows)

SAFA Inspection Preparation — Safety/Cabin (B04)

Tab B04 Hand fire extinguishers

1.   Check if the installed extinguisher(s) is at the indicated location and easily accessible. Check if the installed extinguisher is correctly secured in its bracket. Check if the installed extinguisher(s) is marked with the appropriate operating instructions. Check if the installed extinguisher(s), including the extinguishing agent release mechanism, is serviceable – check pressure gauge (if installed), check expiration date (if any). If considerably low weight, consider it unservice-

able. [EASA SAFA Inspector's Guidance]

Fire extinguishers are checked on each preflight. (See location chart, which appears in Tab A15 of this binder)

2.   Prescribed safety and survival equipment that the crew or passengers are expected to use or operate at the time of an emergency shall be reliable, readily accessible and easily identified, and its method of operation shall be plainly marked.[A8-IIIA-8.3 A8-IIIB-6.3 A8-V-6.3]

Equipment is positioned exactly as installed under the original certificate of airworthiness (See location chart which follows)

3.   A6-I-.2.2(b)(2) An aeroplane shall be equipped with: b) portable fire extinguishers of a type which, when discharged, will not cause dangerous contamination of the air within the aeroplane. At least one shall be located in: 2) each passenger compartment that is separate from the pilot's compartment and that is not readily accessible to the flight crew; Note.- Any portable fire extinguisher so fitted in accordance with the certificate of airworthiness of the aeroplane may count as one prescribed.

Equipment is positioned exactly as installed under the original certificate of airworthiness (See location chart which follows)

SAFA Inspection Preparation — Safety/Cabin (B05)

Tab B05 Life jackets/Flotation devices

1.   6.5.2.1 Land planes shall carry the equipment prescribed in 6.5.2.2: a) when flying over water and at a distance of more than 93 km (50 nm) away from the shore, in the case of land planes operated in accordance with 5.2.9 or 5.2.10; b) when flying en route over water beyond gliding distance from the shore, in the case of all other land planes; and c) when taking off or landing at an aerodrome where, in the opinion of the State of the Operator, the takeoff or approach path is so disposed over water that in the event of a mishap there would be a likelihood of a ditching. 6.5.2.2 The equipment referred to in 6.5.2.1 shall comprise one life jacket or equivalent individual flotation device for each person on board, stowed in a position easily accessible from the seat or berth of the person for whose use it is

provided. [A6-I-6.5.2]

Life jackets are positioned exactly as installed under the original certificate of airworthiness (See location chart which follows)

SAFA Inspection Preparation — Safety/Cabin (B06)

Tab B06 Seat belt and seat condition

1. An aeroplane shall be equipped with: c) 1) a seat or berth for each person over an age to be determined by the State of the Operator; 2) a seat belt for each seat and restraining belts for each berth; [A6-I-6.2.2(c)]

    The aircraft has 16 passenger seats, each with seat belts and restraining belts, installed under the original certificate of airworthiness (See location chart which follows)

2. Aeroplanes over 5700 KG for which application for certification was submitted on or after 2 March 2004. 4.4.1 Seating and restraints Adequate seating and restraints shall be provided for the occupants, taking account of the likely flight and emergency landing loads to be encountered. Attention shall be paid to minimizing injury to occupants due to contact with surrounding structure during the operation of the aeroplane. [A8-IIIB-4.4.1]

    The aircraft has 16 passenger seats, each with seat belts and restraining belts, installed under the original certificate of airworthiness. (See location chart which follows)

SAFA Inspection Preparation — Safety/Cabin (B07)

Tab B07 Emergency exit, lightning and marking, Torches

1. The aeroplane shall be equipped with sufficient emergency exits to allow maximum opportunity for cabin evacuation within an appropriate time period. Items to be considered shall include: a) number of seats and seating configuration; b) number, location and size of exits; c) marking of exits and provision of instructions for use; d) likely blockages of exits; e) operation of exits; and f) positioning and weight of evacuation equipment at exits, e.g. slides and rafts. [A8-IIIB-8.4]

The aircraft has four emergency exits as well as the main entrance and a secondary escape route; as installed under the original certificate of airworthiness. (See diagram which appears at Tab A02 of this binder)

2. All aeroplanes, when operated at night shall be equipped with: f) an electric torch for each crew member station. [A6-I- 6.10(f)]

    Each pilot seat has an electric flashlight readily available, exactly as installed under the original certificate of airworthiness. (See photo which appears at Tab A19 of this binder)

3. Emergency lighting shall be provided and shall have the following characteristics: a) independence from main electrical supply; b) automatic activation upon loss of normal power/impact; c) visual indication of the path to emergency exits in smoke filled cabin conditions; d) illumination both inside and outside the aeroplane during evacuation; and e) no additional hazard in the event of fuel spillage. [A8-IIIB-8.5]

    The aircraft has installed a qualified emergency lighting system. (See description from aircraft operating manual which follows)

SAFA Inspection Preparation — Safety/Cabin (B08)

Tab B08 Slides/Life Rafts, ELT

1. 6.5.3.1 In addition to the equipment prescribed in 6.5.1 or 6.5.2 whichever is applicable, the following equipment shall be installed in all aeroplanes when used over routes on which the aeroplane may be over water and at more than a distance corresponding to 120 minutes at cruising speed or 740 km (400 nm), whichever is the lesser, away from land suitable for making an emergency landing in the case of aircraft operated in accordance with 5.2.9 or 5.2.10, and 30 minutes or 185 km (100 nm), whichever is the lesser, for all other aeroplanes: a) life-saving rafts in sufficient numbers to carry all persons on board, stowed so as to facilitate their ready use in emergency, provided with such life-saving equipment including means of sustaining life as is appropriate to the flight to be undertaken; [A6-I-6.5.3.1(a)]

    There are two life rafts aboard, as originally installed under the original airworthiness certificate. (See diagram which follows)

2.   All aeroplanes authorized to carry 19 passengers or less for which the individual certificate of airworthiness is first issued after 1 July 2008 shall be equipped with at least one automatic ELT. [A6-I-6.17.11]

The aircraft has a qualified ELT, installed under the original airworthiness certificate. (See operating manual extract, which follows)

3.   From 1 January 2005, emergency locator transmitters shall operate on 406 MHz and 121.5 MHz simultaneously. [A10-III-Ch.2- 5.1.4]

The aircraft has a qualified ELT, installed under the original airworthiness certificate. (See operating manual extract, which follows)

SAFA Inspection Preparation — Safety/Cabin (B09)

Tab B09 Oxygen Supply

1.   A flight to be operated at flight altitudes at which the atmospheric pressure in personnel compartments will be less than 700 hPa (10,000 feet) shall not be commenced unless sufficient stored breathing oxygen is carried to supply: a) all crew members and 10 per cent of the passengers for any period in excess of 30 minutes that the pressure in compartments occupied by them will be between 700 hPa and 620 hPa; and b) the crew and passengers for any period that the atmospheric pressure in compartments occupied by them will be less than 620 hPa (13,000 feet). [A6-I-4.3.8.1]

Crews normally plan to be able to continue any flight no higher than 10,000 feet in the event of a pressurization loss and ensure oxygen quantity is sufficient using the chart available in G450-OMS-01, Table III. (See extract at Tab A18)

2.   An aeroplane intended to be operated at flight altitudes at which the atmospheric pressure is less than 700 hPa (10,000 feet) in personnel compartments shall be equipped with oxygen storage and dispensing apparatus capable of storing and dispensing the oxygen supplies required in Annex 6 Part I Chapter 4.3.8.1. [A6-I-6.7.1]

Oxygen masks are readily available, exactly as installed under the original airworthiness certificate. (See operating manual extract at Tab A18)

3.   A flight to be operated at flight altitudes at which the atmospheric

pressure in personnel compartments will be less than 700 hPa (10,000 feet) shall not be commenced unless sufficient stored breathing oxygen is carried to supply: a) all crew members and 10 per cent of the passengers for any period in excess of 30 minutes that the pressure in compartments occupied by them will be between 700 hPa (10,000 feet) and 620 hPa (13,000 feet); and b) the crew and passengers for any period that the atmospheric pressure in compartments occupied by them will be less than 620 hPa (13,000 feet). [A6-I-4.3.8.1]

Crews normally plan to be able to continue any flight no higher than 10,000 feet in the event of a pressurization loss and ensure oxygen quantity is sufficient using the chart available in G450-OMS-01, Table III. (See extract at Tab A18)

4.   An aeroplane intended to be operated at flight altitudes at which the atmospheric pressure is less than 376 hPa (25,000 feet), or which, if operated at flight altitudes at which the atmospheric pressure is more than 376 hPa (25,000 feet), cannot descend safely within four minutes to a flight altitude at which the atmospheric pressure is equal to 620 hPa (13,000 feet) and for which the individual certificate of airworthiness is first issued on or after 9 November 1998, shall be provided with automatically deployable oxygen equipment to satisfy the requirements of Annex 6 Part I Chapter 4.3.8.2. The total number of oxygen dispensing units shall exceed the number of passenger and cabin crew seats by at least 10 per cent. [A6-I-6.7.5]

The aircraft is equipped with an automatically deployable oxygen system, as installed under the original airworthiness certificate. (See operating manual extract at Tab A18)

SAFA Inspection Preparation — Safety/Cabin (B10)

Tab B10 Safety instructions

1.   An operator shall ensure that passengers are made familiar with the location and use of: a) seat belts; b) emergency exits; c) life jackets, if the carriage of life jackets is prescribed; d) oxygen dispensing equipment, if the provision of oxygen for the use of passengers is prescribed; and e) other emergency equipment provided for individual use, including passenger emergency briefing cards. [A6-I-4.2.12.1]

Pilots ensure each passsenger has received an appropriate briefing the first time on the aircraft and thereafter on request. Additionally, all passengers are briefed if any of the equipment has changed location or function. Passenger briefing cards are provided to new passengers and on request. (See copy at Tab B03 of this binder) Pilots are provided a "Aircraft Specific Information Card" to ensure briefings are complete. (See copy at Tab B03 of this binder)

2.   A6-I-6.2.2 (d) An aeroplane shall be equipped with: d) means of ensuring that the following information and instructions are conveyed to passengers: 1) when seat belts are to be fastened; 2) when and how oxygen equipment is to be used if the carriage of oxygen is required; 3) restrictions on smoking; 4) location and use of life jackets or equivalent individual floatation devices where their carriage is required; and 5) location and method of opening emergency exits;

Pilots ensure each pilot has received an appropriate briefing the first time on the aircraft and thereafter on request. Additionally, all passengers are briefed if any of the equipment has changed location or function. Passenger briefing cards are provided to new passengers and on request. (See copy at Tab B03 of this binder) Pilots are provided a "Aircraft Specific Information Card" to ensure briefings are complete. (See copy at Tab B03 of this binder)

SAFA Inspection Preparation — Safety/Cabin (B11)

Tab B11 Cabin crew members

1.   An operator shall establish, to the satisfaction of the State of the Operator, the minimum number of cabin attendants required for each type of aeroplane, based on seating capacity or the number of passengers carried, in order to effect a safe and expeditious evacuation of the aeroplane, and the necessary functions to be performed in an emergency or a situation requiring emergency evacuation. The operator shall assign these functions for each type of aeroplane. [A6-I-12.1]

No cabin attendants are required or used on this aircraft.

2.   An aeroplane shall not be refuelled when passengers are embarking, on board or disembarking unless it is properly attended by qualified

personnel ready to initiate and direct an evacuation of the aeroplane by most practical and expeditious means available. [A6-I-4.3.2]

3.   When refuelling with passengers embarking, on board or disembarking, two-way communication shall be maintained by the aeroplane's inter-communication system or other suitable means between the ground crew supervising the refuelling and the qualified personnel on board the aeroplane. [A6-I-4.3.7]

The company operations manual lists appropriate procedures for refueling operations when passengers are embarking, on board, or disembarking. (See extract which follows)

4.   An operator shall formulate rules to limit flight time and flight duty periods and for the provision of adequate rest periods for all its crew members. These rules shall be in accordance with the regulations established by the State of the Operator, or approved by that State, and included in the operations manual. [A6-I-4.2.11.2]

The company operations manual includes appropriate flight time and duty period limitations. (See extract at Tab A01 of this binder)

SAFA Inspection Preparation — Safety/Cabin (B12)

Tab B12 Access to emergency exits

1.   Aeroplanes over 5700 KG for which application for certification was submitted on or after 2 March 2004. The aeroplane shall be equipped with sufficient emergency exits to allow maximum opportunity for cabin evacuation within an appropriate time period. Items to be considered shall include: a) number of seats and seating configuration; b) number, location and size of exits; c) marking of exits and provision of instructions for use; d) likely blockages of exits; e) operation of exits; and f) positioning and weight of evacuation equipment at exits, e.g. slides and rafts. [A8-IIIB-8.4]

Four emergency escape exits and alternate routes are shown in the Aircraft Flight Manual 4-19-30. (See extract at Tab A02 of this binder)

SAFA Inspection Preparation — Safety/Cabin (B13)

Tab B13 Safety of passenger baggage

1. The operator shall ensure that all baggage carried onto an aeroplane and taken into the passenger cabin is adequately and securely stowed. [A6-I-4.8]

   The aircraft has a secured baggage compartment, equipped with nets, for this purpose. (See photo at Tab B01 of this binder)

SAFA Inspection Preparation — Safety/Cabin (B14)

Tab B14 Seat capacity

1. An aeroplane shall be equipped with: c) 1) a seat or berth for each person over an age to be determined by the State of the Operator. [A6-I-6.2.2(c)(1)]

   The aircraft has 16 passenger seats, each with seat belts and restraining belts, installed under the original certificate of airworthiness. (See location chart at Tab B06 of this binder)

SAFA Inspection Preparation — Aircraft Condition (C01)

Tab C01 General External Condition

1. Check general condition of the airframe: corrosion; cleanliness (related to the ability to inspect the aircraft); presence of ice, snow, frost; legibility of markings. Note: Although missing underwing registrations are a non-compliance with international requirements, the safety relevance is considered low. Therefore, such non-compliance should be recorded as a General Remark (cat G) only. Note: markings may be in languages other than English. Note: ICAO does not require that break-in points need to be marked (however: if such markings are being used, they should be according to a certain format). Note: When inspecting markings and placards, inspectors should differentiate between those required by ICAO and those required only by the manufacturer. Loose or missing fasteners and rivets. Presence and condition of the antennas. Presence and condition of the static dischargers. Condition and functionality of the exterior lights etc. Note: Before raising a finding, the inspector should make sure that the affected light(s) are required for the type of flight

(according to the MEL). Unserviceable lights, not required for the type of flight, should be reported as a General Remark only. [EASA SAFA Inspector's Guidance]

Crews make such an inspection prior to every flight.

2.   Markings and placards or instructions shall be provided to give any information that is essential to the ground crew in order to preclude the possibility of mistakes in ground servicing (e.g. towing, refuelling) that could pass unnoticed and that could jeopardize the safety of the aeroplane in subsequent flights. [A8-IIIA-9.6.2 A8-IIIB-7.6.2 A8-V-7.6.2]

Aircraft is placarded as delivered under the original airworthiness certificate.

3.   All aeroplanes, when operated at night shall be equipped with: b) the lights required by Annex 2 for aircraft in flight or operating on the movement area of an aerodrome; c) two landing lights;

Aircraft is equipped with a full set of suitable exterior lights. (See aircraft operating manual extract, which follows)

4.   A flight to be planned or expected to operate in suspected or known ground icing conditions shall not takeoff unless the aeroplane has been inspected for icing and, if necessary, has been given appropriate de-icing/anti-icing treatment. Accumulation of ice or other naturally occurring contaminants shall be removed so that the aeroplane is kept in an airworthy condition prior to takeoff. [A6-I-4.3.5.4]

Crews conduct pre-flight contamination checks to determine the need for de-icing/anti-icing treatment and further pre-takeoff contamination checks if the aircraft was de-iced and/or the conditions are conducive for icing conditions.

SAFA Inspection Preparation — Aircraft Condition (C02)

Tab C02 Doors and Hatches

1.   Check for: presence and condition of bonding wires; door external markings, operation instructions; Note: only those doors which can be opened from the outside need external markings. Condition of

doors, hatches and associated seals.

Checks are made during every maintenance release inspection, at intervals no longer than 20 flight days or 50 flight hours, and documented in the Maintenance Logbook.

2.   Markings and placards or instructions shall be provided to give any information that is essential to the ground crew in order to preclude the possibility of mistakes in ground servicing (e.g. towing, refuelling) that could pass unnoticed and that could jeopardize the safety of the aeroplane in subsequent flights. [A8-IIIA-9.6.2 A8-IIIB-7.6.2 A8-V-7.6.2]

Aircraft is placarded as delivered under the original airworthiness certificate.

SAFA Inspection Preparation — Aircraft Condition (C03)

Tab C03 Flight Controls

1.   Check external Flight Controls. Check for hydraulic leakage. Check presence and condition of the static dischargers. Check presence and condition of bonding wires.

Crews make such a check prior to every flight.

2.   Any failure to maintain an aircraft in an airworthy condition as defined by the appropriate airworthiness requirements shall render the aircraft ineligible for operation until the aircraft is restored to an airworthy condition. [A8-II-3.5]

3. Crews make conduct a preflight inspection prior to every flight.

SAFA Inspection Preparation — Aircraft Condition (C04)

Tab C04 Wheels, tyres and brakes

1.   Inspect wheels and tyres for damage and wear. When possible, check for correct tyre pressure. Check the condition of the braking system. Check the condition of the landing gear snubbers. Note: some aircraft manufacturers may approve a certain amount of flights with

tires or brakes worn out or damaged beyond AMM limits.

A thorough inspection is made prior to every maintenance release, conducted at intervals no greater than 20 flight days and 50 flight hours. Crews also make a preflight inspection prior to every flight.

SAFA Inspection Preparation — Aircraft Condition (C05)

Tab C05 Undercarriage, skids/floats

1.   Check presence and condition of the water/debris deflectors (if required to be installed). Check skids/floats for obvious damages. Check for presence and legibility of inspection markings/placards. Note: When inspecting markings and placards, inspectors should differentiate between those required by ICAO and those required only by the manufacturer. Check for condition, lubrication, corrosion, leaks, damage and inappropriate strut extension.

A thorough inspection is made prior to every maintenance release, conducted at intervals no greater than 20 flight days and 50 flight hours. Crews also make a preflight inspection prior to every flight.

SAFA Inspection Preparation — Aircraft Condition (C06)

Tab C06 Wheel well

1.   Check for lubrication, leakage & corrosion. Check for lubrication, leakage & corrosion and wear on door fittings and hinges. Check for presence and condition of bonding wires. Check for cleanliness and damage.

A thorough inspection is made prior to every maintenance release, conducted at intervals no greater than 20 flight days and 50 flight hours. Crews also make a preflight inspection prior to every flight.

SAFA Inspection Preparation — Aircraft Condition (C07)

Tab C07 Powerplant and Pylon

1.　　Check for: dents and loose/missing fasteners; LPT/LPC blades (where visible), obvious damage to sensors; cracks; panels are aligned and handles are flushed; unusual damage and leaks; the condition of the thrust reverser; the condition of the Intake acoustic liners; presence and legibility of the markings and placards. Note: When inspecting markings and placards, inspectors should differentiate between those required by ICAO and those required only by the manufacturer.

A thorough inspection is made prior to every maintenance release, conducted at intervals no greater than 20 flight days and 50 flight hours. Crews also make a preflight inspection prior to every flight.

SAFA Inspection Preparation — Aircraft Condition (C08)

Tab C08 Fan blades

1.　　Check for FOD damage, cracks, cuts, corrosion, erosion, etc.

A thorough inspection is made prior to every maintenance release, conducted at intervals no greater than 20 flight days and 50 flight hours. Crews also make a preflight inspection prior to every flight.

SAFA Inspection Preparation — Aircraft Condition (C09)

Tab C09 Propellers, rotors (main/tail)

1.　　Check for corrosion, looseness of blades in hub, stone damage, etc. Check the de-ice boots for damage (where fitted).

Not Applicable.

SAFA Inspection Preparation — Aircraft Condition (C10)

Tab C10 Obvious repairs

1.　　Check for repairs of unusual design or poorly performed. Note: There is no obligation to keep information on board regarding temporary repairs (e.g. on the dent & buckle chart). However, the PIC has to have the knowledge of the status of the temporary repairs in order to be satisfied that the aeroplane remains airworthy.

A thorough inspection is made prior to every maintenance release, conducted at intervals no greater than 20 flight days and 50 flight hours. Crews also make a preflight inspection prior to every flight.

2.   A flight shall not be commenced until flight preparation forms have been completed certifying that the pilot-in-command is satisfied that: a) the aeroplane is airworthy; [A6-I-4.3.1(a)]

Company procedures require the pilot-in-command sign the Flight and Maintenance Log prior to the flight once all preflight inspections have been satisfactorily completed and a maintenance release has been issued.

SAFA Inspection Preparation — Aircraft Condition (C11)

Tab C11 Obvious unrepaired damage

1.   Check for un-assessed and unrecorded damage including corrosion, lightning strike damage, bird strikes etc. Check that any damage is observed, assessed, and possibly recorded on a damage chart/buckle & dent chart.

A thorough inspection is made prior to every maintenance release, conducted at intervals no greater than 20 flight days and 50 flight hours. Crews also make a preflight inspection prior to every flight.

SAFA Inspection Preparation — Aircraft Condition (C12)

Tab C12 Leakage

1.   Check for fuel leaks, hydraulic leaks and (if applicable) toilet liquid leaks (blue ice). Note: Leakages identified when inspecting C03, C04, C05, C06 and C07 should be reported as findings under those inspection items.

A thorough inspection is made prior to every maintenance release, conducted at intervals no greater than 20 flight days and 50 flight hours.

Crews also make a preflight inspection prior to every flight.

SAFA Inspection Preparation — Cargo (D01)

Tab D01 General Condition of Cargo Compartment

1. Check the general condition of cargo compartment. Check lighting, fire protection, detection & extinguishing system (if appropriate). Check side wall and overhead (blow-out) panels, smoke detectors, smoke barrier/curtain. Check the presence and condition of cargo barrier/dividing nets.

    A thorough inspection is made prior to every maintenance release, conducted at intervals no greater than 20 flight days and 50 flight hours. Crews also make a preflight inspection prior to every flight.

SAFA Inspection Preparation — Cargo (D02)

Tab D02 Dangerous Goods

1. The operator of an aircraft in which dangerous goods are to be carried shall provide the pilot-in-command as early as practicable before departure of the aircraft with written information as specified in the Technical Instructions. [A18-9.1]

    We do not carry dangerous goods. (See our company manual extract at Tab A04 of this binder)

2. Packages of dangerous goods bearing the "Cargo aircraft only" label shall be loaded in accordance with the provisions in the Technical Instructions. [A18-8.9]

    We do not carry dangerous goods. (See our company manual extract at Tab A04 of this binder)

3. An operator shall not accept dangerous goods for transport by air: a) unless the dangerous goods are accompanied by a completed dangerous goods transport document, except where the Technical Instructions indicate that such a document is not required; and b) until the package, overpack or freight container containing the dangerous goods has been inspected in accordance with the acceptance procedures contained in the Technical Instructions. [A18-8.1]

We do not carry dangerous goods. (See our company manual extract at Tab A04 of this binder)

SAFA Inspection Preparation — Cargo [D03]

Tab D03 Safety of Cargo on Board

1. Check that loads are properly distributed (floor limits, height limits, pallets and containers maximum gross weight). Note: Not all aircraft have load height restrictions. Check that flight/fly-away kit and spare wheels are correctly secured. Check that cargo is correctly secured. Check the condition of cargo containers, pallets, lock assemblies and lashing nets. Check the condition of the cargo compartment dividing nets.

    Aircraft is loaded considering weight and balance restrictions. (See example weight and balance form at Tab A14 of this binder)

2. A flight shall not be commenced until flight preparation forms have been completed certifying that the pilot-in-command is satisfied that: e) any load carried is properly distributed and safely secured. [A6-I-4.3.1e]

    Company procedures require the pilot-in-command sign the Flight and Maintenance Log prior to the flight once all preflight inspections have been satisfactorily completed and a maintenance release has been issued.

SAFA Inspection Preparation — General (E01)

Tab E01 General

1. Check (if appropriate) for any general item which may have a direct relation with the safety of the aircraft or its occupants.

    Company procedures require the pilot-in-command sign the Flight and Maintenance Log prior to the flight once all preflight inspections have been satisfactorily completed and a maintenance release has been issued.

Slots (European Union)

F *low control is a way of life in the EU; the skies have become so crowded that something had to be done. In 1988 the entire system was automated which enabled more airplanes to fill the sky more efficiently, but it made a complex system too complex for pilots to comprehend. Even if a pilot was emersed into the system for complete familiarity, there is that pesky problem with language. It really pays to have a local handler on your payroll everywhere you go in Europe. But there may be times the handler is unable or unwilling to help. In that case you need to be able to speak the CFMU lingo. There are a lot of acronyms. If you learn the terms, are patient, and remain calm on the phone and radio, you too can negotiate a slot in the European Union.*

Flight Plans

The process begins when you file your flight plan, which you can do up to 120 hours in advance but should do no later than 3 hours prior to your desired takeof time. From this point, your fate is in the hands of the Central Flow Management Unit (CFMU).

[CFMU Handbook, ¶7.4] Integrated Initial Flight Plan Processing System (IFPS):

a.   provides a centralised flight planning system for the States within the CFMU area with the object of rationalising reception, initial processing and distribution of flight plan data to ATC Units;

b.   provides Repetitive Flight Plan (RPL) and Filed Flight Plan (FPL) data for use by the CFMU Operations for ATFCM planning, monitoring and slot allocation.

Every flight plan ends up with the IFPS to be deconflicted so that, in theory, once you takeoff there should be no conflicts with any other en route traffic or with the volume of traffic at your departure and destination airports.

[https://www.eurocontrol.int FAQs] When do I file an FPL? Not later than 3 hours before EOBT. You will get either:

- ACK (FPL accepted).
- MAN (errors in FPL; after manual processing you will get either ACK or REJ) REJ (FPL rejected).
- REJ (FPL rejected).

Slot Allocation

If there are no en route conflicts or no flow issues, your flight plan can be accepted without a slot and you are free to depart unrestricted. If a slot is needed, it will be generated by the Computer Assisted Slot Allocation (CASA) system.

[CFMU Handbook, ¶11.2.1] The CASA System is largely automatic and centralised, and functions from an Aircraft Operator's point of view in passive mode.

[CFMU Handbook, ¶11.2.2.4] At a fixed time before the Estimated Off-Block Time (EOBT) of each pre-allocated flight, called Slot Issue Time (SIT), the slot is allocated to the flight and a Slot Allocation Message (SAM) is sent to the Aircraft Operators and ATC.

The CFMU issues the slot 2 hours prior to your EOBT by sending the SAM. You will also get an Expect Start Engine Time which considers the time to do that and the time to taxi when arriving at a Calculated Takeoff Time (CTOT).

Slot Tolerances

The CTOT is valid from CTOT - 5 to CTOT + 10.

Dealing With the System

Generally speaking, only an airport official or somebody associated with the system between the airport and the CFMU can make changes to an allocated slot. Eurocontrol can be contacted (numbers and email address are given at https://www.eurocontrol.int), but the first question will likely be "have you called the airport?" Your handler should be your "go to" contact. Failing that, you should talk to clearance delivery, ground control, or someone else at the airport first.

Delays

[https://www.eurocontrol.int FAQs] FPL updates - When do I notify a delay? Send a DLA/CHG for any change of EOBT (Estimated Off Block Time) greater than 15 minutes. However, do not update EOBT as a result of delay given by CTOT (Calculated Takeoff Time).

If you cannot make your SLOT time, you should cancel it to free that time up for other aircraft. It is said that the CFMU tracks operators who are habitually unable to make slot times and can penalize you in the future.

- *If the SAM has not yet been issued, you can send a DELAY message.*

- *If the SAM has been issued, you may need to CANCEL your flight plan and restart the entire process.*

- *SSR (Slot Revision Request)*

Early

If you want to depart early, you have several options:

- *You could send a cancellation message (CNL), wait 5 minutes, and resubmit. This could get you an early time but it risks a time even later than your original slot time.*

- *You could just wait until the issued slot time.*

- *You could send a REA (Ready) message, which tells the CFMU you are ready to take the next available slot. But you need to ensure you are really ready with everyone loaded. You also need to make sure the airport can accomodate you. If the airport has its own slot procedures, you could find yourself with a CFMU slot that does not agree with the airport slot. You need to ask the airport. A knowledgeable handler can work both ends of the equation to minimize this possiblity.*

Improving Your Slot Time

[https://www.eurocontrol.int FAQs] Change status - How do I change status of my flight?

By sending : an SWM (Slot Improvement Proposal Wanted Message), if you were in RFI (Ready/Request For direct Improvement) status or an RFI, if you were in SWM status.

Remember the airport has to do this for you, either through your handler or your request.

Missed Slot

[https://www.eurocontrol.int FAQs] What do I do if I have missed my slot?

If your new EOBT (Estimated Off Block Time) is known send DLA/CHG. You will receive either: SRM (Slot Revision Message) , SLC (Slot Requirement Cancellation Message) or FLS (Flight Suspension Message)

If your new EOBT is not known send an SMM (Slot Missed Message). You will receive an FLS (Flight Suspension Message) and will remain suspended until you send a DLA to provide your new EOBT.

Rerouteing

[https://www.eurocontrol.int FAQs] How can I reroute my flight?

Send a new route via a CHG (Change) or CNL (Cancel) and RFP (Replacement Flight Plan), or use AOWIR (Aircraft Operator 'What-If' Re-route) if you have access to ATFCM CHMI/NOP (Network Operation Portal).

Slot Cancellation

[https://www.eurocontrol.int FAQs] What do I do if I get an SLC (Slot Requirement Cancellation Message)?

You are no longer subject to ATFCM measures and may depart without delay. If the SLC is issued after EOBT (Estimated Off Block Time) +15 minutes you must update your EOBT by sending a DLA/CHG.

If You Don't Have a Handler

Having a competent handler can save you hours of delay and make changes much easier. If you don't have a handler or your handler pleads ignorance, start with ground control and ask, "I need help with a slot issue." It is likely they've heard that before.

Chapter 35

Strategic Lateral Offset Procedure (SLOP)

*T*here are SLOP ultra-denyers and SLOP ultra-believers. Me? I'm a SLOP realist.

The SLOP ultra denyers say it is just one more thing to get wrong, let the other guy apply it. Tell that to the survivors of EMBR-135BJ, and more importantly to the victims of Gol 1907, DHL 611, and Bashkirskie Avialinii 2937.

The SLOP ultra-believers are so in tune with the procedure that they apply it everywhere. If it could have prevented the Brazil midair, what about in the remote regions of China, Africa, and Australia? I'm not so sure, the procedure is designed for where tracks are separated by at least 30 nm and if the controlling authority hasn't authorized SLOP, they might have separation issues in mind.

I believe in the concept but it isn't yet approved worldwide. The ICAO says it should be allowed in ADS-C airspace, but only in the NAT is that actually in writing.

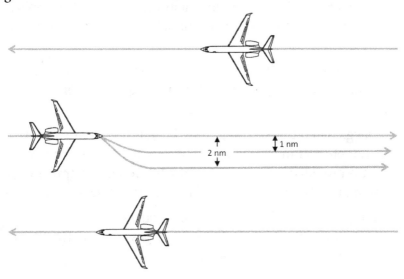

Clearly it can save your life and it is therefore worth using. But you need to know where it is authorized and how to apply it correctly. Also note that while usually no clearance is required to initiate SLOP and no call is needed when returning to centerline, this isn't the case worldwide.

ICAO Guidance

[ICAO Doc 4444 - Amendment No. 2, ¶16.5] Strategic Lateral Offset Procedures (SLOP) in Oceanic and Remote Continental Airspace

16.5.1. SLOP are approved procedures that allow aircraft to fly on a parallel track to the right of the centre line relative to the direction of flight. An aircraft's use of these procedures does not affect the application of prescribed separation standards.

Note 1.— The use of highly accurate navigational systems (such as the global navigation satellite system (GNSS)) by an increasing proportion of the aircraft population has had the effect of reducing the magnitude of lateral deviations from the route centre line and, consequently, increasing the probability of a collision, should a loss of vertical separation between aircraft on the same route occur.

Note 2.— The following incorporates lateral offset procedures for both the mitigation of the increasing lateral overlap probability due to increase navigation accuracy, and wake turbulence encounters.

Note 3.— Annex 2, 3.6.2.1.1, requires authorization for the application of strategic lateral offsets from the appropriate ATS authority responsible for the airspace concerned.

16.5.2. The following shall be taken into account by the appropriate ATS authority when authorizing the use of strategic lateral offsets in a particular airspace;

a.   strategic lateral offsets shall only be authorized in en route oceanic or remote continental airspace. Where part of the airspace in question is provided with an ATS surveillance service, transiting aircraft should normally be allow to initiate or continue offset tracking;

b.   strategic lateral offsets do not affect lateral separation minima and may be authorized for the following types of routes (including where routes or route systems intersect):

1.   uni-directional and bi-directional routes; and

2.   parallel route systems where the spacing between the route centre line is not less than 55.5 km (30 nm);

c.   in some instances it may be necessary to impose restrictions on the use of strategic lateral offsets, e.g. where their application may be inappropriate for reasons related to obstacle clearance;

d.   strategic lateral offset procedures should be implemented on a regional basis after coordination between all States involved;

e.   the routes or airspace where application of strategic lateral offsets is authorized, and the procedures to be followed by pilots, shall be promulgated in aeronautical information publications (AIPs); and

f.   fair traffic controllers shall be made aware of the airspace within which strategic lateral offsets are authorized.

16.5.3. The decision to apply a strategic lateral offset shall be the responsibility of the flight crew. The flight crew shall only apply strategic lateral offsets in airspace where such offsets have been authorized by the appropriate ATS authority and when the aircraft is equipped with automatic offset tracking capability.

16.5.4. The strategic lateral offset shall be established at a distance of 1.85 km (1 nm) or 3.7 km (2 nm) to the right of the centre line relative to the direction of flight.

Note 1.— Pilots may contact other aircraft on the inter-pilot air-to-air frequency 123.45 to coordinate offsets.

Note 2.— The strategic lateral offset procedure has been designed to include offsets to mitigate the effects of wake turbulence of preceding aircraft. If wake turbulence needs to be avoided, one of the three available options (centre line, 1.85 km (1 nm) or 3.7 km (2 nm) right offset) may be used.

Note 3.— Pilots are not required to inform ATC that a strategic lateral offset is being applied.

The ICAO recommends the procedure but does not mandate it and even notes the ATS authority must approve the practice before pilots can opt to use it. Clearly it is up to the pilot to know when it is and isn't authorized.

Where is SLOP Authorized?

It is an expanding list. As of 31 Dec 2013, here is what I've found:

- Africa, various locations (according to the Jeppesen Airways Manual / Air Traffic Control / State Rules and Procedures - Africa).

- Australia administered OCA (according to Australian guidance in Jeppesen Pages).

- China, on routes A1, L642, M771, and N892 (according to China guidance in Jeppesen Pages).

- New York, Oakland and Anchorage Oceanic FIRs (according to U.S. FAA guidance).

- Oceanic airspace in the San Juan FIR (according to U.S. FAA guidance).

- The entire North Atlantic Track Region (according to the North Atlantic Operations and Airspace Manual).

- The Pacific (including the NOPAC, Central East Pacific (CEP) and Pacific Organized Track System (PACOTS)) (according to U.S. FAA guidance).

- South Pacific airspaces (according to U.S. FAA guidance).

African Guidance

Various locations throughout Africa authorize SLOP in specified areas or routes. You will have to check each country's state pages. For example:

[Jeppesen Airway Manual/Air Traffic Control/State Rules and Procedures - Africa / Madagascar - Rules and Procedures] Madagascar has implemented in its upper airspace between FL280 and FL460 the strategic lateral offset procedures (SLOP) in its entire continental Antananarivo FIR. The pilot must report to the controller when normal navigation is resumed after a lateral deviation of 1 or 2 nm right of the axis of the nominal route. Pilots may contact other aircraft on the Interpilot frequency 123.45MHz to coordinate offset.

Australian Guidance

[Jeppesen Airway Manual/Air Traffic Control/State Rules and Procedures - Australia/General Flight Procedures]

6.4.1. Aircraft operating in OCA within Australian administered airspace are authorized to use strategic lateral offset procedures (SLOP) in accordance with the requirements detailed below.

6.4.2. The following requirements apply to the use of SLOP:

a.   The offset must only be applied by aircraft with automatic offset tracking capability.

b.   The offset must be established at a distance of 1 nm or 2 nm to the RIGHT of track relative to the direction of flight.

Note: Offsets to the left of track are not permitted.

c.   The offset must only be applied during the en route phase of flight.

d.   The offset may only be used in OCA. Pilots must fly the centerline for any portion within CTA. Pilots must return to centerline before leaving OCA or, where the subsequent state does not allow SLOP, prior to leaving Australian administered airspace.

e.   The offset must not be used in addition to diversions or other offsets; eg, weather or wake turbulence.

f.   The offset must not be applied at levels where obstacle clearance would be affected.

g.   Identified aircraft:

1.   may continue an offset in OCA; and

2.   must advise ATC prior to initiating or changing an offset.

6.4.3. The decision to apply SLOP is the responsibility of the pilot in command — a clearance is not required. Except when an identified aircraft initiates or changes a lateral offset, pilots are not required to notify ATC that SLOP are being applied.

6.4.4. The use of SLOP is recommended in OCA for aircraft cruising at levels not in compliance with the Table of Cruising Levels.

Canadian Guidance

[Jeppesen Airway Manual/Air Traffic Control/State Rules and Procedures - Canada/North Atlantic (NAT) Operations, ¶11.22] The Strategic Lateral Offset Procedure (SLOP) is now a standard operating procedure throughout the North Atlantic (NAT) Region. This procedure mitigates collision risk and wake turbulence encounters. Pilots conducting oceanic flights within the NAT Region with automatic offset programming capability are recommended to fly lateral offsets of either 1 or 2 nm right of center line.

P.R. of China Guidance

[Jeppesen Airway Manual/Air Traffic Control/State Rules and Procedures - China/China, P.R. - Rules and Procedures]

Offsets are only applied on routes A1, L642, M771 and N892.

The following requirements apply to the use of the offset:

- the decision to apply a strategic lateral offset is the responsibility of the flight crew;

- the offset shall be established at a distance of one or two nautical miles to RIGHT of the center line relative to the direction of flight;

- in airspace where the use of lateral offsets has been authorized, pilots are not required to inform ATC that an offset is being applied.

- offsets are only applied by aircraft with automatic offset tracking capability.

Be careful dealing with SLOP in the People's Republic of China. The rules have changed several times over the years and the guidance out there is contradictory. SLOP used to be at the discretion of ATC and was to the left as well as the right. Current guidance, what is out there, limits SLOP to the routes shown above.

FAA Guidance

[AC 91-70A, ¶3-9.] Pilots should use the Strategic Lateral Offset Procedure (SLOP) as standard operating practice in the course of normal operations to mitigate collision risk and wake turbulence. The SLOP is in force throughout the New York, Oakland and Anchorage Oceanic FIRs and in oceanic airspace in the San Juan FIR. Internationally, operators implement the SLOP in the NAT, the Pacific (including the NOPAC, Central East Pacific (CEP) and Pacific Organized Track System (PACOTS)) and South Pacific airspaces. Use this procedure for both the heightened risk of collision when non-normal events such as operational altitude deviation errors and turbulence-induced altitude deviations occur due to highly-accurate navigational systems and to mitigate wake vortex encounters.

a.   Guidelines. Apply SLOP using the following guidelines:

1.   Make strategic lateral offsets and those executed to mitigate the effects of wake turbulence to the right of a route or track only.

2.   In relation to a route or track, there are three positions that an aircraft may fly: centerline (CL) and 1 or 2 nm right.

3.   Offsets are not to exceed 2 nm right of CL.

b.   Reducing Risk. The intent of this procedure is to reduce risk (increase the safety margin) by distributing aircraft laterally and equally across the three available positions. In this connection, pilots must take into account the following:

1.   Aircraft without automatic offset programming capability must fly the CL.

2.   Aircraft programmed with automatic offsets may fly the CL or offset 1 or 2 nm right of CL to obtain lateral spacing from nearby aircraft.

3.   Pilots should use whatever means are available (e.g., TCAS, communications, visual acquisition, ground proximity warning system (GPWS)) to determine the best flight path to fly.

4.   Any aircraft overtaking another aircraft is to offset within the confines of this procedure, if capable, so as to create the least amount of wake turbulence for the overtaken aircraft.

5.   For wake turbulence purposes, pilots are also to fly one of the three positions in the second bullet above and never offset to the left of the CL nor offset more than 2 nm right of CL, appropriate to any given situation and have the final authority and responsibility for the safe operation of the aircraft.

NOTE: The FAA recognizes that the pilot will use his/her judgment to determine the action most appropriate to any given situation and has the final authority and responsibility for the safe operation of the aircraft. You may use air-to-air frequency 123.45 to coordinate the best wake turbulence offset option.

6.   Pilots may apply an offset outbound at the oceanic entry point, but must return to CL at the oceanic exit point.

7.   Aircraft transiting radar-controlled airspace (e.g., Bermuda) may remain on their established offset positions.

8.   This procedure does not require ATC clearance and it is not necessary to advise ATC.

9.   Base voice position reports on the current ATC clearance and not the offset positions.

[AC 91-70A, Appendix 2, ¶2.g.(4)] The SLOP should be SOP for all oceanic crossings. This procedure reduces the risk from highly accurate navigation systems or operational errors involving the ATC clearance. SLOP also replaced the contingency procedure developed for aircraft encountering wake turbulence. Depending upon winds aloft, coordination between aircraft to avoid wake turbulence may be necessary. This procedure of flying centerline (CL), 1 nm or 2 nm right of CL, greatly reduces the risk to the airspace by the nature of the randomness. Aircraft that do not have an automatic offset capability (that can be programmed in the LRNS) should fly the CL only. SLOP is not for operators to use only in contingency situations.

North Atlantic Guidance

[ICAO NAT Doc 007, ¶8.5.1.] ATC clearances are designed to ensure that separation standards are continually maintained for all traffic. However, the chain of clearance definition, delivery and execution involves a series of technical system processes and human actions. Errors are very rare but they do occur. Neither pilots nor controllers are infallible. Gross Navigation Errors (usually involving whole latitude degree mistakes in route waypoints) are made, and aircraft are sometimes flown at flight levels other than those expected by the controller. When such errors are made, ironically, the extreme accuracies of modern navigation and height keeping systems themselves increase the risk of an actual collision. Within an SSR environment the controller is alerted to such errors and can, using VHF voice communications, intervene in a timely fashion. This is not the case in Oceanic airspace, such as the North Atlantic, where the controller's awareness of the disposition of a significant proportion of the traffic is reliant largely upon pilot position reports through communication links utilising HF or SATCOM Voice via third party radio operators. And furthermore, even among that proportion of traffic utilising data link for automated position reporting, and perhaps ATS communications, navigation errors continue to occur. Consequently, it has been determined that allowing aircraft conducting oceanic flight to fly self-selected lateral offsets will provide an additional safety margin and mitigate the risk of traffic conflict when non-normal events such as aircraft navigation errors, height deviation errors and turbulence induced altitude-keeping errors do occur. Collision risk is significantly reduced by application of these offsets. These procedures are known as "Strategic Lateral Offset Procedures (SLOP)".

[ICAO NAT Doc 007, ¶8.5.2.] This procedure provides for offsets within the following guidelines:

- along a route or track there will be three positions that an aircraft may fly: centreline or one or two miles right;
- offsets will not exceed 2 nm right of centreline; and
- offsets left of centreline must not be made.

[ICAO NAT Doc 007, ¶8.5.3.] Distributing aircraft laterally and equally across the three available positions adds an additional safety margin and reduces collision risk. Consequently, SLOP is now a standard operating procedure for the entire NAT Region and pilots are required to adopt this procedure as is appropriate. In this connection, it should be noted that:

- Aircraft without automatic offset programming capability must fly the centreline.

- Pilots of aircraft capable of programming automatic offsets should preferably not fly the centre line but rather elect to fly an offset one or two nautical miles to the right of the centre line in order to obtain lateral spacing from nearby aircraft (ie those immediately above and/or below). Pilots should use whatever means are available (e.g. ACAS/TCAS, communications, visual acquisition, GPWS) to determine the best flight path to fly.

- An aircraft overtaking another aircraft should offset within the confines of this procedure, if capable, so as to create the least amount of wake turbulence for the aircraft being overtaken.

- For wake turbulence purposes, pilots should fly one of the three positions shown above. Pilots should not offset to the left of centreline nor offset more than 2 nm right of centreline. Pilots may contact other aircraft on the air-to-air channel, 123.45 MHz, as necessary; to coordinate the best wake turbulence mutual offset option. (Note. It is recognised that the pilot will use his/her judgement to determine the action most appropriate to any given situation and that the pilot has the final authority and responsibility for the safe operations of the aeroplane. See also Chapter 12, paragraph 13.5.) As indicated below, contact with ATC is not required.

- Pilots may apply an offset outbound at the oceanic entry point and must return to centreline prior to the oceanic exit point unless otherwise authorised by the appropriate ATS authority or directed by the appropriate ATC unit.

- Aircraft transiting ATS Surveillance-controlled airspace mid-ocean should remain on their already established offset positions.

- There is no ATC clearance required for this procedure and it is not necessary that ATC be advised.

- Voice Position reports should be based on the waypoints of the current ATC clearance and not the offset positions.

[ICAO NAT Doc 007, ¶8.5.4.] SLOP has been implemented as a standard operating procedure in the NAT region since 2004. An indication of the proportion of pilots adopting a SLOP offset here is obtained through study of ADS-C position reports. Such study has shown that during 2012 more than 40% of aircraft flying in the NAT MNPS Airspace selected the 1 nm Right option and about 20% chose the 2 nm Right option. As indicated above, system safety would be further enhanced if aircraft were more evenly distributed between the centreline, 1 and 2 nm Right options. As proposed in paragraph 8.5.3 b) above, pilots should attempt to determine the offsets (if any) being flown by aircraft immediately ahead on the same track one flight level above and one flight level below. And then select an offset which differs from those. If this is not possible or practical, then pilots should randomly choose one of the three flight path options.

[NAT Doc 007, ¶8.5.5] The previously mentioned study of ADS-C position reports has also shown that some aircraft continue to adopt an offset LEFT of cleared track centre-line. The standard SLOP procedures are designed to provide safety enhancements for both uni-directional and bi-directional flows. On bi-directional routes a LEFT offset will INCREASE collision risk rather than decrease it. There are areas in the NAT Region where bi-directional traffic flows are routinely used. And there are times when opposite direction traffic may be encountered in any part of the Region. Pilots must therefore recognise that LEFT offsets from the cleared track centre-line must not be adopted. After the introduction of RVSM and before the adoption of SLOP, a NAT offsetting procedure was promulgated for wake-turbulence avoidance. This procedure allowed both right and left offsets to be flown. The procedure was developed primarily with a view to the unique traffic flows of the NAT OTS, where uni-directional traffic occupied every flight level from FL310 to FL390. That procedure is no longer in place. The avoidance of wake turbulence (even in the OTS) can be accomplished effectively within the confines of the SLOP procedures, as specified in paragraph 8.5.3 d) above. Pilots should communicate with the other aircraft involved to co-ordinate a pair of mutual offsets from within the allowed three options, in order to mitigate any wake-turbulence issue.

Random Route SLOP?

Many Gulfstream pilots feel immune to the SLOP issue, saying they always fly above the tracks and they usually fly random routing. As you can see from the drawing, there is one problem with that argument. If you are on the track, chances are you are flying the same direction as your nearest neighbor and while the sky is considerably more crowded, the chance of a collision is reduced. The guy behind you might make an altitude error but he is behind you and likely to stay behind you.

You might be on the random track because you are flying an unusual city pair or for some other reason. But what if there is somebody flying the same city pair in the opposite direction? Now what if that guy makes an altitude error? Wouldn't an extra mile of separation be nice?

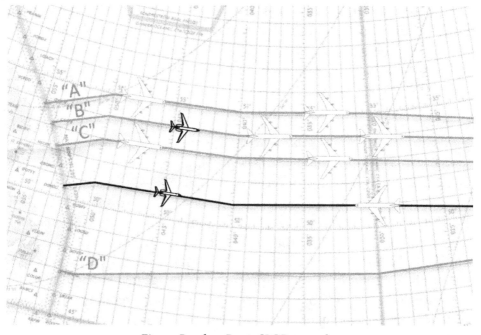

Figure: Random Route SLOP example.

540

Section VIII - Appendices

Chapter 36

Traffic Information Broadcast by Aircraft (TIBA)

*T*he IATA calls them "In-Flight Broadcast Procedures" or IFBP. The ICAO calls them Traffic Information Broadcasts by Aircraft" or TIBA. As pilots we've known them as "Broadcast in the Blind." Whatever you call them, they used to be the staple of remote flight operations in places like Africa, South America, India, and parts of Australia. There aren't many TIBA regions left but you still find them. So if you find a note on the chart calling for TIBA or IFBP, you should know this. So what's it all about?

You are broadcasting your position in space to everyone on an agreed upon frequency in hopes they are paying attention. You are listening to everyone else, hoping to decipher their English into figuring out if somebody else will be on the same airway and altitude about your time, or perhaps an intersection. If there is a conflict, you negotiate avoidance actions.

Of course all that is theory and you hope those deconflicting flight plans have done a good job. All this was really terrifying about twenty years ago. (In some parts of the world they didn't even make the pretense of speaking English.) Now your biggest fear is that they don't have TCAS or for some reason have it turned off.

Introduction and applicability of broadcasts

[ICAO Annex 11 Attachment B, para;1]

1.1 Traffic information broadcasts by aircraft are intended to permit reports and relevant supplementary information of an advisory nature to be transmitted by pilots on a designated VHF radiotelephone (RTF) frequency for the information of pilots of other aircraft in the vicinity.

1.2 TIBAs should be introduced only when necessary and as a temporary measure.

541

1.3 The broadcast procedures should be applied in designated airspace where:

- there is a need to supplement collision hazard information provided by air traffic services outside controlled airspace; or

- there is a temporary disruption of normal air traffic services.

1.4 Such airspaces should be identified by the States responsible for provision of air traffic services within these airspaces, if necessary with the assistance of the appropriate ICAO Regional Office(s), and duly promulgated in aeronautical information publications or NOTAM, together with the VHF RTF frequency, the message formats and the procedures to be used. Where, in the case of 1.3 a), more than one State is involved, the airspace should be designated on the basis of regional air navigation agreements and promulgated in Doc 7030.

1.5 When establishing a designated airspace, dates for the review of its applicability at intervals not exceeding 12 months should be agreed by the appropriate ATS authority(ies).

Details of broadcasts

[ICAO Annex 11 Attachment B, para;2]

VHF RTF frequency to be used

2.1.1 The VHF RTF frequency to be used should be determined and promulgated on a regional basis. However, in the case of temporary disruption occurring in controlled airspace, the States responsible may promulgate, as the VHF RTF frequency to be used within the limits of that airspace, a frequency used normally for the provision of air traffic control service within that airspace.

2.1.2 Where VHF is used for air-ground communications with ATS and an aircraft has only two serviceable VHF sets, one should be tuned to the appropriate ATS frequency and the other to the TIBA frequency.

Listening watch

A listening watch should be maintained on the TIBA frequency 10 minutes before entering the designated airspace until leaving this airspace. For an aircraft taking off from an aerodrome located within the lateral limits of the designated airspace listening watch should start as soon as appropriate after takeoff and be maintained until leaving the airspace.

Time of broadcasts

- A broadcast should be made:
- 10 minutes before entering the designated airspace or, for a pilot taking off from an aerodrome located within the lateral limits of the designated airspace, as soon as appropriate after takeoff;
- 10 minutes prior to crossing a reporting point;
- 10 minutes prior to crossing or joining an ATS route;
- at 20-minute intervals between distant reporting points;
- 2 to 5 minutes, where possible, before a change in flight level;
- at the time of a change in flight level; and
- at any other time considered necessary by the pilot.

Forms of broadcast

2.4.1 The broadcasts other than those indicating changes in flight level, should be in the following form:

- ALL STATIONS (necessary to identify a traffic information broadcast)
- (call sign)
- FLIGHT LEVEL (number) (or CLIMBING* TO FLIGHT LEVEL (number))
- (direction)
- (ATS route) (or DIRECT FROM (position) TO (position))
- POSITION (position**) AT (time)
- ESTIMATING (next reporting point, or the point of crossing or joining a designated ATS route) AT (time)
- (call sign)
- FLIGHT LEVEL (number)
- (direction)

Fictitious example

"ALL STATIONS WINDAR 671 FLIGHT LEVEL 350 NORTHWEST BOUND DIRECT FROM PUNTA SAGA TO PAMPA POSITION 5040 SOUTH 2010 EAST AT 2358 ESTIMATING CROSSING ROUTE LIMA THREE ONE AT 4930 SOUTH 1920 EAST AT 0012 WINDAR 671 FLIGHT LEVEL 350 NORTHWEST BOUND OUT"

2.4.2 Before a change in flight level, the broadcast (referred to in 2.3 e)) should be in the following form:

- ALL STATIONS
- (call sign)
- (direction)
- (ATS route) (or DIRECT FROM (position) TO (position))
- LEAVING FLIGHT LEVEL (number) FOR FLIGHT LEVEL (number) AT (position and time)

2.4.3 Except as provided in 2.4.4, the broadcast at the time of a change in flight level (referred to in 2.3 f)) should be in the following form:

- ALL STATIONS
- (call sign)
- (direction)
- (ATS route) (or DIRECT FROM (position) TO (position))
- LEAVING FLIGHT LEVEL (number) NOW FOR FLIGHT LEVEL (number) followed by:
- ALL STATIONS
- (call sign)
- MAINTAINING FLIGHT LEVEL (number)

2.4.4 Broadcasts reporting a temporary flight level change to avoid an imminent collision risk should be in the following form:

- ALL STATIONS
- (call sign)
- LEAVING FLIGHT LEVEL (number) NOW FOR FLIGHT LEVEL (number) followed as soon as practicable by:

- ALL STATIONS
- (call sign)
- RETURNING TO FLIGHT LEVEL (number) NOW

Acknowledgement of the broadcasts

The broadcasts should not be acknowledged unless a potential collision risk is perceived.

Related operating procedures

[ICAO Annex 11 Attachment B, para;3]

Changes of cruising level

3.1.1 Cruising level changes should not be made within the designated airspace, unless considered necessary by pilots to avoid traffic conflicts, for weather avoidance or for other valid operational reasons.

3.1.2 When cruising level changes are unavoidable, all available aircraft lighting which would improve the visual detection of the aircraft should be displayed while changing levels.

Collision avoidance

- If, on receipt of a traffic information broadcast from another aircraft, a pilot decides that immediate action is necessary to avoid an imminent collision risk, and this cannot be achieved in accordance with the right-of-way provisions of Annex 2, the pilot should:
- unless an alternative manoeuvre appears more appropriate, immediately descend 150 m (500 ft), or 300 m (1,000 ft) if above FL 290 in an area where a vertical separation minimum of 600 m (2,000 ft) is applied;
- display all available aircraft lighting which would improve the visual detection of the aircraft;
- as soon as possible, reply to the broadcast advising action being taken;
- notify the action taken on the appropriate ATS frequency; and
- as soon as practicable, resume normal flight level, notifying the action on the appropriate ATS frequency.

Normal position reporting procedures

Normal position reporting procedures should be continued at all times, regardless of any action taken to initiate or acknowledge a traffic information broadcast.

Chapter 37

True Course 10-Degree Tables

*B*ack in the old days if you were presented with a reroute when oceanic, you pulled out the charts and plotter and got to work building a new flight plan. If you were good, you could churn out three thousand miles of master document in about fifteen minutes. If you were really good, you had a book of ten-degree tables and could cut that time in half.

These days I would just call in the change to my flight planning service and have them fax, e-mail, or just read them to me over the phone. What if you don't have that kind of connectivity or if you just want to be old school for a day?

Purpose

If required to fly an unplanned oceanic flight plan — you got a reroute just prior to coast out — you need to build a new master document with courses and distances between waypoints so you can still make all the necessary checks before each point and also so you can make your post position plot. The 10-degree tables below provide your true courses and distances between any two positions expressed as latitudes (to the nearest degree) and the next position expressed as a longitude 10 degrees east or west.

For example, say you are 50°N 030°W heading to Europe and your next position will be at 51°N 020°W. You could pull out a plotter and come up with a course, add the variation, and end up with the correct true course. Then you could measure the distance, compare that to the nearest line of longitude and come up with a distance. You would probably do this a few times to make sure you didn't make a mistake, either with the plotter or your ad hoc measuring device. Or you could go to the From 50° Latitude table, check the course provided on the 51° row and Northern Hemisphere / East column and see your true course will be 081° and reading across see that the distance between these two points is 386 nautical miles.

The Tables

From 0° Lat	Northern Hemisphere		Southern Hemisphere		Distance
To Latitude	East	West	East	West	(nm)
10°	045°	315°	135°	225°	846
09	048	312	132	228	805
08	051	309	129	231	767
07	055	305	125	235	731
06	059	301	121	239	699
05	063	297	117	243	670
04	068	292	112	248	646
03	073	287	107	253	626
02	078	282	102	258	612
01	084	276	096	264	603
00	090	270	090	270	600

From 1° Lat	Northern Hemisphere		Southern Hemisphere		Distance
To Latitude	East	West	East	West	(nm)
11°	044°	316°	136°	224°	846
10	048	312	132	228	805
09	051	309	129	231	766
08	055	305	125	235	731
07	059	301	121	239	698
06	063	297	117	243	670
05	068	292	112	248	645
04	073	287	107	253	626
03	079	281	101	259	611
02	084	276	096	264	603
01	090	270	090	270	600
00	096	264	084	276	603
01	101	259	079	281	612
02	106	254	074	286	626
03	112	248	068	292	646
04	117	243	063	297	670
05	121	239	059	301	699
06	125	235	055	305	732
07	129	231	051	309	767
08	132	228	048	312	806
09	135	225	045	315	847

From 2° Lat	Northern Hemisphere		Southern Hemisphere		Distance
To Latitude	East	West	East	West	(nm)
12°	044°	316°	136°	224°	845
11	047	313	133	227	804
10	051	309	129	231	765
09	055	305	125	235	730
08	059	301	121	239	697
07	063	297	117	243	669
06	068	292	112	248	645
05	073	287	107	253	625
04	078	282	102	258	611
03	084	276	096	264	602
02	090	270	090	270	600
01	096	264	084	276	603
00	101	259	079	281	612
01	107	253	073	287	626
02	112	248	068	292	646
03	117	243	063	297	671
04	121	239	059	301	699
05	125	235	055	305	732
06	129	231	051	309	768
07	132	228	048	312	806
08	135	225	045	315	847

From 3° Lat	Northern Hemisphere		Southern Hemisphere		Distance
To Latitude	East	West	East	West	(nm)
13°	044°	316°	136°	224°	844
12	047	313	133	227	803
11	051	309	129	231	764
10	054	306	126	234	729
09	058	302	122	238	697
08	063	297	117	243	668
07	068	292	112	248	644
06	073	287	107	253	625
05	078	282	102	258	610
04	084	276	096	264	602
03	090	270	090	270	599
02	096	264	084	276	602
01	101	259	079	281	611
00	107	253	073	287	626
01	112	248	068	292	646
02	117	243	063	297	671
03	121	239	059	301	699
04	125	235	055	305	732
05	129	231	051	309	768
06	132	228	048	312	807
07	135	225	045	315	848

From 4° Lat	Northern Hemisphere		Southern Hemisphere		Distance
To Latitude	East	West	East	West	(nm)
14°	044°	316°	136°	224°	843
13	047	313	133	227	802
12	051	309	129	231	763
11	054	306	126	234	728
10	058	302	122	238	696
09	063	297	117	243	667
08	068	292	112	248	643
07	073	287	107	253	624
06	078	282	102	258	610
05	084	276	096	264	601
04	090	270	090	270	598
03	095	265	085	275	602
02	101	259	079	281	611
01	107	253	073	287	626
00	112	248	068	292	646
01	116	244	064	296	670
02	121	239	059	301	699
03	125	235	055	305	732
04	129	231	051	309	768
05	132	228	048	312	807
06	135	225	045	315	848

From 5° Lat	Northern Hemisphere		Southern Hemisphere		Distance
To Latitude	East	West	East	West	(nm)
15°	044°	316°	36°	224°	841
14	047	313	133	227	801
13	050	310	130	230	762
12	054	306	126	234	727
11	058	302	122	238	694
10	063	297	117	243	666
09	068	292	112	248	642
08	073	287	107	253	623
07	078	282	102	258	609
06	084	276	096	264	600
05	090	270	090	270	598
04	095	265	085	275	601
03	101	259	079	281	610
02	106	254	074	286	625
01	112	248	068	292	645
00	116	244	064	296	670
01	121	239	059	301	699
02	125	235	055	305	732
03	129	231	051	309	768
04	132	228	048	312	807
05	135	225	045	315	848

From 6° Lat	Northern Hemisphere		Southern Hemisphere		Distance
To Latitude	East	West	East	West	(nm)
16°	044°	316°	136°	224°	840
15	047	313	133	227	799
14	050	310	130	230	761
13	054	306	126	234	725
12	058	302	122	238	693
11	063	297	117	243	665
10	067	293	113	247	641
09	073	287	107	253	621
08	078	282	102	258	607
07	084	276	096	264	599
06	090	270	090	270	597
05	095	265	085	275	600
04	101	259	079	281	610
03	106	254	074	286	625
02	111	249	069	291	645
01	116	244	064	296	670
00	121	239	059	301	699
01	125	235	055	305	732
02	128	232	052	308	768
03	132	228	048	312	807
04	135	225	045	315	848

From 7° Lat	Northern Hemisphere		Southern Hemisphere		Distance
To Latitude	East	West	East	West	(nm)
17°	043°	317°	137°	223°	839
16	047	313	133	227	797
15	050	310	130	230	759
14	054	306	126	234	724
13	058	302	122	238	692
12	062	298	118	242	663
11	067	293	113	247	639
10	072	288	108	252	620
09	078	282	102	258	606
08	084	276	096	264	598
07	090	270	090	270	595
06	095	265	085	275	599
05	101	259	079	281	609
04	106	254	074	286	624
03	111	249	069	291	644
02	116	244	064	296	669
01	121	239	059	301	698
00	125	235	055	305	731
01	128	232	052	308	767
02	132	328	048	312	806
03	135	225	045	315	848

Section VIII - Appendices

From 8° Lat	Northern Hemisphere		Southern Hemisphere		Distance
To Latitude	East	West	East	West	(nm)
18	044	316	136	224	837
17	047	313	133	227	797
16	051	309	129	231	758
15	055	305	125	235	722
14	059	301	121	239	690
13	063	297	117	243	665
12	068	292	112	248	639
11	073	287	107	253	620
10	078	282	102	258	607
09	084	276	096	264	598
08	090	270	090	270	597
07	096	264	084	276	600
06	101	259	079	281	612
05	106	254	074	286	624
04	111	249	069	291	645
03	116	244	064	296	669
02	121	239	059	301	698
01	125	235	055	305	732
00	129	231	051	309	767
01	132	228	048	312	807
02	135	225	045	315	848

From 9° Lat	Northern Hemisphere		Southern Hemisphere		Distance
To Latitude	East	West	East	West	(nm)
19	044	316	136	224	832
18	047	313	133	227	794
17	051	309	129	231	756
16	054	306	126	234	721
15	059	301	121	239	689
14	063	297	117	243	662
13	068	292	112	248	638
12	073	287	107	253	620
11	078	282	102	258	605
10	084	276	096	264	598
09	090	270	090	270	596
08	096	264	084	276	598
07	101	259	079	281	600
06	106	254	074	286	623
05	112	248	068	292	643
04	116	244	064	296	668
03	121	239	059	301	697
02	125	235	055	305	730
01	129	231	051	309	766
00	132	228	048	312	805
01	135	225	045	315	847

From 10° Lat	Northern Hemisphere		Southern Hemisphere		Distance
To Latitude	East	West	East	West	(nm)
20	044	316	136	224	834
19	047	313	133	227	793
18	051	309	129	221	754
17	054	306	126	234	719
16	058	302	122	238	686
15	063	297	117	243	658
14	068	292	112	248	634
13	073	287	107	253	615
12	078	282	102	258	601
11	084	276	096	264	593
10	090	270	090	270	590
9	096	264	084	276	595
8	101	259	079	281	605
7	107	253	073	287	620
6	112	248	068	292	641
5	117	243	063	297	666
4	121	239	059	301	696
3	125	235	055	305	729
2	129	231	051	309	765
1	132	228	048	312	805
0	135	225	045	315	846

From 11° Lat	Northern Hemisphere		Southern Hemisphere		Distance
To Latitude	East	West	East	West	(nm)
21	044	316	136	224	832
20	047	313	133	227	791
19	050	310	130	230	752
18	054	306	126	234	716
17	058	302	122	238	684
16	063	297	117	243	656
15	068	292	112	248	632
14	073	287	107	253	613
13	078	282	102	258	599
12	084	276	096	264	591
11	090	270	090	270	589
10	096	264	084	276	593
09	101	259	079	281	603
08	107	253	073	287	619
07	112	248	068	292	639
06	117	243	063	297	665
05	121	239	059	301	695
04	125	235	055	305	728
03	129	231	051	309	765
02	132	228	048	312	804
01	135	225	045	315	846

From 12° Lat	Northern Hemisphere		Southern Hemisphere		Distance
To Latitude	East	West	East	West	(nm)
22	044	316	136	224	830
21	047	313	133	227	788
20	050	310	130	230	750
19	054	306	126	234	714
18	058	302	122	238	682
17	063	297	117	243	654
16	068	292	112	248	630
15	073	287	107	253	610
14	078	282	102	258	597
13	084	276	096	264	589
12	090	270	090	270	587
11	096	264	084	276	591
10	102	258	078	282	601
09	107	253	073	287	617
08	112	248	068	292	638
07	117	243	063	297	663
06	121	239	059	301	693
05	125	235	055	305	727
04	129	231	051	309	763
03	132	228	048	312	803
02	135	225	045	315	845

From 13° Lat	Northern Hemisphere		Southern Hemisphere		Distance
To Latitude	East	West	East	West	(nm)
23	044	316	136	224	827
22	047	313	133	227	786
21	050	310	130	230	748
20	054	306	126	234	712
19	058	302	122	238	680
18	063	297	117	243	651
17	068	292	112	248	627
16	073	287	107	253	608
15	078	282	102	258	594
14	084	276	096	264	587
13	090	270	090	270	585
12	096	264	084	276	589
11	101	259	079	281	599
10	107	253	073	287	615
09	112	248	068	292	636
08	117	243	063	297	662
07	121	239	059	301	692
06	125	235	055	305	725
05	129	231	051	309	762
04	132	228	048	312	802
03	135	225	045	315	844

From 14° Lat	Northern Hemisphere		Southern Hemisphere		Distance
To Latitude	East	West	East	West	(nm)
24	044	316	136	224	825
23	047	313	133	227	784
22	050	310	130	230	745
21	054	306	126	234	709
20	058	302	122	238	677
19	063	297	117	243	649
18	068	292	112	248	625
17	073	287	107	253	605
16	078	282	102	258	592
15	084	276	096	264	584
14	090	270	090	270	582
13	096	264	084	276	587
12	102	258	078	282	597
11	107	253	073	287	613
10	112	248	068	292	634
09	117	243	063	297	660
08	121	239	059	301	690
07	125	235	055	305	724
06	129	231	051	309	761
05	132	228	049	312	801
04	135	225	045	315	843

From 15° Lat	Northern Hemisphere		Southern Hemisphere		Distance
To Latitude	East	West	East	West	(nm)
25	043	317	137	223	823
24	046	314	134	226	781
23	050	310	130	230	743
22	054	306	126	234	707
21	058	302	122	238	674
20	062	298	118	242	646
19	067	293	113	247	622
18	073	287	107	253	603
17	078	282	102	258	589
16	084	276	096	264	581
15	090	270	090	270	580
14	096	264	084	276	584
13	102	258	078	282	594
12	107	253	073	287	610
11	112	248	068	292	632
10	117	243	063	297	658
09	121	239	059	301	688
08	125	235	055	305	722
07	129	231	051	309	759
06	132	228	048	312	799
05	135	225	045	315	842

From 16° Lat	Northern Hemisphere		Southern Hemisphere		Distance
To Latitude	East	West	East	West	(nm)
26	043	317	137	223	820
25	046	314	134	226	779
24	050	310	130	230	740
23	054	306	126	234	704
22	058	302	122	238	672
21	062	298	118	242	643
20	067	293	113	247	619
19	073	287	107	253	600
18	078	282	102	258	586
17	084	276	096	264	578
16	090	270	090	270	577
15	096	264	084	276	581
14	102	258	078	282	592
13	107	253	073	287	608
12	112	248	068	292	630
11	117	243	063	297	656
10	122	238	058	302	686
9	126	234	054	306	720
8	129	231	051	309	758
7	133	227	047	313	798
6	135	224	044	316	840

From 17° Lat	Northern Hemisphere		Southern Hemisphere		Distance
To Latitude	East	West	East	West	(nm)
27	043	317	137	223	817
26	046	314	134	226	776
25	050	310	130	230	737
24	053	307	127	233	701
23	058	302	122	238	669
22	062	298	118	242	640
21	067	293	113	247	616
20	073	287	107	253	596
19	078	282	102	258	583
18	084	276	096	264	575
17	090	270	090	270	574
16	096	264	084	276	578
15	102	258	078	282	589
14	107	253	073	287	606
13	112	248	068	292	627
12	117	243	063	297	653
11	122	238	058	302	684
10	126	234	054	306	718
09	129	231	051	309	756
08	133	227	047	313	796
07	136	224	044	316	838

From 18° Lat	Northern Hemisphere		Southern Hemisphere		Distance
To Latitude	East	West	East	West	(nm)
28	043	317	137	223	815
27	046	314	134	226	773
26	049	311	131	229	734
25	053	307	127	233	698
24	057	303	123	237	666
23	062	298	118	242	637
22	067	293	113	247	613
21	072	288	108	252	593
20	078	282	102	258	580
19	084	276	096	264	572
18	090	270	090	270	571
17	096	264	084	276	575
16	102	258	078	282	586
15	107	253	073	287	603
14	113	247	067	293	625
13	117	243	063	297	651
12	122	238	058	302	682
11	126	234	054	306	716
10	129	231	051	309	754
09	133	227	047	313	794
08	136	224	044	316	837

From 19° Lat	Northern Hemisphere		Southern Hemisphere		Distance
To Latitude	East	West	East	West	(nm)
29	043	317	137	223	812
28	046	314	134	226	770
27	049	311	131	229	731
26	053	307	127	233	695
25	057	303	123	237	662
24	062	298	118	242	633
23	067	293	113	247	609
22	072	288	108	252	590
21	078	282	102	258	576
20	084	276	096	264	569
19	090	270	090	270	567
18	096	264	084	276	572
17	102	258	078	282	583
16	107	253	073	287	600
15	113	247	067	293	622
14	118	242	002	298	649
13	122	238	058	302	680
12	126	234	054	306	714
11	130	230	050	310	752
10	133	227	047	313	793
09	136	224	044	316	835

From 20° Lat	Northern Hemisphere		Southern Hemisphere		Distance
To Latitude	East	West	East	West	(nm)
30	042	318	138	222	809
29	045	315	135	225	767
28	049	311	131	229	728
27	053	307	127	233	692
26	057	303	123	237	659
25	062	298	118	242	630
24	067	293	113	247	606
23	072	288	108	252	586
22	078	282	102	258	573
21	084	276	096	264	565
20	090	270	090	270	564
19	096	264	084	276	569
18	102	258	078	282	580
17	108	252	072	288	597
16	113	247	067	293	619
15	118	242	062	298	646
14	122	238	058	302	677
13	126	234	054	306	712
12	130	230	050	310	750
11	133	227	047	313	791
10	136	224	044	316	834

From 21° Lat	Northern Hemisphere		Southern Hemisphere		Distance
To Latitude	East	West	East	West	(nm)
31	042	318	138	222	806
30	045	315	135	225	764
29	049	311	131	229	725
28	053	307	127	233	688
27	057	303	123	237	655
26	062	298	118	242	626
25	067	293	113	247	602
24	072	288	108	252	583
23	078	282	102	258	569
22	084	276	096	264	561
21	090	270	090	270	560
20	096	264	084	276	565
19	102	258	078	282	576
18	108	252	072	288	593
17	113	247	067	293	616
16	118	242	062	298	643
15	122	238	058	302	674
14	126	234	054	306	709
13	130	230	050	310	748
12	133	227	047	313	788
11	136	224	044	316	832

25

From 22° Lat	Northern Hemisphere		Southern Hemisphere		Distance
To Latitude	East	West	East	West	(nm)
32	042	318	138	222	803
31	045	315	135	225	761
30	048	312	132	228	721
29	052	308	128	232	685
28	057	303	123	237	652
27	061	299	119	241	623
26	066	294	114	246	598
25	072	288	108	252	579
24	078	282	102	258	565
23	084	276	096	264	558
22	090	270	090	270	556
21	096	264	084	276	561
20	102	258	078	282	573
19	108	252	072	288	590
18	113	247	067	293	613
17	118	242	062	298	640
16	122	238	058	302	672
15	126	234	054	306	707
14	130	230	050	310	745
13	133	227	047	313	786
12	136	224	044	316	830

From 23° Lat	Northern Hemisphere		Southern Hemisphere		Distance
To Latitude	East	West	East	West	(nm)
33	042	318	138	222	800
32	045	315	135	225	757
31	048	312	132	228	718
30	052	308	128	232	681
29	056	304	124	236	648
28	061	299	119	241	619
27	066	294	114	246	594
26	072	288	108	252	575
25	078	282	102	258	561
24	084	276	096	264	553
23	090	270	090	270	552
22	096	264	084	276	558
21	102	258	078	282	569
20	108	252	072	288	586
19	113	247	067	293	609
18	118	242	062	298	637
17	123	237	057	303	669
16	127	233	053	307	704
15	130	230	050	310	743
14	133	227	047	313	784
13	136	224	044	316	827

From 24° Lat	Northern Hemisphere		Southern Hemisphere		Distance
To Latitude	East	West	East	West	(nm)
34	041	319	13	221	796
33	044	316	136	224	754
32	048	312	132	228	714
31	052	308	128	232	677
30	056	304	124	236	644
29	061	299	119	241	615
28	066	294	114	246	590
27	072	288	108	252	570
26	078	282	102	258	557
25	084	276	096	264	549
24	090	270	090	270	548
23	096	264	084	276	553
22	102	258	078	282	565
21	108	252	072	288	583
20	113	247	067	293	606
19	118	242	062	298	633
18	123	237	057	303	665
17	127	233	053	307	701
16	130	230	050	310	740
15	134	226	046	314	781
14	137	223	043	317	825

From 25° Lat	Northern Hemisphere		Southern Hemisphere		Distance
To Latitude	East	West	East	West	(nm)
35	041	319	139	221	793
34	044	316	136	224	750
33	048	312	132	228	710
32	052	308	128	232	673
31	056	304	124	236	640
30	061	299	119	241	610
29	066	294	114	246	586
28	072	288	108	252	566
27	078	282	102	258	552
26	084	276	096	264	545
25	090	270	090	270	544
24	096	264	084	276	549
23	102	258	078	282	561
22	108	252	072	288	579
21	113	247	067	293	602
20	118	242	062	298	630
19	123	237	057	303	662
18	127	233	053	307	698
17	131	229	049	311	737
16	134	226	046	314	779
15	137	223	043	317	823

From 26° Lat	Northern Hemisphere		Southern Hemisphere		Distance
To Latitude	East	West	East	West	(nm)
36	041	319	139	221	789
35	044	316	136	224	747
34	047	313	133	227	707
33	051	309	129	231	670
32	056	304	124	236	636
31	060	300	120	240	606
30	066	294	114	246	581
29	071	289	109	251	562
28	077	283	103	257	547
27	084	276	096	264	540
26	090	220	090	270	539
25	096	264	084	276	545
24	102	258	078	282	557
23	108	252	072	288	575
22	114	246	066	294	598
21	119	241	061	299	626
20	123	237	057	303	659
19	127	233	053	307	695
18	131	229	049	311	734
17	134	226	046	314	776
16	137	223	043	317	820

From 27° Lat	Northern Hemisphere		Southern Hemisphere		Distance
To Latitude	East	West	East	West	(nm)
37	040	320	140	220	786
36	044	316	136	224	743
35	047	313	133	227	703
34	051	309	129	231	665
33	055	305	125	235	632
32	060	300	120	240	602
31	066	294	114	246	577
30	071	289	109	251	557
29	077	283	103	255	543
28	084	276	096	264	535
27	090	270	090	270	534
26	096	264	084	276	540
25	102	258	078	282	552
24	108	252	072	288	571
23	114	246	066	294	594
22	119	241	063	299	623
21	123	237	057	303	655
20	127	233	053	307	692
19	131	229	049	311	731
18	134	226	046	314	773
17	137	223	043	317	817

Section VIII - Appendices

From 28° Lat	Northern Hemisphere		Southern Hemisphere		Distance
To Latitude	East	West	East	West	(nm)
38	040	320	140	220	782
37	043	317	137	223	739
36	047	313	133	227	699
35	051	309	129	231	661
34	055	305	125	235	627
33	060	300	120	240	597
32	065	255	115	245	572
31	071	289	109	251	552
30	077	283	103	257	538
29	084	276	096	263	531
28	090	270	090	270	530
27	096	264	084	276	535
26	103	257	077	283	548
25	109	251	071	289	566
24	114	246	066	294	590
23	119	241	061	299	619
22	123	237	057	303	652
21	128	232	052	308	688
20	131	229	049	311	728
19	134	226	046	314	770
18	137	223	043	317	815

From 29° Lat	Northern Hemisphere		Southern Hemisphere		Distance
To Latitude	East	West	East	West	(nm)
39	040	320	140	210	778
38	043	317	137	223	735
37	046	314	134	226	695
36	050	310	130	230	657
35	055	305	125	233	623
34	060	300	120	240	593
33	065	295	115	245	567
32	071	289	109	251	547
31	077	283	103	257	333
30	083	274	109	263	526
29	090	270	090	270	325
28	097	263	083	277	530
27	103	257	077	283	543
26	109	251	071	289	562
25	114	246	066	294	586
24	119	241	061	299	615
23	124	236	056	304	648
22	128	232	052	308	685
21	131	229	049	311	725
20	135	225	045	315	767
19	138	222	042	318	812

From 30° Lat	Northern Hemisphere		Southern Hemisphere		Distance
To Latitude	East	West	East	West	(nm)
40	039	321	141	219	775
39	043	317	137	223	731
38	046	314	134	226	690
37	050	310	130	230	653
36	055	305	125	235	618
35	059	301	121	239	588
34	065	295	115	245	562
33	071	289	109	251	542
32	077	283	103	257	528
31	083	2770	097	263	520
30	090	270	090	270	519
29	096	264	084	276	525
28	103	237	077	283	538
27	109	251	071	289	55
26	114	246	066	294	581
25	119	241	061	299	611
24	124	236	056	304	644
23	128	232	052	308	681
22	132	228	048	312	721
21	135	225	045	315	764
20	138	222	042	318	809

From 31° Lat	Northern Hemisphere		Southern Hemisphere		Distance
To Latitude	East	West	East	West	(nm)
41	039	321	141	219	771
40	042	318	138	222	727
39	046	314	134	226	686
38	050	310	130	230	648
37	054	306	126	234	613
36	059	301	127	239	583
35	065	295	115	245	557
34	071	289	109	231	537
33	077	283	103	257	523
32	083	277	097	263	515
31	090	270	095	270	514
30	097	263	083	277	520
29	103	257	077	283	533
28	109	251	071	289	552
27	115	245	065	295	577
26	120	240	060	300 ·	606
25	124	236	056	304	640
24	128	232	052	308	677
23	132	228	048	312	718
22	135	225	045	315	761
21	138	222	042	318	806

563

From 32° Lat	Northern Hemisphere		Southern Hemisphere		Distance
To Latitude	East	West	East	West	(nm)
42	039	321	141	219	767
41	042	318	138	222	723
40	045	315	135	225	682
39	049	311	131	229	644
38	054	306	126	234	609
37	059	301	121	239	578
36	064	296	116	244	552
35	070	290	110	250	531
34	077	283	103	257	517
33	083	277	097	263	509
32	090	270	090	270	508
31	097	263	083	277	515
30	103	257	077	283	528
29	109	251	071	289	547
28	115	245	065	295	572
27	120	240	060	300	602
26	124	236	056	304	636
25	128	232	052	308	674
24	132	228	048	312	714
23	135	225	045	315	757
22	138	222	042	318	803

From 33° Lat	Northern Hemisphere		Southern Hemisphere		Distance
To Latitude	East	West	East	West	(nm)
43	038	322	142	218	763
42	042	318	138	222	719
41	045	315	135	225	677
40	049	311	131	229	639
39	054	306	126	234	604
38	059	301	121	239	573
37	064	296	116	244	547
36	070	290	110	250	526
35	077	283	103	257	511
34	083	274	097	263	504
33	090	270	090	270	503
32	097	263	083	277	509
31	103	257	077	283	523
30	109	251	071	289	542
29	115	245	065	295	567
28	120	240	060	300	597
27	125	235	055	305	632
26	129	231	051	309	670
25	132	228	048	312	711
24	136	224	044	316	754
23	138	222	042	318	800

From 34° Lat	Northern Hemisphere		Southern Hemisphere		Distance
To Latitude	East	West	East	West	(nm)
44	038	322	142	218	759
43	041	319	139	221	715
42	045	315	135	225	673
41	049	311	131	229	634
40	053	307	127	233	599
39	058	302	122	238	568
38	064	296	116	244	541
37	070	290	110	250	520
36	076	284	104	256	506
35	083	277	097	263	498
34	090	270	090	270	497
33	097	263	083	277	504
32	103	257	077	283	517
31	110	250	071	289	537
30	115	245	065	295	562
29	120	240	060	300	593
28	125	235	055	305	627
27	129	231	051	309	665
26	133	227	047	313	707
25	136	224	044	316	750
24	139	221	041	319	796

From 35° Lat	Northern Hemisphere		Southern Hemisphere		Distance
To Latitude	East	West	East	West	(nm)
45	038	322	142	218	754
44	041	319	139	221	710
43	044	316	136	224	668
42	048	312	132	228	629
41	053	307	127	233	594
40	058	302	122	238	562
39	064	296	116	244	536
38	070	290	110	250	515
37	076	284	104	256	500
36	083	277	097	263	492
35	090	270	090	270	491
34	097	263	083	277	498
33	104	256	076	283	511
32	110	250	070	290	531
31	115	245	065	295	557
30	121	239	059	301	588
29	125	235	055	305	623
28	129	231	051	309	661
27	133	227	047	333	703
26	136	224	044	316	747
25	139	221	041	319	793

From 36° Lat	Northern Hemisphere		Southern Hemisphere		Distance
To Latitude	East	West	East	West	(nm)
46	037	323	143	217	750
45	040	320	140	220	706
44	044	316	136	224	664
43	048	312	132	228	624
42	052	308	128	232	588
41	058	302	122	238	557
40	063	297	117	243	530
39	069	291	111	249	509
38	076	284	104	256	494
37	083	277	097	263	486
36	090	270	090	270	485
35	097	263	083	277	492
34	104	256	076	284	506
33	110	250	070	293	526
32	116	244	064	296	552
31	121	239	059	301	583
30	126	234	054	306	618
29	130	230	050	310	657
28	133	227	047	313	699
27	136	224	044	316	743
26	139	221	041	319	789

From 37° Lat	Northern Hemisphere		Southern Hemisphere		Distance
To Latitude	East	West	East	West	(nm)
47	037	323	143	217	746
46	040	320	140	220	701
45	043	317	137	223	659
44	048	312	132	228	619
43	052	308	128	232	583
42	057	303	123	237	551
41	063	297	117	243	524
40	069	291	111	249	503
39	076	284	104	256	488
38	083	277	097	263	480
37	090	270	090	270	478
36	097	263	083	277	486
35	104	256	076	284	500
34	110	250	070	290	520
33	116	244	064	296	547
32	121	238	059	301	578
31	126	234	054	306	613
30	130	230	050	310	653
29	134	226	046	314	695
28	137	223	043	317	739
27	140	220	040	320	786

From 38° Lat	Northern Hemisphere		Southern Hemisphere		Distance
To Latitude	East	West	East	West	(nm)
48	036	324	144	216	742
47	039	321	141	219	697
46	043	317	137	223	654
45	047	313	133	227	614
44	052	308	128	232	579
43	057	303	123	237	545
42	063	297	117	243	518
41	069	291	111	249	496
40	076	284	104	256	481
39	083	277	097	263	473
38	090	270	090	270	472
37	097	263	083	277	479
36	104	256	076	284	494
35	110	250	070	290	515
34	116	244	064	296	541
33	122	238	058	302	573
32	126	234	054	306	609
31	130	230	050	310	648
30	134	226	046	314	690
29	137	223	043	317	735
28	140	220	040	320	782

From 39° Lat	Northern Hemisphere		Southern Hemisphere		Distance
To Latitude	East	West	East	West	(nm)
49	036	324	144	216	738
48	039	321	141	219	692
47	043	317	137	223	649
46	047	313	133	227	609
45	051	309	129	231	572
44	056	304	124	236	540
43	062	298	118	242	512
42	069	291	111	249	490
41	075	285	105	255	474
40	083	277	097	263	467
39	090	270	090	270	466
38	097	263	083	277	473
37	104	256	076	284	487
36	111	249	069	291	509
35	117	243	063	297	536
34	122	238	058	302	568
33	127	233	053	307	604
32	131	229	049	311	644
31	134	226	046	314	686
30	137	223	043	317	731
29	140	220	040	320	778

From 40° Lat	Northern Hemisphere		Southern Hemisphere		Distance
To Latitude	East	West	East	West	(nm)
50	035	325	145	215	733
49	039	321	141	219	688
48	042	318	138	222	644
47	046	314	134	226	604
46	051	309	129	231	567
45	056	304	124	236	534
44	062	298	118	242	506
43	068	292	112	248	484
42	075	285	105	255	468
41	083	277	097	263	460
40	090	270	090	270	459
39	097	263	083	277	467
38	104	256	076	284	481
37	111	249	069	291	503
36	117	243	063	297	530
35	122	238	058	302	562
34	127	233	053	301	599
33	131	229	049	311	639
32	135	225	045	315	682
31	138	222	042	318	727
30	141	219	039	321	775

From 41° Lat	Northern Hemisphere		Southern Hemisphere		Distance
To Latitude	East	West	East	West	(nm)
51	03	325	145	215	729
50	038	322	142	218	683
49	042	318	138	222	640
48	046	314	134	226	599
47	050	310	130	230	561
46	056	304	124	236	528
45	061	299	119	241	500
44	068	292	112	248	477
43	075	285	105	255	461
42	082	228	098	262	453
41	090	270	090	270	453
40	098	262	082	278	460
39	105	255	075	285	475
38	111	249	069	291	496
37	117	243	063	297	524
36	123	237	057	303	557
35	127	233	053	307	594
34	131	229	049	311	634
33	13	225	045	315	677
32	138	222	042	318	723
31	141	219	039	321	771

From 42° Lat	Northern Hemisphere		Southern Hemisphere		Distance
To Latitude	East	West	East	West	(nm)
52	034	326	146	214	725
51	038	322	142	218	679
50	041	319	139	221	635
49	045	315	135	225	593
48	050	310	130	230	556
47	055	305	125	235	522
46	061	299	119	241	493
45	068	292	112	248	471
44	075	285	105	255	455
43	082	278	098	262	446
42	090	270	090	270	446
41	098	262	082	278	453
40	105	255	075	285	468
39	112	248	068	292	490
38	118	242	062	298	518
37	123	237	057	303	551
36	128	232	052	308	588
35	132	228	048	312	629
34	135	225	045	315	673
33	139	221	041	319	719
32	141	219	039	321	767

From 43° Lat	Northern Hemisphere		Southern Hemisphere		Distance
To Latitude	East	West	East	West	(nm)
53	034	326	146	214	720
52	037	323	143	217	674
51	041	319	139	221	630
50	045	315	135	225	588
49	049	311	131	229	550
48	055	305	125	235	516
47	061	299	119	241	487
46	067	293	113	247	464
45	075	285	105	255	448
44	082	278	098	262	439
43	090	270	090	270	439
42	098	262	082	278	446
41	105	255	075	285	461
40	112	248	068	292	484
39	118	242	062	298	512
38	123	237	057	303	545
37	128	232	052	308	583
36	132	228	048	312	624
35	136	224	044	316	668
34	139	221	041	319	715
33	142	218	038	322	763

From 44° Lat	Northern Hemisphere		Southern Hemisphere		Distance
To Latitude	East	West	East	West	(nm)
54	031	327	147	213	716
53	037	323	143	217	669
52	040	320	140	220	625
51	044	316	166	224	583
50	049	311	131	229	544
49	054	306	126	234	510
48	060	300	120	240	480
47	067	293	113	247	457
46	074	286	106	254	441
45	082	278	098	262	432
44	090	270	090	270	431
43	098	262	082	278	439
42	105	255	075	285	455
41	112	248	068	292	477
40	118	242	062	298	506
39	124	236	056	304	540
38	128	232	052	308	578
37	133	227	047	313	619
36	136	224	044	316	664
35	139	221	041	319	710
34	142	218	038	322	759

From 45° Lat	Northern Hemisphere		Southern Hemisphere		Distance
To Latitude	East	West	East	West	(nm)
55	033	327	147	213	712
54	036	324	144	216	665
53	039	321	141	219	620
52	044	346	136	224	577
51	048	312	132	228	538
50	054	306	126	234	504
49	060	300	120	240	474
48	067	293	113	247	450
47	074	286	106	254	433
46	082	278	098	262	425
45	090	270	090	270	424
44	098	262	082	278	432
43	106	254	074	286	448
42	112	248	068	292	471
41	119	241	061	299	500
40	124	236	056	304	534
39	129	231	051	309	522
38	133	227	047	313	614
37	137	223	043	317	659
36	140	220	040	320	706
35	142	218	038	322	755

From 46° Lat	Northern Hemisphere		Southern Hemisphere		Distance
To Latitude	East	West	East	West	(nm)
56	032	328	148	212	707
55	035	325	145	215	660
54	039	321	141	219	615
53	043	317	137	223	572
52	048	312	132	228	533
51	053	307	127	233	497
50	059	301	121	239	467
49	066	294	114	246	443
48	074	286	106	254	426
47	082	278	098	262	417
46	090	270	090	270	417
45	098	262	082	278	425
44	106	254	074	286	441
43	113	247	067	293	464
42	119	241	061	299	493
41	125	235	055	305	528
40	129	231	051	309	567
39	133	227	047	313	609
38	137	223	043	317	654
37	140	220	040	320	701
36	143	217	037	323	750

From 47° Lat	Northern Hemisphere		Southern Hemisphere		Distance
To Latitude	East	West	East	West	(nm)
57	032	328	148	212	703
56	035	325	145	215	655
55	038	322	142	218	610
54	042	318	138	222	566
53	047	313	133	227	527
52	053	307	127	233	491
51	059	301	121	239	460
50	066	294	114	246	436
49	073	287	107	253	419
48	082	278	098	262	410
47	090	270	090	270	409
46	098	262	082	278	417
45	106	254	074	286	433
44	113	247	067	293	457
43	119	241	061	299	487
42	125	235	055	305	522
41	130	230	050	310	561
40	134	226	046	314	604
39	138	222	042	318	649
38	141	219	039	321	697
37	143	217	037	323	746

From 48° Lat	Northern Hemisphere		Southern Hemisphere		Distance
To Latitude	East	West	East	West	(nm)
58	031	329	149	211	699
57	034	326	146	214	651
56	038	322	142	218	604
55	042	318	138	222	561
54	047	313	133	227	521
53	052	308	128	232	485
52	058	302	122	238	454
51	065	295	115	245	428
50	073	287	107	253	401
49	081	279	099	261	402
48	090	270	090	270	401
47	098	262	082	278	410
46	106	254	074	286	426
45	114	246	066	294	450
44	120	240	060	300	480
43	125	235	055	305	516
42	130	230	050	310	556
41	134	226	046	314	599
40	138	222	042	318	644
39	141	219	039	321	692
38	144	216	036	324	742

From 49° Lat	Northern Hemisphere		Southern Hemisphere		Distance
To Latitude	East	West	East	West	(nm)
59	031	329	149	211	694
58	034	326	146	214	646
57	037	323	143	217	599
56	041	319	139	221	556
55	046	314	134	226	515
54	051	309	129	231	478
53	058	302	122	238	447
52	065	295	115	245	422
51	073	287	107	253	404
50	081	279	099	261	394
49	090	270	090	270	393
48	099	261	081	279	402
47	107	253	073	287	419
46	114	246	066	294	443
45	120	240	060	300	474
44	126	234	054	306	510
43	131	229	049	311	550
42	135	225	045	315	593
41	138	222	042	318	640
40	142	218	038	322	688
39	144	215	036	324	738

From 50° Lat	Northern Hemisphere		Southern Hemisphere		Distance
To Latitude	East	West	East	West	(nm)
60	030	330	150	210	690
59	033	327	147	213	641
58	036	324	144	216	594
57	040	320	140	220	550
56	045	315	135	225	509
55	051	309	129	231	472
54	057	303	123	237	440
53	064	296	116	244	414
52	072	288	108	252	396
51	081	279	099	261	386
50	090	270	090	270	385
49	099	261	081	279	394
48	107	253	073	287	411
47	114	246	066	294	436
46	121	239	059	301	467
45	126	234	054	306	504
44	131	229	049	311	544
43	135	225	045	315	588
42	139	221	041	319	635
41	142	218	038	322	683
40	145	215	035	325	733

From 51° Lat	Northern Hemisphere		Southern Hemisphere		Distance
To Latitude	East	West	East	West	(nm)
61	029	331	151	209	686
60	032	328	148	212	637
59	036	324	144	126	589
58	040	320	140	220	545
57	045	315	135	225	503
56	050	310	130	230	465
55	057	303	123	237	433
54	064	296	116	244	407
53	072	288	108	252	388
52	081	229	099	261	378
51	090	270	090	270	377
50	099	261	081	279	386
49	107	253	073	287	404
48	115	245	065	295	429
47	121	239	059	301	460
46	127	233	053	307	497
45	132	228	048	312	538
44	136	224	044	316	583
43	140	220	040	320	630
42	143	217	037	323	679
41	145	215	035	325	729

From 52° Lat	Northern Hemisphere		Southern Hemisphere		Distance
To Latitude	East	West	East	West	(nm)
62	029	331	151	209	682
61	032	328	148	212	632
60	035	325	145	215	584
59	039	321	141	219	539
58	044	316	136	224	497
57	049	311	131	229	459
56	056	304	124	236	426
55	063	297	117	243	399
54	072	288	108	252	380
53	081	279	099	261	370
52	090	270	090	270	369
51	099	261	081	279	378
50	108	252	072	288	396
49	115	245	065	295	422
48	122	238	058	302	454
47	128	232	052	308	491
46	132	228	048	312	533
45	137	223	043	317	577
44	140	220	040	320	625
43	143	217	037	323	674
42	146	214	034	326	725

From 53° Lat	Northern Hemisphere		Southern Hemisphere		Distance
To Latitude	East	West	East	West	(nm)
63	028	332	152	208	677
62	031	329	149	211	627
61	034	326	146	214	579
60	038	322	142	218	534
59	043	317	137	223	491
58	049	311	131	229	453
57	055	303	125	235	419
56	063	297	117	243	392
55	071	289	109	251	372
54	081	279	099	261	362
53	090	270	090	270	361
52	099	261	081	279	370
51	108	252	072	288	388
50	116	244	064	296	414
49	122	238	058	302	447
48	128	232	052	308	485
47	133	227	047	313	527
46	137	223	043	317	572
45	141	219	039	321	620
44	144	216	036	324	669
43	146	214	034	326	720

From 54° Lat	Northern Hemisphere		Southern Hemisphere		Distance
To Latitude	East	West	East	West	(nm)
64	027	333	153	207	673
63	030	330	150	210	623
62	034	326	146	214	574
61	038	322	142	218	528
60	042	318	138	222	485
59	048	312	132	228	446
58	055	305	125	235	412
57	062	298	118	242	384
56	071	289	109	251	364
55	080	280	100	260	353
54	090	270	090	270	352
53	100	260	080	280	362 ¬
52	108	252	072	288	380
51	116	244	064	296	407
50	123	237	057	303	440
49	129	231	051	309	478
48	134	226	046	314	521
47	138	222	042	318	566
46	141	219	039	321	615
45	144	216	036	324	665
44	147	213	033	327	716

From 55° Lat	Northern Hemisphere		Southern Hemisphere		Distance
To Latitude	East	West	East	West	(nm)
65	027	333	153	207	669
64	030	330	150	210	618
63	033	327	147	213	570
62	037	323	143	217	523
61	042	318	138	222	479
60	047	313	133	227	440
59	054	306	126	234	405
58	062	298	118	242	376
57	070	290	110	250	356
56	080	280	100	260	345
55	090	270	090	270	344 ¬
54	100	260	080	280	353
53	109	251	071	289	372
52	117	243	063	297	399
51	124	236	056	304	433
50	129	231	051	309	472
49	134	226	046	314	515
48	138	222	042	318	561
47	142	218	038	322	610
46	145	215	035	325	660
45	147	213	033	327	712

From 56° Lat	Northern Hemisphere		Southern Hemisphere		Distance
To Latitude	East	West	East	West	(nm)
66	026	334	154	206	665
65	029	331	151	209	614
64	032	328	148	212	565
63	036	324	144	216	318
62	041	319	139	221	473
61	046	314	134	226	433
60	053	307	127	233	398
59	061	299	119	241	369
58	070	290	110	250	348
57	080	280	100	260	336
56	090	270	090	270	335
55	100	260	080	280	345
54	109	251	071	289	364
53	117	243	063	297	392
52	124	236	056	304	426
51	130	230	050	310	465
50	134	226	046	314	509
49	139	221	041	319	556
48	142	218	038	322	604
47	145	215	035	325	655
46	148	212	032	328	707

From 57° Lat	Northern Hemisphere		Southern Hemisphere		Distance
To Latitude	East	West	East	West	(nm)
67	025	335	155	205	661
66	028	332	152	208	610
65	031	329	149	211	560
64	035	325	145	215	512
63	040	320	140	220	468
62	046	314	134	226	427
61	052	308	128	232	391
60	060	300	120	240	361
59	069	291	111	249	339
58	079	281	101	259	328
57	090	270	090	270	327
56	100	260	080	280	336
55	110	250	070	290	355
54	118	242	062	298	384
53	125	235	055	305	419
52	131	229	049	311	459
51	136	224	044	316	503
50	140	220	040	320	550
49	143	217	037	323	599
48	146	214	034	326	651
47	148	212	032	328	703

From 58° Lat	Northern Hemisphere		Southern Hemisphere		Distance
To Latitude	East	West	East	West	(nm)
68	025	335	155	205	657
67	027	333	153	207	605
66	031	329	149	211	555
65	034	326	146	214	507
64	039	321	141	219	462
63	045	315	135	225	420
62	051	309	129	231	384
61	060	300	120	240	353
60	069	291	111	249	331
59	079	281	101	259	319
58	090	270	090	270	318
57	101	259	079	281	328
56	110	250	070	290	348
55	119	241	061	299	376
54	126	234	054	306	412
53	131	229	049	311	453
52	136	224	044	316	497
51	140	220	040	320	545
50	144	216	036	324	594
49	146	214	034	326	646
48	149	211	031	329	699

From 59° Lat	Northern Hemisphere		Southern Hemisphere		Distance
To Latitude	East	West	East	West	(nm)
69	024	336	156	204	653
68	027	333	153	207	601
67	030	330	150	210	550
66	034	326	146	214	502
65	038	322	142	218	456
64	044	316	136	224	414
63	051	309	129	231	376
62	059	301	121	239	345
61	068	292	112	248	323
60	079	281	101	259	310
59	090	270	090	270	309
58	101	259	079	281	319
57	111	249	069	291	339
56	119	241	061	299	369
55	126	234	054	306	405
54	132	228	048	312	446
53	137	223	043	317	491
52	141	219	039	321	539
51	144	216	036	324	589
50	147	213	033	327	641
49	150	210	030	330	694

From 60° Lat	Northern Hemisphere		Southern Hemisphere		Distance
To Latitude	East	West	East	West	(nm)
70	023	337	157	203	649
69	026	334	154	206	597
68	029	331	151	209	546
67	033	327	147	213	497
66	037	323	143	217	450
65	043	317	137	223	408
64	050	310	130	230	369
63	058	302	122	238	338
62	068	292	112	248	314
61	079	281	101	259	301
60	090	270	090	270	300
59	101	259	079	281	310
58	111	249	069	291	331
57	120	240	060	300	361
56	127	233	053	307	398
55	133	227	047	313	440
54	138	222	042	318	485
53	142	218	038	322	534
52	145	215	035	325	584
51	148	212	032	328	637
50	150	210	030	330	690

From 61° Lat	Northern Hemisphere		Southern Hemisphere		Distance
To Latitude	East	West	East	West	(nm)
71	022	338	158	202	646
70	025	335	155	205	593
69	028	332	152	208	541
68	032	328	148	212	492
67	036	324	144	216	445
66	042	318	138	222	401
65	049	311	131	229	362
64	057	303	123	237	330
63	067	293	113	247	306
62	078	282	102	258	292
61	090	270	090	270	291
60	102	258	078	282	301
59	112	248	068	292	323
58	121	239	059	301	353
57	128	232	052	308	391
56	134	226	046	314	433
55	139	221	041	319	479
54	142	218	038	322	528
53	146	214	034	326	579
52	148	212	032	328	632
51	151	209	029	331	686

From 62° Lat	Northern Hemisphere		Southern Hemisphere		Distance
To Latitude	East	West	East	West	(nm)
72	021	339	159	201	642
71	024	336	156	204	589
70	027	333	153	207	537
69	031	329	149	211	487
68	035	325	145	215	439
67	041	319	139	221	395
66	048	312	132	228	355
65	056	304	124	236	322
64	066	294	114	246	297
63	078	282	102	258	283
62	090	270	090	270	281
61	102	258	078	282	292
60	112	248	068	292	314
59	121	239	059	301	345
58	129	231	051	309	384
57	135	225	045	315	427
56	139	221	041	319	473
55	143	217	037	323	523
54	146	216	034	326	574
53	149	211	031	329	627
52	151	209	029	331	682

From 63° Lat	Northern Hemisphere		Southern Hemisphere		Distance
To Latitude	East	West	East	West	(nm)
73	021	339	159	201	639
72	023	337	157	203	585
71	026	334	154	206	533
70	030	330	150	210	482
69	034	326	146	214	434
68	040	320	140	220	389
67	047	313	133	227	348
66	055	305	125	235	314
65	066	294	114	246	289
64	077	283	103	257	274
63	090	270	090	270	272
62	102	258	078	282	283
61	113	247	067	293	306
60	122	238	058	302	338
59	129	231	051	309	376
58	135	225	045	315	420
57	140	220	040	320	468
56	144	216	036	324	518
55	147	213	033	327	570
54	150	210	030	330	623
53	152	208	028	332	677

From 64° Lat	Northern Hemisphere		Southern Hemisphere		Distance
To Latitude	East	West	East	West	(nm)
73	022	338	158	202	582
72	025	335	155	205	529
71	029	331	151	209	478
70	033	327	147	213	429
69	039	321	141	219	383
68	046	314	134	226	342
67	054	306	126	234	307
66	065	295	115	245	281
65	077	283	103	257	265
64	090	270	090	270	263
63	103	257	077	283	275
62	114	246	066	294	298
61	123	237	057	303	330
60	130	230	050	310	370
59	136	224	044	316	414
58	141	219	039	321	462
57	145	215	035	325	513
56	148	212	032	328	565
55	150	210	030	330	619
54	153	207	027	333	674
0	135	225	045	315	846

From 65° Lat	Northern Hemisphere		Southern Hemisphere		Distance
To Latitude	East	West	East	West	(nm)
74	021	339	159	201	578
73	024	336	156	204	524
72	028	332	152	208	473
71	032	328	148	212	423
70	037	323	143	217	377
69	044	316	136	224	335
68	053	307	127	233	299
67	064	296	116	244	272
66	076	284	104	256	256
65	270	090	270	270	254
64	103	257	077	283	265
63	114	246	066	294	289
62	124	236	056	304	322
61	131	229	049	311	363
60	137	223	043	317	408
59	142	218	038	322	456
58	146	214	034	326	507
57	149	211	031	329	559
56	151	209	029	331	614
55	153	207	027	333	669
01	135	225	045	315	846

Chapter 38

Visa Waiver Program

*W*ill a foreign national need a Visa when entering the United States? That depends on their nationality, the purpose of the visit, duration of stay, and many other variables. Fortunately the U.S. Department of State has a nifty "Visa Wizard" that gives you an easy answer to this complicated question: http://travel.state.gov/content/visas/english/general/visa-wizard.html.*

An operator requires State Department approval to carry pasengers under the VWP. Part 91 operators are eligible.

Visa Basics

[http://travel.state.gov/content/visas/english/visit.html]

- Foreign travelers to the United States for short visits, for example tourism, vacation, visiting family and friends, or medical treatment, need visitor visas unless they qualify for entry under the VWP.

- Most citizens of participating countries may travel to the United States for short visits without a visa through the Visa Waiver Program.

- Citizens of Canada and Bermuda generally do not need visas for tourism and visits.

- There are several types of Visas, including B - Visitor, E1 through E5 - Employment, and H - Temporary Worker

It is up to you, or an agent working on your behalf, to ensure you and your pasengers have what they need in terms of Visas to enter the United States. The particulars of their Visa may also impact the manner in which they can leave the country too. It is all getting easier, thanks to the electronic record keeping in place at the U.S. Department of State and at the Customs and Border Protection agency. The State Department's Visa Wizard can get you started in the right direction: http://travel.state.gov/content/visas/english/general/visa-wizard.html.

Applying for a Visa is simple enough, but it can be time consuming. If your prospective passenger is eligible for the Visa Waiver Program, that is the way to go. More about that . . .

Visa Waiver Program — Participating Countries

[http://travel.state.gov/content/visas/english/visit.html] Andorra, Australia, Austria, Belgium, Brunei, Chile, Czech Republic, Denmark, Estonia, Finland, France, Germany, Greece, Hungary, Iceland, Ireland, Italy, Japan, Latvia, Liechtenstein, Lithuania, Luxembourg, Malta, Monaco, Netherlands, New Zealand, Norway, Portugal, San Marino, Singapore, Slovakia, Slovenia, South Korea, Spain, Sweden, Switzerland, Taiwan, United Kingdom.

Non-immigrant Visitors on Visa Waiver Program (VWP)

[Visa Waiver Program]

- The VWP allows citizens of participating countries to travel to the United States without a visa for stays of 90 days or less, when they meet all requirements explained below. Travelers must be eligible to use the VWP and have a valid Electronic System for Travel Authorization (ESTA) approval prior to travel.

- If you are eligible to travel on the VWP, but prefer to have a visa in your passport, you may still apply for a visitor (B) visa.

- Each Traveler Must have authorization under ESTA. In order to travel without a visa on the VWP, you must have authorization through the ESTA prior to boarding a U.S. bound air or sea carrier. ESTA is the Department of Homeland Security (DHS), Customs and Border Protection's (CBP) automated web-based system to determine eligibility to travel without a visa to the United States for tourism or business. Visit the ESTA web page on the CBP website for more detailed information, to apply for ESTA, and pay the fee.

- Travel Must be on an Approved Carrier — If arriving by air or sea, you must be arriving on an approved air or sea carrier. You must also have a round trip ticket indicating return passage to a country outside the United States.

If under 14 CFR 135, your certificate holder must be approved under the VWP. If under 14 CFR 91, you as an operator must be approved.

- Previous Compliance and No Prior Visa Ineligibilities — If you have had a U.S. visa before or previously traveled to the United States under the VWP or another status, you must have complied with the conditions of previous admissions to the United States, and you must not have previously been found ineligible for a U.S. visa. Travelers should be aware that by requesting admission under the Visa Waiver Program, they are generally waiving their right to review or appeal a CBP officer's decision as to their application for admission at the port of entry. See the CBP website for additional details.

- Have the Correct Type of Passport — You must have a passport that is valid for at least 6 months after your planned departure from the United States (unless exempted by country-specific agreements). For families, each member of your family, including infants and children, must have his/her own passport.

Generally speaking, the passenger will need an e-Passport, one with an electronic chip integrated into the passports. Some countries still allow machine-readable passports without the chip. Traveler's should contact their country's passport issuing authority.

ESTA Facts

[ESTA]

- All Visa Waiver Program (VWP) travelers are required to obtain a travel authorization via the Electronic System for Travel Authorization (ESTA) prior to traveling to the U.S. under the VWP.

- The VWP allows visitors from participating countries to travel to the U.S. for business or pleasure for 90 days or less without obtaining a visa. ESTA enhances the security of the VWP and has allowed the U.S. government to expand membership in the program.

- Travel authorizations are generally valid for two years or until your passport expires, whichever comes first. A visitor may travel to the U.S. repeatedly within the validity period without having to apply for another ESTA authorization.

- If I am approved through ESTA to travel to the U.S., does that mean I can enter the country? Not necessarily. Approval only authorizes a traveler to board a plane or ship for travel to the United States without a visa. In all cases, U.S. Customs and Border Protection officers make admissibility determinations at ports of entry or preclearance facilities.

- Do VWP travelers need to bring a paper printout of their ESTA approval to the airport? No. DHS communicates a traveler's ESTA status to the carriers. However, DHS recommends that travelers print out the ESTA application response as a record of their ESTA application number.

If you have passengers on the Visa Waiver Program, it is up to them to complete the ESTA steps. It is no longer necessary for you to fill out, give out, or collect the green cards.

Visa Waiver Program Signatory Carriers

Only carriers who are specifically approved and listed by the U.S. Customs and Border Protection department are allowed to carry passengers taking advantage of the Visa Waiver Program. This used to be the special domain of commercial carriers but 14 CFR 91 operators can be approved.

The U.S. Customs and Border Protection department maintains a list of VWP Signatory Carriers on their website: http://www.cbp.gov/travel/international-visitors/visa-waiver-program. You need to be on that list to participate as a carrier, even if you are flying strictly 14 CFR 91.

To apply for VWP Signatory Status, refer to the CBP website page on the subject: http://www.cbp.gov/travel/international-visitors/business-pleasure/vwp/signatory-status. They reorganize their website often and if this link goes dead, go to the www.cbp.gov website and do a search for "VWP Signatory Status Application."

We did this about five years ago and it was pretty easy, taking one phone call, one letter, and a few weeks of waiting. Our contract was written with 7 years of validity.

Chapter 39

Waypoint Symbology

*T*here are various U.S. and international regulations with opinions on how to best annotate your master document, but no one way. Whatever method you choose, you should be able to explain it if an inspector ever comes knocking on your door.

Technique

Here is the method I grew up with, it has served me well for years . . .

The waypoint or waypoint number (for aircraft LRNS requiring numbered waypoints) is circled to indicate that the course and distance information has been compared to the plotting chart and its database coordinates have been checked.

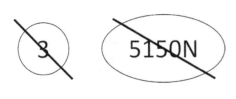

A diagonal line will be drawn through the circled waypoint to show that the course and distance displayed in the FMS has been verified against the master document and plotting or en route chart.

Following acknowledgement of the position report, a second diagonal line will be drawn through the circled waypoint (creating an "X") on the master document to indicate these duties have been completed.

Of course there are other techniques out there . . .

Advisory Circular

[AC 91-70A, ¶3-5.b.]

- Circle the waypoint, waypoint number, or symbol to signify that another crewmember independently crosschecks the entry of the coordinates in the navigation computer;

- Tick or diagonally slash the circled waypoint, waypoint number, or symbol to signify the crosschecking of track and distance information within a specified tolerance; and

  NOTE: Some operators use a diagonal line approaching a waypoint to confirm a subsequent waypoint to include coordinates, track, and distance.

- Cross out the circled waypoint, waypoint number, or symbol to signify that the aircraft has passed the waypoint. Pilots must verify all navigational information contained in the master document against the best available primary data source. Cross out old waypoints and insert the new information.

North Atlantic

[ICAO NAT Doc 007, ¶ 8.2.7.]

a. The waypoint number is entered against the relevant waypoint coordinates to indicate that the waypoint has been inserted into the navigation computers.

b. The waypoint number is circled, to signify that insertion of the correct coordinates in the navigation computers has been double-checked independently by another crew member.

c. The circled waypoint number is ticked, to signify that the relevant track and distance information has been double-checked.

d. The circled waypoint number is crossed out, to signify that the aircraft has overflown the waypoint concerned.

Chapter 40

World Geodetic System (WGS-84)

*F*or those pilots who want to avoid all things tech, or understanding all things tech, here is what you need to know about WGS-84 in a nutshell:

- *The United States Department of Defense first developed GPS for military uses and that eventually morphed into a worldwide civil system of navigation.*

- *Various entities around the world started cataloging the positions of things on earth as a way of finding them and, of course, avoiding them. The standard most of us use is known as the World Geodetic System of 1984, or WGS-84.*

- *If your aircraft and its database uses WGS-84 — and most do — then it is critically important that your navigation and approach charts are based on WGS-84 too.*

- *Part of your mission planning to international destinations needs to ask this question for every procedure you fly: is this WGS-84 compliant?*

- *You aircraft manufacturer might require you to deselect GPS in non-WGS-84 areas while en route (Gulfstream does not in the G450) and for approach (Gulfstream does).*

Oblate Spheroid

7,901 miles
(12,715.43 km)

7,926.41 miles
(12,756.32 kilometers)

Sphere "Flattening"

The earth is basically round because gravity pulls with equal strength in all directions, tending to smooth variations towards a norm. But it isn't perfectly round, the centrifugal effects of its rotation tends to make it wider in the middle than it is tall. Technically, you would call the basic shape an oblate spheroid.

Sphere versus Geoid

It is helpful to think of the earth's shape as a "geoid," the shape it would most closely resemble figuring the effects of gravity.

[National Geodetic Survey] geoid: The equipotential surface of the Earth's gravity field which best fits, in a least squares sense, global mean sea level.

Even though we adopt a definition, that does not mean we are perfect in the realization of that definition. For example, altimetry is often used to define "mean sea level" in the oceans, but altimetry is not global (missing the near polar regions). As such, the fit between "global" mean sea level and the geoid is not entirely confirmable.

The earth doesn't conform to the geoid because the magnetic field isn't uniform and the earth's surface is filled with varying heights of land as well as a sea that does not maintain the same level throughout.

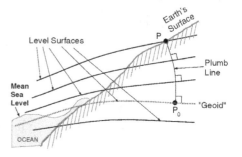

Level Surface = Equipotential Surface
H (Orthometric Height) = Distance along Plumb line (P_0 to P)

Figure: Schematic diagram, from National Geodetic Survey.

Mapping the Earth

[Geodesy for the Layman, Ch. 8] The Department of Defense, in the late 1950's began to develop the needed world system to which geodetic datums could be referred and compatibility established between the coordinates of widely separated sites of interest. Efforts of the Army, Navy and Air Force were combined leading to the DoD World Geodetic System 1960 (WGS 60).

The survey was updated in 1966, 1972, and finally in 1984, hence . . .

Adopting a Standard

["FAQs for Operations in Non WGS 84 Airspace," pg. 11]

With the deployment of the GPS constellation, the surveying process was updated in 1984 to incorporate GPS as the primary method of reference. Therefore, the '84' is appended to the name to identify the year that the system was last updated.

Throughout history, there have been numerous methods to survey the surface of the earth, but the WGS-84 system is the most accurate, having an overall fidelity of less than 1 meter. As an example, the WGS-84 system placed the actual Prime Meridian (0° line of longitude) approximately 100 meters east of where it traditionally lies in Greenwich, UK. This is a prime example of how different methodologies can yield different results.

In 1989, ICAO officially adopted WGS-84 as the standard geodetic reference system for future navigation with respect to international civil aviation. With this policy, virtually all countries use the WGS-84 standard to publish waypoint coordinates for navigation (e.g., airports, runways, navaids, etc.).

Technical Definition

[NIMA, ¶2.1] The WGS 84 Coordinate System is a Conventional Terrestrial Reference System (CTRS). The definition of this coordinate system follows the criteria outlined in the International Earth Rotation Service (IERS) Technical Note 21 [1]. These criteria are repeated below:

- It is geocentric, the center of mass being defined for the whole Earth including oceans and atmosphere

- Its scale is that of the local Earth frame, in the meaning of a relativistic theory of gravitation

- Its orientation was initially given by the Bureau International de l'Heure (BIH) orientation of 1984.0

- Its time evolution in orientation will create no residual global rotation with regards to the crust

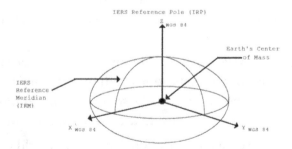

Figure: WGS84 Coordinate System Definition, from NIMA, Figure 2.1

The WGS 84 Coordinate System is a right-handed, Earth-fixed orthogonal coordinate system and is graphically depicted in [the figure].

- Origin = Earth's center of mass

- Z-Axis = The direction of the IERS Reference Pole (IRP). This direction corresponds to the direction of the BIH Conventional Terrestrial Pole (CTP) (epoch 1984.0) with an uncertainty of 0.005

- X-Axis = Intersection of the IERS Reference Meridian (IRM) and the plane passing through the origin and normal to the Z-axis. The IRM is coincident with the BIH Zero Meridian (epoch 1984.0) with an uncertainty of 0.005

- Y-Axis = Completes a right-handed, Earth-Centered Earth-Fixed (ECEF) orthogonal coordinate system

The WGS 84 Coordinate System origin also serves as the geometric center of the WGS 84 Ellipsoid and the Z-axis serves as the rotational axis of this ellipsoid of revolution.

The World Geodetic System 84 is a standard used by most of the world to define exactly where a set of coordinates are on the earth. The issues on using one standard versus another are more than just determining where something is left, right, forward, and aft. Another issue is that the world isn't a perfect sphere, or geoid, and defining where something is can also vary in height above the center of the earth.

ICAO Requirement

[ICAO Doc 9613 ¶1.2.5.2] The navigation data published in the State AIP for the routes and supporting navigation aids must meet the requirements of Annex 15 — Aeronautical Information Services. All routes must be based upon WGS-84 coordinates.

[ICAO Doc 9613 ¶3.4] Navigation data may originate from survey observations, from equipment specifications/settings or from the airspace and procedure design process. Whatever the source, the generation and the subsequent processing of the data must take account of the following:

a.   all coordinate data must be referenced to the World Geodetic System — 1984 (WGS-84);

b.   all surveys must be based upon the International Terrestrial Reference Frame;

c.   all data must be traceable to their source;

d.   equipment used for surveys must be adequately calibrated;

WGS-84 Compliance

The Jeppesen State pages list WGS-84 compliance but are not always up-to-date. Jeppesen offers a better list at: http://www.jeppesen.com/company/publications/wgs-84.jsp.

Non-WGS-84 Airspace

["FAQs for Operations in Non WGS 84 Airspace," pg. 11] Several countries such as China and Russia have not adopted the WGS-84 standard, and continue to use their own methods to survey their airports and navaids. Although the fidelity of their methods are not in question, the simple fact that using different methods exposes the possibility that position information may not match when compared to WGS-84 methods. In any event, non-WGS-84 countries publish their navigational information in similar fashion to WGS-84 countries. This information is also compiled and disseminated in formats such as navigation charts and FMS Navigation Databases.

For the purposes of navigation, the FMS normally compares actual GPS location against the location of waypoints defined in the navigation database. Since these waypoints were derived using WGS-84 methods, the comparison between actual GPS position relative location among waypoints is consistent. This allows for accurate navigation since the aircraft's computed position is using the same reference as how the waypoints were surveyed.

In non-WGS-84 airspace, a GPS-derived position may not yield accurate results because the associated waypoints were not surveyed using WGS-84 methods. Therefore, pilots are instructed to deselect GPS and use DME/DME to determine position. This position is compared against the location of the waypoints defined in the navigation database. By using DME/DME, a consistent reference is being used between the actual position and the position relative to nearby waypoints because the navigation database uses the non WGS-84 data. One might notice a difference between the DME/DME position and a GPS position, but this is irrelevant due to the fact that the

FMS is still comparing its position against the navigation database data supplied by the country developing the procedure or route.

Most AFMs advise pilots to deselect GPS and use DME/DME as the primary navigation method when operating in non WGS-84 airspace. This is acceptable when navigating to the airport or when maneuvering to a conventional approach. It is important to note that aircraft with advanced navigation displays and EGPWS or RAAS must consider that much of the information displayed is based on WGS-84 data. For example, the terrain mapping data that is depicted on the INAV on EPIC platforms was developed using WGS-84 data. Therefore, it is possible that the depiction of terrain on the INAV will be inconsistent when compared to local charts and maps. The terrain data on the INAV is correct, but the relation between terrain and non WGS-84 information (airports, navaids, etc.) could be different. Other WGS-84 derived information, such as geopolitical boundaries could also show some inconsistencies.

There is no doubt you are better off flying an ILS in Russia or China than hoping your GPS coordinates are the same as theirs. But what about en route? Honeywell says to deselect GPS and rely on DME/DME. But the DME/DME network is spotty in China and Russia, and when at altitude wouldn't the WGS-84 coordinates in your FMS be close enough? You decide. Many manufacturers have decided you can use GPS while en route but should deselect it while on approach.

References

Articles and Books

[Radio Communications] "Radio Communications in the Digital Age," Volume 1, HF Technology, Edition 2, Harris Corporation, October 2005

["FAQs for Operations in Non WGS 84 Airspace"] Honeywell Direct-To, FMS Quarterly Update and Newsletter, December 2011

[Finneran, Michael] "Thousand-fold Rise in Polar Flights Hikes Radiation Risk," http://www.nasa.gov/centers/langley/science/polar-radiation.html, NASA Langley Research Center, 02.18.11

["Flying to Europe? Think Again"] National Business Aviation Association, April 4, 2005

[Geerts, B. and Linacre, E.] "The Height of the Tropopause," University of Wyoming, Atmospheric Science, 11/97.

["Geodesy for the Layman"] Defense Mapping Agency, Building 56 U.S. Naval Observatory DMA TR 80-003, Washington DC 20305, 16 March 1984

[McLaren, Grant, 2012] "Insurance Considerations For Overseas Missions," Professional Pilot, December 2012

[McLaren, Grant, 2013] "Dealing With the New Rules of Worldwide Documentation," Professional Pilot, July 2013

[Sobel, Dava] "Longitude: The true story of a long genius who solved the greatest scientific problem of his time," Thomas Allen & Sons Canada Limited, Markham, Ontario, 1995

Australia

[Australia Advisory Circular 21-45(1)] Airworthiness Approval of Airborne Automatic Dependent Surveillance Broadcast Equipment, February 2012, Australian Government Civil Aviation Safety Authority

[Australia Aeronautical Information Service H09/11] Transition to Satellite Technology for Navigation and Surveillance, 15 Jun 11

[Australian Civil Aviation Order 82.3] Conditions on Air Operators' Certificates authorising regular public transport operations other than high capacity aircraft, 27 June 2011, Australian Government Civil Aviation Safety Authority

Canada

[Canadian Aviation Regulations] Transport Canada, http://www.tc.gc.ca/eng/acts-regulations/menu.htm

[CANPASS] http://www.cbsa-asfc.gc.ca/prog/canpass/generalavi-eng.html

[Nav Canada Aeronautical Information Circular 31/11] Air Traffic Services Associated with Automatic Dependent Surveillance-Broadcast Out Surveillance (Hudson Bay and Minto Sectors), 20 Oct 11

[Nav Canada Aeronautical Information Circular 44/11] Air Traffic Services Associated with Automatic Dependent Surveillance-Broadcast Service in the Gander Oceanic Control Area, 15 Dec 11

[Transport Canada Advisory Circular 700-009] Automatic Dependent Surveillance - Broadcast, 2011-03-11, Transport Canada Standards

[Transport Canada Aeronautical Information Manual] TP 14371, October 15, 2015, http://www.tc.gc.ca/eng/civilaviation/publications/tp14371-menu-3092.htm

Commercial Vendors

[ARINC Handbook] ARINC Voice Services Operating Procedures Handbook, ARINC Headquarters, Aviation Voice Services Support, www.arinc.com, September 27, 2006

[Jeppesen] "Jeppesen" generally refers to the Jeppesen Airway Manual suite of products, including instrument approach plates, en route charts, and text pages. Available at: http://ww1.jeppesen.com/aviation/business/

[PetroValue] Aviation Fuel Handling and Quality Control Procedures Manual, PetroValue Products Canada, Inc., August 2008

EASA / EU

[European Aviation Safety Agency (EASA) Acceptable Means of Compliance (AMC) 20-24] Certification Considerations for the Enhance ATS in Non-Radar Areas using ADS-B Surveillance (ADS-B-NRA) Application via 1090 MHz Extended Squitter, February 5, 2008

[European Aviation Safety Agency (EASA) Acceptable Means of Compliance (AMC) and Guidance Material (GM) to Annex III - Part-ORO], EASA, 20 February 2015

[Eurocontrol CFMU Handbook] General & CFMU Systems, Edition No. 14.0, 18 Mar 2010

[European Union Regulation No 859/2008] Technical requirements and administrative procedures applicable to commercial transportation by aeroplane, 20 August 2008

[European Union Regulation No 965/2012] Technical requirements and administrative procedures related to air operations, 5 October 2012

[SAFA Ramp Inspections Guidance Material] European Aviation Safety Agency, Approvals & Standardisation Directorate, Version 2.0, 2012

Hong Kong

[Hong Kong AIRAC AIP Supplement A11/14] Automatic Dependent Surveillance Broadcast (ADS-B) Out Operations, 29 August 2014, Hong Kong Special Administrative Region, People's Republic of China

International Civil Aviation Organization

[Chicago Convention] "Convention on International Civil Aviation Done at Chicago on the 7th Day of December 1944"

[ICAO Annex 1] Personnel Licensing, International Standards and Recommended Practices, Annex 1 to the Convention on International Civil Aviation, July 2011

[ICAO Annex 2] Rules of the Air, International Standards, Annex 2 to the Convention on International Civil Aviation, July 2005

[ICAO Annex 3] Meteorological Service for International Air Navigation, International Standards and Recommended Practices, Annex 3 to the Convention on International Civil Aviation, July 2010

[ICAO Annex 4] Aeronautical Charts, International Standards and Recommended Practices, Annex 4 to the Convention on International Civil Aviation, July 2009

[ICAO Annex 5] Units of Measurement to be used in Air and Ground Operations, International Standards and Recommended Practices, Annex 5 to the Convention on International Civil Aviation, July 1979

[ICAO Annex 6 Part 1] Operation of Aircraft - Commercial Aircraft, International Standards and Recommended Practices, Annex 6 to the Convention on International Civil Aviation, Part I, July 2010

[ICAO Annex 6 Part 2] Operation of Aircraft - General Aviation, International Standards and Recommended Practices, Annex 6 to the Convention on International Civil Aviation, Part II, July 2008

[ICAO Annex 7] Aircraft Nationality and Registration Marks, International Standards, Annex 7 to the Convention on International Civil Aviation, July 2003

[ICAO Annex 8] Airworthiness of Aircraft, International Standards and Recommended Practices, Annex 8 to the Convention on International Civil Aviation, July 2010

[ICAO Annex 9] Facilitation, International Standards and Recommended Practices, Annex 9 to the Convention on International Civil Aviation, July 2005

[ICAO Annex 10 Vol I] Aeronautical Telecommunications, Radio Navigation Aids, International Standards and Recommended Practices, Annex 10 to the Convention on International Civil Aviation, Vol I, July 2006

[ICAO Annex 10 Vol II] Aeronautical Telecommunications, Communications Procedures, International Standards and Recommended Practices, Annex 10 to the Convention on International Civil Aviation, Vol II, October 2001

[ICAO Annex 10 Vol III] Aeronautical Telecommunications, Communications Systems, International Standards and Recommended Practices, Annex 10 to the Convention on International Civil Aviation, Vol III, July 2007

[ICAO Annex 10 Vol IV] Aeronautical Telecommunications, Surveillance and Collision Avoidance Systems, International Standards and Recommended Practices, Annex 10 to the Convention on International Civil Aviation, Vol IV, July 2007

[ICAO Annex 10 Vol V] Aeronautical Radio Frequency Spectrum Utilization, International Standards and Recommended Practices, Annex 10 to the Convention on International Civil Aviation, Vol V, July 2001

[ICAO Annex 11] Air Traffic Services, International Standards, Annex 11 to the Convention on International Civil Aviation, July 2001

[ICAO Annex 12] Search and Rescue, International Standards, Annex 12 to the Convention on International Civil Aviation, July 2004

[ICAO Annex 13] Aircraft Accident and Incident Investigation, International Standards, Annex 13 to the Convention on International Civil Aviation, July 2010

[ICAO Annex 14 Vol I] Aerodrome Construction and Design, International Standards and Recommended Practices, Annex 14 to the Convention on International Civil Aviation, Vol I, July 2009

[ICAO Annex 14 Vol II] Heliports, International Standards and Recommended Practices, Annex 14 to the Convention on International Civil Aviation, Vol II, July 2009

[ICAO Annex 15] Aeronautical Information Services, International Standards and Recommended Practices, Annex 15 to the Convention on International Civil Aviation, July 2010

[ICAO Annex 16 Vol I] Environmental Protection - Aircraft Noise, International Standards and Recommended Practices, Annex 16 to the Convention on International Civil Aviation, Vol I, July 2008

[ICAO Annex 16 Vol II] Environmental Protection - Aircraft Engine Emissions, International Standards and Recommended Practices, Annex 16 to the Convention on International Civil Aviation, Vol II, July 2008

[ICAO Annex 17] Security, International Standards and Recommended Practices, Annex 17 to the Convention on International Civil Aviation, March 2011

[ICAO Annex 18] The Safe Transport of Dangerous Goods by Air, International Standards and Recommended Practices, Annex 18 to the Convention on International Civil Aviation, July 2001

[ICAO Doc 4444] Air Traffic Management, Fifteenth Edition, Procedures for Air Navigation Services, International Civil Aviation Organization, 2007

[ICAO Doc 7030] Regional Supplementary Procedures, International Civil Aviation Organization, 2008

[ICAO Doc 7300] Convention on International Civil Aviation, International Civil Aviation Organization, 2006

[ICAO Doc 7910] Location Indentifiers, International Civil Aviation Organization, 2009

[ICAO Doc 8168 Vol I] Aircraft Operations - Flight Procedures, Procedures for Air Navigation Services, International Civil Aviation Organization, 2006

[ICAO Doc 8168 Vol II] Aircraft Operations - Construction of Visual and Instrument Flight Procedures, Procedures for Air Navigation Services, International Civil Aviation Organization, 2006

[ICAO Doc 8168] ICAO Abbreviations and Codes, Procedures for Air Navigation Services, International Civil Aviation Organization, 2006

[ICAO Doc 9574] Manual on Implementation of a 300 m (1,000 ft) Vertical Separation Minimum Between FL 290 and FL 410 Inclusive, Second Edition, International Civil Aviation Organization, 2001

[ICAO Doc 9613] Performance Based Navigation (PBN) Manual, International Civil Aviation Organization, 2008

[ICAO Doc 9859] Safety Management Manual (SMM), International Civil Aviation Organization, 2006

[ICAO Doc 9869] Manual on Required Communication Performance (RCP) (Draft), International Civil Aviation Organization, 2006

[ICAO Doc 9691] Manual on Volcanic Ash, Radioactive Material and Toxic Chemical Clouds, First Edition, 2001

[ICAO Global Operational Data Link Document (GOLD)] International Civil Aviation Organization, Second Edition, 26 April 2013

[ICAO NAT Doc 001] Guidance and Information Material Concerning Air Navigation in the North Atlantic Region, Seventh Edition, January 2002

[ICAO NAT Doc 003] North Atlantic Operations and Airspace Manual, International Civil Aviation Organization, Edition 2014/2015

[ICAO NAT Doc 007] High Frequency Management Guidance Material for the North Atlantic Region, International Civil Aviation Organization, June 2015

[ICAO Satellite Voice Guidance Material (SVGM)] International Civil Aviation Organization, First Edition, 24 July 2012

Singapore

[Singapore AIP Supplement 254] Implementation of Automatic Dependent Surveillance Broadcast (ADS-B) Out Service Within Part of the Singapore FIR, 6th November 2013, Civil Aviation Authority of Singapore

United States

"CFR" Refers to the U.S. Code of Federal Regulations

[14 CFR 1] Title 14 Part 1: Aeronautics and Space, Definitions and Abbreviations, U.S. Department of Transportation

[14 CFR 45] Title 14 Part 45: Aeronautics and Space, Identification and Registration Marking, U.S. Department of Transportation

[14 CFR 61] Title 14 Part 61: Aeronautics and Space, Certification: Pilots, Flight Instructors, and Ground Instructors, Federal Aviation Administration, Department of Transportation

[14 CFR 91] Title 14 Part 91: Aeronautics and Space, General Operating and Flight Rules, U.S. Department of Transportation

[14 CFR 97] Title 14 Part 97: Aeronautics and Space, Standard Instrument Procedures, Federal Aviation Administration, Department of Transportation

[14 CFR 135] Title 14 Part 135: Aeronautics and Space, Operating Requirements: Commuter and On Demand Operations and Rules Governing Persons on Board Such Aircraft, U.S. Department of Transportation

[14 CFR 139] Title 14 Part 139: Aeronautics and Space, Certification of Airports, U.S. Department of Transportation

[19 CFR 122] Title 19 Part 122: Air Commerce Regulations

"AC" refers to U.S. Advisory Circulars

[AC 20-138D] Positioning and Navigation Systems, 5/8/12, U.S. Department of Transportation

[AC 20-165A] Airworthiness Approval of Automatic Dependent Surveillance - Broadcast (ADS-B) Out Systems, 11/07/12, U.S. Department of Transportation

[AC 90-96A] Approval of U.S. Operators and Aircraft to Operate Under Instrument Flight Rules (IFR) in European Airspace Designated for Basic Area Navigation (B-RNAV) and Precision Area Navigation (P-RNAV), 1/13/05, U.S. Department of Transportation

[AC 90-100A] U.S. Terminal and En Route Area Navigation (RNAV) Operations, 03/01/07, U.S. Department of Transportation

[AC 90-107] Guidance for Localizer Performance with Vertical Guidance and Localizer Performance without Vertical Guidance Approach Operations in the U.S. National Airspace System, 2/11/11, U.S. Department of Transportation

[AC 90-114] Automatic Dependent Surveillance-Broadcast (ADS-B) Operations, 9/21/12, U.S. Department of Transportation

[AC 91-70A] Oceanic and International Operations, 8/12/10, U.S. Department of Transportation

[AC 91-85] Authorization of Aircraft and Operators for Flight in Reduced Vertical Separation Minimum Airspace, 8/21/09, U.S. Department of Transportation

[AC 120-42B] Extended Operations (ETOPS and Polar Ops), 6/13/08, U.S. Department of Transportation

[AC 120-47] Survival Equipment for use in Overwater Operations, 6/12/87, U.S. Department of Transportation

[AC 120-61A] In-flight Radiation Exposure, 7/6/06, U.S. Department of Transportation

[AC 120-70B] Operational Authorization Process for Use of Data Link Communication System, 8/24/10, U.S. Department of Transportation

[AC 120-108] Continuous Descent Final Approach, 1/20/11, U.S. Department of Transportation

[Advisory Circular 120-42B] Extended Operations (ETOPS and Polar Ops), 6/13/08, U.S. Department of Transportation

[AC 135-42] Extended Operations (ETOPS) and Operations in the North Polar Area, 6/10/08, U.S. Department of Transportation

[AFAIS] Air Force Advanced Instrument School, various presentations, 2009, United States Air Force

[Air Force Manual (AFM) 51-37] Instrument Flying, 1 December 1976, United States Air Force

[Air Force Manual (AFM) 51-40] Air Navigation, Flying Training, 1 July 1973, United States Air Force

[Air Traffic Organization Policy Order JO 7110.65U] Air Traffic Control, February 9, 2012, U.S. Department of Transportation

[Department of Defense (DoD) Dictionary of Military and Associated Terms] Joint Publication 1-02, 15 November 2013

[ESTA] Electronic System for Travel Authorization, http://www.cbp.gov/travel/international-visitors/esta

[FAA MMEL Policy Letter] High Frequency (HF) Communications, MMEL Policy Letter (PL)106, Revision 5 GC, June 6, 2014, U.S. Department of Transportation

[FAA-H-8083-15] Instrument Flying Handbook, U.S. Department of Transportation, 2001

[FAA-H-8083-15B] Instrument Flying Handbook, U.S. Department of Transportation, 2012

[FANS-1/A Operations Manual] FAA Aeronautical Communications Aviation Safety (AVS), Version 6.0, 25 September 2008, U.S. Department of Transportation

[Information for Operators (InFO) 13009] Operations Specification (OpSpec)/Management Specification (MSpec)/Letter of Agreement (LOA) Paragraph A353, Automatic Dependent Surveillance-Broadcast (ADS-B) Operations Outside of U.S. Designated Airspace, 6/17/13, U.S. Department of Transportation

[National Geodetic Survey] http://www.ngs.noaa.gov/GEOID/geoid_def.htm

[NIMA] World Geodetic System 1984, Department of Defense, National Imagery and Mapping Agency (NIMA), NSN 7643-01-402-0347, NIMA TR8350.2, Third Edition, Amendment 1, 3 Janaury 2000

[Notice of Public Rule Making (NPRM), 19 CFR 122, Federal Register, Vol. 73, No 223] Advance Information on Private Aircraft Arriving and Departing the United States, November 18, 2008.

[Order 8400.12A] Required Navigation Performance 10 (RNP-10) Operational Approval, 2/9/98, U.S. Department of Transportation

[Order 8400.33] Procedures for Obtaining Authorization for Required Navigation Performance 4 (RNP-4) Oceanic and Remote Area Operations, 9/15/05, U.S. Department of Transportation

[Order 8900.1 Vol 3] General Technical Administration, U.S. Department of Transportation

[Order 8900.1 Vol 4] Aircraft Equipment and Operational Authorizations, U.S. Department of Transportation

[United States Aeronautical Information Manual (AIM)] Official Guide to Basic Flight Information and ATC Procedures, Change 3, June 25, 2015, U.S. Department of Transportation

[United States Aeronautical Information Publication] Updated by NOTAM, U.S. Department of Transportation

[USGS, Encounters of Aircraft with Volcanic Ash Clouds: A Compilation of Known Incidents, 1953-2009] U.S. Department of the Interior, U.S. Geological Survey, Data Series 545, Version 1.0, 2010

[Visa Waiver Program] http://travel.state.gov/content/visas/en/visit/visa-waiver-program.html, U.S. Department of State

[www.aphis.usda.gov] http://www.aphis.usda.gov/wps/portal/aphis/home]

Index

James Albright is an average pilot with average stick and rudder skills, but has an above average desire to learn and instruct. He spent twenty years in the United States Air Force as an aircraft commander, instructor pilot, evaluator pilot, and squadron commander. After retiring as a lieutenant colonel, he went on to fly for several private and commercial operators as an international captain, check airman, and chief pilot. His logbook includes the T-37B, T-38A, KC-135A, Boeing 707, Boeing 747, Challenger 604, and the Gulfstream III, IV, V, and 450.

His website, www.code7700.com attracts nearly two million hits each month and his articles have appeared in several magazines, most notably Business & Commercial Aviation.

CPSIA information can be obtained
at www.ICGtesting.com
Printed in the USA
BVHW062233240520
580210BV00003B/23/J

9 780986 263040